THE KIROV AFFAIR

BY ADAM ULAM

THE BOLSHEVIKS

STALIN: THE MAN AND HIS ERA

THE UNFINISHED REVOLUTION

THE NEW FACE OF SOVIET TOTALITARIANISM

RUSSIA'S FAILED REVOLUTIONS

TITOISM AND THE COMINFORM

IN THE NAME OF THE PEOPLE

DANGEROUS RELATIONS

A HISTORY OF SOVIET RUSSIA

PATTERNS OF GOVERNMENT

THE KIROV AFFAIR

ADAM · ULAM

HARCOURT BRACE JOVANOVICH, PUBLISHERS
SAN DIEGO · NEW YORK · LONDON

LIBRARY OF CONGRESS CATALOGING-IN-PUBLICATION DATA
Ulam, Adam Bruno, 1922–
The Kirov affair.
1. Kirov, Sergei Mironovich, 1886–1934—Fiction.
2. Soviet Union—History—1917–1936—Fiction. I. Title.
PS3571.L52K5 1988 813′.54 87-12055
ISBN 0-15-147277-7

Designed by Ann Gold

Printed in the United States of America

First edition

A B C D E

HISTORICAL NOTE

In the afternoon of December 1, 1934, Sergei Mironovich Kirov, the Communist boss of Leningrad, was murdered in the Smolny Institute, the city's Party Headquarters. The victim was one of the most important Soviet leaders, a member of the Politburo and a secretary of the Party's Central Committee. On the news of his death Stalin and several of his highest-ranking henchmen rushed to Leningrad. The dictator in person supervised the investigation, which according to the official communiqué established that the assassination was part of a wide-ranging conspiracy, its instigators having planned to murder the leading personages of the Soviet regime, including Stalin.

Kirov's death and the execution of the fourteen people declared guilty of the crime ushered in a period of mass purges throughout the Soviet Union, the terror reaching its most ferocious proportions in 1936 and 1937. Among those sent to their deaths were practically all of Lenin's closest companions, those who under his leadership conquered Russia for Communism in 1917. But also countless others, ranging from the highest-ranking officials to rank-and-file Communists, and just plain citizens, were branded as "enemies of the people" and as such either summarily executed or imprisoned in the *lagers*—forced labor camps, whose population at the height of the terror numbered in the millions.

THE KIROV AFFAIR

CHAPTER 1

GENEVA, JULY 1982

There seemed to be no compelling reason for Kondratiev to dress up for the dinner. In their peregrinations throughout the capitalist world, the state and Party leaders, himself included, had habitually adhered to the business suit, even when entertained at Buckingham Palace, not to mention the White House. But on this occasion Kondratiev felt that donning a tuxedo would provide just the right psychological touch for the dinner party hosted by his American counterpart, which was to mark the conclusion of the latest, and fruitless, round of strategic arms control talks. The past six weeks had been spent in acrimonious debates, filled with charges and countercharges, veiled and not-so-veiled threats. So now was the moment when the Soviet delegates should inject a note of urbanity and conviviality into what had hitherto been a strained and frigid relationship. For all their discomfiture, the Americans must not depart from the conference feeling that there was simply no point in negotiating with the Russians. Tonight they would see the Soviet emissaries, impeccably attired, indulging in small talk; surely not the kind of people who were plotting to subjugate or incinerate the West. Members of the delegation had been carefully coached by Kondratiev on the right degree of sociability they were to display toward their hosts. If the mood of the evening warranted it, he himself might drop some carefully phrased indiscretion about what supposedly transpired behind the Kremlin walls. Westerners were always tantalized by such tales, craving the slightest inkling that those outwardly stern and ominous figures ruling the Soviet colossus were not free from human frailties or the political worries that beset their opposite numbers in the capitalist world.

Quite aside from such calculations, Kondratiev enjoyed diplomatic parties, especially ones given by the Americans. Having lived in the States, he believed he had got to know, and in a way like, those strange people. He felt at ease with them, quite unlike his fellow oligarchs who, he realized, could not endure even a casual chat with their transatlantic antagonists without revealing a sizable chip on their shoulders or, contrariwise, giving vent to irritation that grown-up men representing a world power could be so childish when it came to international politics. For all the expected verbal fencing, he looked forward to an enjoyable evening.

His pleasant feeling was enhanced by what he saw in the mirror: at sixty-nine, Mikhail Alexandrovich Kondratiev cast the figure of a man in his early fifties, slim, slightly above the average height, his thick black hair becomingly touched with silver at the temples. Servant as well as one of the masters of the USSR, he looked perfectly natural in his Italian-tailored evening clothes. At times like this, Kondratiev could not help thinking of yet another characteristic that distinguished him from his fellow Politburo members: he came from an old, if impecunious, noble family that for two centuries had provided the imperial government with military and civil officers. He smiled, remembering his confusion during his first appearance at the Council of Ministers, when Stalin had turned to him and said, "And what does our hereditary nobleman think about the problem?" Those who began to smirk had quickly changed their expression when the Boss added, "It is a sign of the maturity of our socialist society that old and senseless prejudices are vanishing. We may joke about them, but of what importance are a man's class origins, as against his services to the Fatherland?" And a few weeks later, when alone with Kondratiev, Stalin recalled the occasion: "Yes, there are still dunderheads among us who believe that a man is qualified for a high position if he was born the son of a village whore or a Jewish peddler, but not if he came from a family that has served Russia for so long and so faithfully. Well, there will soon be changes around here, and some people are in for a surprise." He still recalled the shiver that went down his spine as he watched the dictator pronounce those last words. But that was many years ago, and now such memories—even some hideous ones—seemed as if they had happened in another life.

His musings were interrupted by a knock on the door. "I am almost ready, Mitya, come in," said Kondratiev, fixing the final stud in his shirt front. But instead of his secretary, Dmitri Gorbunov, it was the ungainly figure of Ivan Pluyev that materialized in the antechamber opening of his suite. Officially listed as a press attaché, Pluyev, a plump little man in his forties, was a colonel in the KGB and chief security officer of the delegation. "I beg your pardon, Comrade Kondratiev," he began somewhat nervously and without stepping into the drawing room, "but there is something I thought I should bring to your attention."

"Whatever it is, it must wait; I shall be late for the Americans!"

"But this is a letter addressed personally to you and mailed from the United States," said Pluyev, groping in his briefcase.

Kondratiev approached him and took the envelope; it had been opened. "Of course you looked at the contents," he said good-naturedly.

"We are under strict orders to examine all mail not delivered by the official courier."

Kondratiev suddenly moved so close to the secret policeman that the latter stepped back, colliding with the door. "And that, I suppose, gives you the right to spy on the head of the State Delegation, and member of the Politburo," said Kondratiev, still in an even voice, but using the second person singular, a form of address indicating familiarity or, as in this case, indicating contempt.

"I . . . I thought I was doing my duty. There could have been explosives."

"I congratulate you on your vigilance, which will not go unrewarded. Turn over your duties to Yudin, and remain in your room until the delegation leaves tomorrow for Moscow. Now go. It is right behind you," he added as in his panic Pluyev seemed unable to move, his eyes searching vainly for an exit.

As his victim left the room, Kondratiev began to read the letter, at first impatiently, then with growing attention. Finally, with a frown, he put it in the safe. The letter itself was not of great consequence, though potentially embarrassing if that fool of an American professor should publish what he had learned. And was that all he knew? Well, no one but himself could any longer know the secret, and yet the idiotic letter made him relive the one memory he had tried desperately for the past forty-eight years to push out of his mind.

When Gorbunov finally arrived, he found his boss in his usual jovial pre-party mood, nothing suggesting that Mikhail Kondratiev had just seen the ghost of his past. It was with some relish that he recounted his chastisement of Pluyev. "Unless you press hard on some of those people, they will never learn. In general there has been a great improvement in this respect, for which we ought to be grateful to Comrade Andronnikov, but the Pluyevs are still around, and they cannot get it through their thick skulls that we no longer live in the thirties or forties."

"But shouldn't we perhaps transmit the text of the letter to Moscow?" asked Gorbunov, who for all of his three years of work for a Politburo member, and the realization that as such his chief ought to be immune to the fears and cautions afflicting the ordinary Soviet mortal, could not quite rid his mind of the awe of the secret police.

"Dear Mitya, of course it has already been transmitted, and Andronnikov knows that I know that he has the full text. Much as I like him, I do not want to indulge the KGB's sense of self-importance and to act as if we were schoolboys, afraid of being caught playing hooky. And if they question you about it in Moscow, you can repeat word for word what I just said." Kondratiev looked fixedly at his young assistant, and noted inwardly that it was the first time in a very long while that he had seen a Soviet official blush. A rather encouraging sign. "But we must not keep the Americans waiting. This will make them even more nervous than they probably are after we broke off the negotiations."

The lobby of the hotel was crowded with journalists and Soviet security people, and the Swiss police had difficulty clearing the path for the delegates.

"Just a word, Mr. Chairman," cried one of the correspondents frantically, thrusting his head and microphone between the two agents.

"I believe I said everything that needed to be said at the press conference." But recognizing a correspondent of a Paris journal, whom he had met in Moscow, Kondratiev paused and addressed him in French: "Well, let me repeat. We are always ready to resume the negotiations if the United States comes forth with reasonable proposals, rather than demands that our country should unilaterally disarm. . . . Oh, yes, it certainly does not help Soviet-American relations or world peace if U.S. political leaders lecture us as if we were children . . . some fantasies about our socialist state harboring aggressive designs, the nonsense about our violating human rights. Such fabrications certainly do not create an atmosphere conducive to resolving the most important question facing the international community, how to banish forever the specter of nuclear war."

"How is Mr. Leontiev's health?" shouted someone else in the crowd, in English.

"I am grateful for your solicitude. The chairman of the Presidium of the Supreme Soviet has for all his other and stupendous duties kept abreast of every single detail of our discussions. I wish your leaders were equally alert and concerned about this all-important problem," replied Kondratiev, icily. Then, with a smile, "You must excuse us. If we keep our American hosts waiting, some might think that we were drawing up plans for invading Switzerland." There was a burst of laughter and a spattering of applause.

"Yet, my dear Chairman, how sad that we could not have got at least closer in our respective proposals. We hoped that when a man of your stature and knowledge of the West was named the chief of your delegation that your people were surely counting on the conference bringing concrete results." Charles Amon could not help reverting to the subject, even though both sides had agreed that occasions such as this were to be free of any contentious business.

The Russian took some time in relighting his cigar. This was the time for dropping one of those tantalizing hints. "Your disappointment cannot be any greater than mine," said Kondratiev slowly, "and I am probably being indiscreet in telling you that some of us wish not only for correct, but for cordial relations between our two great countries. But whenever I try to reassure my colleagues that the Americans are in the habit of saying things they really don't mean, someone thrusts under my nose one of your own newspaper headlines. 'Secretary of Defense to Discuss Arms Sales to Beijing,' 'Pentagon to Test Potential First-Strike Weapon.' Fortunately, the head of our government is a man of patience and understanding. But it is at least open to question whether someone else in his position could keep our hotheads, especially the military ones, as firmly in hand."

The American diplomat sighed. This was not the first time he had heard this theme, but never before from a member of the Politburo. Certainly Kondratiev was a different breed from the other Soviets he had encountered in previous negotiations. Not like their foreign minister with his sneering manner. Not like their younger diplomats with their robotlike reactions. Perhaps there really were "doves" and "hawks" in the Politburo, and probably the present administration in Washington was making a major mistake in talking and acting as if they had all been cast from the same stuff: cheaters, deceivers, haters of the West.

As if reading his thoughts, Kondratiev said reflectively, "No, you must not think that there are wild men among us who might wish to destroy the world. But without some give-and-take on your part, how can such as myself persuade the others that you are not out to subvert our socialist allies in Eastern Europe or allow Israel to grind down the Arabs? What am I to tell my military friends when they point out that missiles you are planning to deploy could in a few minutes reach our command posts—why, Moscow itself!"

The deputy chief of the American delegation, who was on Kondratiev's left, allowed himself a chuckle. "And your own weapons, I suppose, are aimed at the North Pole, and not London, Paris, or Bonn?"

The Russian smiled agreeably. There was little point in rehearsing once more the tedious argument. This rather impudent man, Doherty, he recalled from his dossier, had been stationed as a young diplomat in Moscow. The KGB surprised him in bed with a winsome secret service operative, but the matter was not pursued. Instead of cringing, Doherty had asked for enlargements of the photos, so, he said, he could add them to his collection.

Amon was anxious to turn the conversation in another direction. "It has been quite a while since you visited our country, Mr. Chairman."

"Not since the sixties, when I went to the United Nations."

"But your really long stay in the States was when?" asked Doherty.

"In the early thirties, when I worked as an apprentice engineer in a Ford factory. Not a very happy time for either of our countries." Was there anything behind the question, and how could the FBI, the CIA, or whatever, have failed to brief them that he had been in Detroit precisely from October 1932 to June 1934? If he had only stayed in America a few more months!

But evidently Doherty was just making conversation, for he now launched into the theme of how big cities like New York or Detroit gave one a rather flawed picture of American life, and that one had to savor a small New England or Midwestern town to appreciate what America was really like. "You should send your people to visit such places rather than sticking to big cities where they spend their free time at discotheques and watch X-rated movies."

Amon frowned, but Kondratiev fell in with the spirit of the chatter. "We would love dearly to preserve our young men's socialist virtues, but now I understand why your government, by restricting Soviet diplomats' travel, virtually compels them to resort to such sinful diversions."

"For a man of my strict upbringing," continued Doherty relentlessly, clearly showing the cumulative effects of vodka, wine, and brandy, "it was a shock to discover that even here in Geneva, the city of Calvin, there are two very advanced striptease cabarets. I had a very instructive discussion on the merits of the various performers with your public relations man—Pluyev, is it?—who is evidently quite a connoisseur of the art. By the way, I don't see him here."

"He is unwell," replied Kondratiev curtly.

After initial awkwardness, the atmosphere grew more relaxed as the dinner progressed, and now there was animated conversation around the table. The arguments and contentions of the past six weeks were laid aside, and the post mortems on the conference and "what next" would come later. Amon, who was exactly his own age, recounted to Kondratiev how during the Depression his family had lost its fortune and how he had to work his way through college and law school. "In your country you had, I understand, a lot of trouble with agriculture, but I don't suppose it interfered with your education."

Oh, no, if the American only knew what kind of education he had received during those years.

Alcohol also seemed to trigger memories of the past in the old General Savitsky, the chief official military expert of the delegation. In fact, since Moscow had decided even before the conference started that it would lead to no tangible agreements, Savitsky was chosen not because of any technical expertise—the gallant ex–cavalry man could hardly tell the difference between a cruise missile and an ICBM—but because of his martial air and brusque manner. It was thus hoped that he would impress the Americans with how dangerous it was to keep rejecting the Soviet government's reasonable proposals—the military might get the upper hand, and, judging by Savitsky, they seemed frighteningly ignorant of what an all-out war would portend. The trouble was that the old warrior called out of his semiretirement found his stint so enjoyable that it was difficult for him to play the assigned role convincingly.

"But Mikhail Alexandrovich," he expostulated with Kondratiev when the latter urged him to be more circumspect, "I understand that these are our enemies, but I find them so much more pleasant to deal with than those Arabs, Vietnamese, and all the other *svoloch* [riffraff] from what you call the Third World who are supposed to be our friends." He was now bending the ear of General Powell with his wartime recollections. "And so my army moved into Serbia. We had been told that it would be just a mopping-up operation, for the Yugoslav partisans had taken care of most of the German units. It was fortunate that I had not quite believed our Slav brothers' boasting and prepared for a German counterattack. I love the Serbs; they are a brave people, but those partisans were no more than armed rabble. They were all right when fighting the Italians or their own Fascists, but how could you expect them to stand up to the German tanks? I could never understand how you people had so much trouble with the Vietcong."

It was fortunate that the representative of the Joint Chiefs of Staff, who believed that because of his two years of Russian at West Point he could dispense with an interpreter, found it difficult both to follow and to sustain the conversation in that language. Before the American had time to compose a rejoinder such as, "But you haven't been doing so well in Afghanistan," the alert foreign-office man on his other side broke in hastily. "General Savitsky must tell you about his great wartime feat, how he led his divisions out of an encirclement when surrounded by a whole German army."

Savitsky nodded happily and launched into the story, not omitting such details as how he had to shoot with his own hand his chief of staff, who had panicked and wanted to surrender.

Kondratiev glanced at another corner of the table where Boris Davidovich Feldman was evidently discussing some problem in theoretical physics with his American counterpart. There had been some raised eyebrows when he proposed taking Academician Feldman as his chief scientific adviser. "Are you sure that he would not bolt to join his aunt in Israel?" asked Marshal Vorontsov, the minister of defense, only half in jest. Kondratiev had had to remind the marshal that Feldman had been one of the principal experts in his own ministry, and that his presence on the delegation would go far in refuting all that slander spread by the Zionists. Besides, Feldman had the reputation of being an excellent chess player. Geneva was a dull city with no amusements suitable to a man of Kondratiev's age, and he would need some relaxation from the Americans, and from those weapons of mass destruction.

"But of course, Misha, that is a sufficient reason in itself," exclaimed Lunin, who in Leontiev's absence presided over the session of the Defense Council. "Do take the Jew along." Some members of the delegation affected to snub Feldman, but Kondratiev quickly put an end to that.

There was a burst of laughter at the other end of the table where junior members of both teams had been cracking jokes. "How well our people get along, once we forget politics," said Amon wistfully.

The Russian felt, unexpectedly, a surge of warmth toward his antagonist. They had gone through weeks of arguments, often heated, but Amon never let drop a discourteous or barbed word, unlike that pip-squeak (he was actually in his forties) Doherty, with his sarcastic manner. The older American conformed to the qualities that men of Kondratiev's father's generation associated with the term *true gentleman*. Yes, the breed was vanishing in the Western world, just as in his own the same fate had befallen that seemingly prehistoric species, the *true Marxist-Leninist*. Well, at least we don't have any illusions about the kind of world we live in, and that is why we must prevail and their way of life is doomed.

"We shall never see eye to eye on politics, Mr. Ambassador," he said, raising his glass, "but let us drink to the time when we shall firmly agree as to the ways of preventing the cataclysm of a war between our two countries."

Amon appeared deeply moved as they clicked glasses. This was the first concrete indication that the Soviets had not precluded returning to the conference table. "And when—I don't say if—an opportunity for our getting together arises, would you again lead your country's delegation, Mr. Chairman? I certainly hope so."

"I am always at the disposal of my government." But my return in this capacity is most unlikely, thought Kondratiev to himself. With the Chief getting ever weaker and more disorganized, no Politburo member should absent himself from Russia for any lengthy period of time. And this will be even truer when Leontiev's ashes are finally deposited in the Kremlin wall.

"Many thanks for your hospitality. We older people must go to bed, while Mr. Doherty and the other youngsters are undoubtedly eager to catch a show in one of those striptease places."

Once back in his hotel, Kondratiev decided he was not ready for bed and invited Savitsky for a nightcap. The old soldier's tales often amused him, but above all he wanted to postpone having to reread the damned letter, something he realized he would have to do before going to sleep, and which indeed might keep him from sleeping altogether. The general vetoed brandy and opted for Johnny Walker.

"I don't see why foreigners always think that we drink nothing but vodka, and only our Russian one at that." He, during his military career that had taken him to all of the People's Democracies, had reached the sorrowful conclusion that the domestic product was greatly inferior to those manufactured in the fraternal socialist countries, especially Poland and Czechoslovakia. His cosmopolitan tastes in strong spirits once threatened to have dire consequences. At a party in the British embassy he instructed its military attaché about the numerous varieties of vodka, and their respective merits. The Englishman, who had hitherto believed that there was but one kind, was so enchanted by a whole new world opening before him that he sent Savitsky a case of Scotch.

"That was in 1951, and I don't have to tell you, Mikhail Alexandrovich, what things were like then." Savitsky was summoned before the chief military procurator and asked point-blank about his connection with the British intelligence. He was then confined to headquarters and told that his case would be turned over to the Ministry of State Security.

"That, you understand, would have been curtains." Fortunately the procurator felt it prudent to have a case involving a lieutenant general and thrice Hero of the Soviet Union brought to the personal attention of the generalissimo.

"And so, before those hyenas could get their teeth into me, I received a note: 'Ivan Alexeyevich, forgive this idiocy. Tasted whiskey only once in London in 1907 and did not like it. But I hope you enjoy it. Do you still remember our little joke?' Signed, 'Stalin.' The procurator practically cried when begging me to forget the unfortunate misunderstanding."

"What was the little joke?" asked Kondratiev.

"Oh, at the time it had not seemed funny at all. In 1943, the Fifth Guards division that I commanded entered Kursk. My neighbor on the left was dilatory in covering us, and the Germans counterattacked, pushing us out of the city. Well, it took two days' fighting to turn the scales and put Fritz to flight. We were in the midst of pursuit when I was ordered to turn over the division to my deputy and to report to the Stavka. My friend, assistant chief of the General Staff, greeted me in Moscow with a long face. 'Vanya, you're in deep trouble.' 'What is the matter? We are advancing!' 'The Supreme was extremely irritated when you announced the recovery of Kursk when the city was in fact still in German hands.' 'But for Heaven's sake, Anton, we went back within forty-eight hours!' 'So I told him, and also that if it was anyone's fault, it was Tolmachiev's, who exposed your flank. No, he said, we must teach our generals not to lie so they could fraudulently obtain decorations and see their names in orders of the day. He will summon you. God be with you.' Next day, a telephone call, and then a limousine picked me up. I thought that the major who was my escort looked at me as if I were a lost man, but that shows my state of mind. How could he have known that I was not going to the Kremlin to be decorated? Well, after going through those three checkpoints, I am finally in Poskryobishev's office. I sit and wait. Finally, the door opens and *he* comes out. I stand up and report. Stalin picks up some papers and without looking at me goes back to his cabinet. Just before closing the door behind him he says, 'I see, Savitsky, you haven't been shot yet.' I keep standing, stupidly looking at Poskryobishev, who keeps scribbling, with the light shining on his bald pate. I badly needed to relieve myself, but tell me, Mikhail Alexandrovich, would *you* have had the courage even to ask?"

Kondratiev laughed. Here was the man, he remembered, who performed incredible feats of heroism under enemy fire.

"Finally a ring. Poskryobishev lifts up his mug, listens, and says, 'You can go now, Comrade General.' I went home. My family had been evacuated. So I sit alone, looking at my service revolver. One voice in me says: 'Shoot yourself. They will call it an accident, and your wife will get a pension instead of going to a camp.' Another: 'But they really couldn't kill you. These are not the thirties. You will be reduced to the ranks and sent to a penal battalion at the front—a much better way to die.' Finally, I drank myself into a stupor and slept until noon. I was awakened by a telephone. It was my friend from the General Staff.

" 'You must have luck and fantastic powers of persuasion. Pack your things. In four hours you are to fly to the headquarters of the Eleventh Army to take over as its deputy commander. And get your orderly to sew another stripe on your shoulder straps. You've been promoted to lieutenant general.' "

"A happy ending," Kondratiev pronounced.

"Not yet. At the victory banquet in May 1945, Josif Vissarionovich was surrounded by the Politburo and the marshals. I was sitting with mere generals, but he spotted me and came to click glasses.

" 'Well, old friend, we've been through some terrible years. But we didn't lose our sense of humor and even found occasions for a joke, here and there. Didn't we?'

"What a man," concluded Savitsky.

"A terrible man in some ways, but without him the Germans would have eaten us up alive during the war, and the Americans might have done the same, of course in a much more civilized manner, after the war."

Savitsky, who was not stupid, noted the stilted way Kondratiev pronounced this verdict—the official Party line on Stalin, as of the moment.

"Forgive me, Mikhail Alexandrovich, but it is we, the Russian people, who defeated Hitler. And it did not help that *he* let Yezhov, Beria, and other scoundrels kill so many of our best people before the war. As for the Americans—what could they have done? Sure, their capitalists hate us. But they are not a martial nation. That general who sat next to me, with his glasses and his entire manner he looked like a schoolteacher rather than a military man. I could not understand much of what he was saying, but I did get that he was looking forward to his retirement and to spending most of his time fishing and playing golf. Imagine that from an officer who is fifty-four."

Himself seventy-two, Savitsky still felt bitter at being considered too old for an army command, and having to adjust to the unexciting job of head of a military academy.

"They may not be military minded, but their leaders occasionally do get vicious. And besides, it is the Americans' very childishness that is a major source of trouble. They let others manipulate them against us. Yesterday it was Churchill and Adenauer, today it is the Israelis. Tomorrow in all likelihood it will be our dear Chinese comrades. Much as I like them, we must never let the Americans become unafraid of us. If we do, they will try to push us around. Would you like to see Poland, Czechoslovakia, those other countries we liberated in 1944 and '45 slip from our grip?"

"Never," said Savitsky. "We earned our domination over them with the blood we spilled there during the war."

"Precisely. And without Stalin, we probably could not have managed it. At the time we were bloodied and exhausted, while the Americans were at the peak of their power. We would have had the capitalists right at our doorstep stirring up trouble in the Ukraine, Byelorussia, our Baltic republics. I remember when Stalin announced that West Berlin must be blockaded. We all sat dumbfounded, until finally Molotov stuttered, 'But Josif, they h-have the b-bomb.' 'It counts for nothing because we have stronger nerves than the capitalists.' Yes, they were terrified by him . . . almost as much as ourselves."

Did he himself believe in what he was telling Savitsky? In a way, yes, but there was also another image of Stalin that he found difficult to banish from his mind: a deceitful sadist caring for little but his own power, ready for its sake, or simply out of a whim or delusion, to order the deaths of hundreds of thousands, while beneath the veneer of a man of steel was often a frightened, haunted creature. In any case, the discussion had taken an untoward turn and was bringing back those painful memories.

"I must not detain you any longer, Ivan Alexeyevich. We take off early tomorrow, and from the minute we land in Moscow it is work, work: reports, conferences, interviews."

When the door closed behind the general, Kondratiev summoned Gorbunov and dictated an account of the dinner with the Americans. "What was all that uproar at your end of the table?" he asked when the secretary finished taking notes.

"We had a very spirited discussion as to whether the condition of weightlessness in space vehicles decreases or enhances the sexual drive."

"I am glad our two sides found a common ground for discussion of at least one important issue. Good night, Mitya."

Alone, he sat for a while, still sipping brandy and trying to convince himself that the letter business would be best attended to in the morning, with his mind fresh. Or, perhaps, even back in Moscow where he could consult his diary and establish for sure when he had met this wretched American professor. No, that was a child's way of coping with an unpleasant task. He had to make sure right now that the whole matter was of trifling importance; otherwise it would continue to prey on his mind more and more and his preoccupation would become obvious to his entourage on the plane, and to the people meeting him at home. A man in his position was constantly on display, with any departure from the habitual mood immediately registered by those around him. "What is eating Kondratiev, he is usually so lively and jovial?" His dear colleagues would soon hear about this and, with the Pluyev business, might put two and two together. "Misha is showing the first signs of old age—agonizing over the sins of his youth." Personal, as distinct from political, failings of a Politburo member were usually tolerated by that body as a whole. Having had to struggle with constant fear for their lives under Stalin and for their jobs under Khrushchev, the oligarchs had entered upon an unwritten and unspoken compact: once a man was within the charmed circle, such peccadilloes as drunkenness, philandering, or even loafing would not, unless of course carried scandalously far, result in dismissal or disgrace. Even though useless for serious work—the others would cover up for him—the culprit would often retain a position on the Soviet Olympus until his utter decrepitude. But two personal failings were held as inadmissible and incompatible with membership in the ruling council: excessive moral sensitivity and the loss of one's nerve. Brooding about the past fell clearly under both categories.

▬

In another hotel in Geneva, Charles Amon was also keeping late hours, reviewing with his staff their impressions of the dinner.

"I must say that after having been quite depressed, I was somewhat cheered up this evening. The affair went off much better than we had any right to expect. Yesterday, when breaking up the conference, the Russians ranted and raved as if doomsday was at hand: 'There is no way we can even talk with the present American administration. While it tries to drag out the negotiations, NATO is preparing an armed crusade against the Soviet Union. The capitalists seem to be bent on starting a worldwide conflagration.' Tonight they were hinting that under certain conditions they might indeed come back to the conference table."

Doherty snorted. "They are full of nonsense." Out of consideration for Amon's age, he refrained from using a more graphic noun. "That is the way they negotiate, first kick you in the balls, and then when you are doubled up, they smile and explain that all they really desire is a meaningful dialogue, and won't you please try to see things from where they sit."

"You have a very vivid way of expressing yourself, Jim," said Amon reproachfully, "but won't you admit that some of them are not impervious to reason? Take Kondratiev. I am sure that if it depended only on him, we would not be breaking off the negotiations."

"Oh, yes, he is very smooth, but he is the same Kondratiev who went to Hungary in 1957 to impress the local Communists that they must shoot more people if they want to avoid another rebellion, and who was on a similar mission to Prague in 1969 to deliver the final kick to Dubcek. On both occasions he was undoubtedly very polite, passing his message over brandy and cigars." "Well, it is possible he has mellowed with age," he added lamely, noticing the obvious discomfiture of the older man.

"No one can think me naive about Russians. I spent two years in Moscow as ambassador. And after practicing law for forty years, one gets to know something about human nature. Of course, Kondratiev is a devout Marxist-Leninist, otherwise he wouldn't be where he is. But beneath the ideological armor, I detect a civilized and reasonable human being. If only more of their leading people were like him. God help us if characters like this Savitsky take over."

"I rather got to like him," said General Powell, "but I must admit that for a man who has been through what he has in war, he seems remarkably lighthearted about the whole business. He told me he almost regretted that there had been no armed uprising in Poland and said that he would not have minded having a hand in teaching that ungrateful and perfidious people a lesson."

"There," Amon turned to Doherty. "Would you have the Savitskys rather than the Kondratievs as Soviet policymakers?"

"But he has about as much chance of being one as I do."

"Savitsky is a member of the Central Committee." The tone of Amon's voice implied that no one had to instruct him in the intricacies of the Soviet power structure.

Doherty was about to rejoin, "But so are about four hundred other people, including an occasional champion dairy maid and textile worker," but a look from a State Department man made him desist; he just shrugged his shoulders.

"And what were your impressions, Hilmar?" Amon, having subdued Doherty, pursued his inquest with the chief scientific expert of the delegation.

"I did not have the feeling that Feldman was really at ease and empowered to go into actual technical details of possible variants of the agreements."

Turnquist was thinking hard to make sense of the Soviets' evasions and detours in the last six weeks. "On most occasions Boris would say, 'I am a theoretical physicist, not a missile expert. Ask Baranov.' He in turn would protest, 'It is Boris Davidovich who has all the data in his mind. I am just his assistant.' Feldman could and did relax only when we talked about scientific problems having nothing to do with arms. He was quite nostalgic about the year he spent at Stanford as an exchange professor, and was very much au courant about the latest advances in his field in the States. Stiffened up when I tried to probe him, needless to say quite delicately, on the Jewish question in the USSR. 'I would not be a member of the Academy or on this delegation if our leaders were anti-Semitic. Of course, you can always find ignorant and bigoted individuals in our country, just as in yours. The Americans are doing themselves, and for that matter also Israel, much harm by listening to those Zionist fanatics who hate the Soviet Union. For many of them it is still the old Russia from which their ancestors had fled, the country of pogroms, where Jews were treated the way you still do treat your Negroes. Things now are completely different.' I could not help asking him about the quota system for Jewish admissions to the universities. 'But I understand American schools have a similar system and you call it affirmative action.' "

"Touché," cried Doherty. They certainly know, he thought to himself, how to pick people to be exhibited abroad.

"I sometimes wonder myself," interjected Amon, hesitantly, "whether our policy is not excessively affected by Zionist influence. Kondratiev was quite revealing in this connection. 'Your and my countries, Mr. Ambassador, must not allow themselves to be bullied by our allies. Old Khrushchev got us too deep into the Mideastern mess, and we have been trying to get out of it ever since. Personally, I am glad that you took the Egyptians off our hands, they had been nothing but a source of trouble and vast expense to us. But we cannot pull out of that damnable region, so to speak, under fire. You ought to persuade your Israeli friends to be more sensible. Why should our two great nations be constantly dragged into other peoples' quarrels?' I had to remind him that this was quite beyond the subject of our negotiations, but in a way, I think, he has a point."

Again Doherty had to resist the urge to intervene and ask whether training and arming Palestinian terrorists, and sending arms and military personnel to Libya and Syria, could be interpreted as the USSR trying to get out of the Mideastern mess. Instead, he said, "Speaking of our business, while we were sitting and chatting here in Geneva, the Soviets added ten SS-20s to their tactical force, and flight-tested a new, powerful, strategic rocket."

"We have not been entirely idle," objected General Powell.

"Oh, yes, the Congress has blocked the funds for an antiballistic missile system, and the Air Force and the Navy have entered on a furious quarrel over which of them is to have the principal deterrent role in the nineties."

"What, then, is your prescription, Jim?" asked Amon.

"What I have been saying all along: avoid giving the Russians an impression that we are simply desperate for an agreement. If they go on with their games, let us match them weapon for weapon, threaten to help the Chinese with their nuclear and other arms. *That* will bring them back to the table in a hurry."

"You will have an opportunity to present your views to the National Security Council. As for me, I believe a bit of give-and-take and less harsh rhetoric from our side would bring speedier results. And the consequences of not reaching an agreement, and soon, may be simply too dreadful to contemplate." Amon's tone clearly indicated that the discussion, as well as the meeting, was now concluded.

In the corridor, Doherty grabbed Arthur Hill's arm. "You must think I've already had too many, but what I badly need is a drink to soothe my nerves."

"As behooves an assistant secretary of state, I always keep a bottle in my room."

"No, let's go to the Bataclan. The sight of bouncing tits and asses will help me regain my composure."

"We can't talk there; we are bound to run into some journalists. And really, Jim, neither of us should be seen in a place like that at two o'clock at night." Though grumbling, Doherty let himself be persuaded.

His mood brightened at the array of bottles produced by his host. "Do you suppose these rooms are bugged?"

"By the Swiss secret service? Jim, perhaps you've had enough."

"Nonsense. In my days in Russia I could outdrink most of the natives. No, I am naturally upset by the session with our leader. He really let Kondratiev sell him a bill of goods. And I expected support from your people, while you kept signaling me to shut up."

"You are on the Security Council, and after a stint there you can with your law degree go into practice, business, or teaching. I am strictly a career officer, and Amon may become secretary of state."

"I like the old gent. He would have been an ideal ambassador to Russia . . . in 1910, or a secretary of state under Coolidge. You know those people, Art. How can you expect a man of his background and personality to see through them? It is we who should have walked out of the conference in the very beginning when it became obvious that they meant it as a charade. Instead, we stayed, offering a fresh concession every week only to be kicked repeatedly in the teeth."

"You underestimate Amon, Jim. His very reputation is such that it should still all those voices back home and in Europe saying we do not negotiate in good faith. And for the moment that is the main thing. The Russians do respect him. They are such snobs. He may be a trifle old-fashioned, but that is why you and I have been here to keep things in balance and ward off their tricks."

"To be sure, he is not an unmitigated ass, such as ———." Doherty named several of America's most eminent senior statesmen and Sovietologists. "But how could anyone with the slightest knowledge of that miserable country believe that an old fart like Savitsky could become politically important? And he has virtually fallen in love with Kondratiev."

"Well, he is an impressive fellow, and in human terms more attractive than most of their crowd."

"Yes, every Mafia-like organization has a character like him to front for it and delude the ignorant with his urbanity and charm. How do we know what he is really like when he's with those other gangsters?"

"You simply don't like the Russians, Jim."

"On the contrary, I am very fond of them as people and feel sorry that most of their rulers throughout history have been scoundrels or dolts. The thing I do detest is the stupidity of our own people whenever they deal with those crooks. And that is why after my tour in Moscow—and I'll tell you sometime about my experience there—I resigned from the service and went into law. I came back thinking it would be different under this administration, but so far we have had much noise, but otherwise little change."

"Your little adventure had become quite a legend in the embassy by the time I got there."

"Oh," said Doherty, surprised but not displeased: his encounter with Sonia and her KGB pimps had been confided only to the ambassador, and had happened five years before Hill got there.

"Oh, yes, we were all warned to watch out for such traps, but my own story was kind of the reverse of yours and not quite as satisfactory to my *amour propre*."

"Do tell," said Doherty, pouring himself another drink.

"Well, I was in the habit of frequenting the Lenin Library. One day its assistant director, a man I had assumed to be entirely engrossed in medieval manuscripts, invited me to have tea in his basement office. There I found another gentleman who was very solicitous as to whether I was enjoying myself in Moscow. He then informed me that my wife, not of course my present one, was indeed having the time of her life, ably assisted in that respect by a certain British newspaperman. After much hemming and hawing he then implied that his employers, evidently solicitous about the sanctity of the matrimonial bond, could arrange for something quite unpleasant to happen to the man in question, but wouldn't I in return provide them with a few bits of innocuous information? I thanked him for his concern, but added that I knew perfectly well what was going on and did not give a damn. As for the Englishman, they should make him a Hero of Socialist Labor. You should have seen his face."

It could not really have appeared so funny to Art at the time, thought Doherty. "Delightful people. And do you suppose your Kondratiev would not authorize similar tricks? No, where he sits now, I believe, he is above getting mixed up in such minor forms of swinishness, only in the very major ones."

"I honestly don't know, Jim. From what I have heard, he is not really anti-American. Of course he would not pass up those opportunities to screw us that we offer them so frequently, but basically he would like to see some kind of Soviet-American understanding. And I know for a fact that he helped many literary and artistic people when they got into trouble. No, he is different from that general run of troglodytes. I would not mind seeing him as successor to Leontiev."

"You can never tell what they would be like at the very top. I doubt Kondratiev has a serious chance, partly because he is smarter than the others. But in addition there is something not quite kosher about his past. That phony press officer/policeman in their delegation, with whom I got quite palsy, seemed to hint at some mystery about his boss's career under Stalin. He probably hesitated a day or two before countersigning a police protocol branding his grandmother an 'enemy of the people.' No wonder he has the reputation of a liberal."

"You are incorrigible, Jim. You must admit there has been an improvement since Uncle Joe's time. And so we must believe that there is at least a possibility of further changes for the better. If not, what hope is there for Russia, for the world? Let us give such as Kondratiev the benefit of the doubt."

"Of course, one must keep hoping, Art." Doherty suddenly sounded completely sober. "Otherwise I would not have come back to government, and probably would be drinking much more than I am. But there will never be any improvement in their behavior toward us if we keep making asses of ourselves."

▬

No, there was no reason to get excited about the letter, Kondratiev decided after rereading it for the third time. Still, there was something both irritating and puzzling about it. He had had plenty of personal letters from Americans. People he had completely forgotten—fellow workers from the Ford plant in Detroit fifty years ago, businessmen and journalists he had encountered both in Russia and in the States, or the occasional university student assigned a theme like "Is Soviet policy more influenced by ideology or by Russian nationalism"—sought help at the very source, writing to the man whom both *Time* and *Newsweek* identified as the only Politburo member with complete mastery of English. Most of such mail was handled by his secretaries, with only a few letters deemed important or amusing enough brought to his attention. All requests for personal favors—a son's request that his father be allowed to join him in Israel, a mother's plea that the Russian boy who married and impregnated her daughter while the girl was an exchange student at Leningrad University not be denied an exit permit, and so on—were invariably returned to the senders with an explanation that such requests should be addressed to the proper state officials. Letters imploring him to prevent the outbreak of a nuclear war were reassuringly acknowledged, but with the admonition that the USSR was a constitutional state and such letters should have been sent to the Presidium of the Supreme Soviet. His staff was on guard against answering any letters from the very young. Leontiev was very solicitous about his reputation as a great friend of children, and he insisted that all such correspondence be referred to his office where it was handled by a special assistant, a hoydenish spinster who had spent a year in America and had a degree in child psychology. It was her job to ghost Konstantin Leonidovich's answers to that twelve-year-old in Hackensack, New Jersey, or college freshman in Iowa.

Superficially this letter, except for one sentence, did not differ from the general run of such trash. It bore the postmark of a city boasting one of America's major universities; its writer, Valentin Kerner, identified himself as a professor of Russian politics and history. He asserted that he had met Kondratiev two years before, at the meeting of the International Political Science Association in Moscow. Kondratiev thought hard. On account of his chairmanship of the Committee for Scientific and Cultural Relations, he had attended innumerable social functions connected with such organizations during the past few years. But the job was really a sideline and the people he encountered at those functions usually of no importance, so he seldom concentrated on trying to remember their names or faces, leaving the gathering after a couple of drinks and a perfunctory chat with the officers of the given organization. He had more important things to do and think about, and begrudged the time wasted in meaningless socializing with people who, though undoubtedly authorities in their field, were as a rule uninteresting and awkward in their conversation. The only things that stood out in his mind were a few jarring or funny episodes: a Scandinavian hydrographer who asked whether the Soviet Union was going to plant nuclear missiles on the Baltic seabed; several psychiatrists who attempted to question him about dissidents incarcerated in mental institutions; that preposterous French Communist professor who announced that his researches proved that the theory of relativity could be best understood in terms of Marxist dialectic.

In 1980—at the International Political Science Association? Was it the little man who wondered why in Kazakhstan 99.88 percent of those eligible to vote cast their ballots for the Supreme Soviet, while the corresponding figure in Latvia was only 99.58 percent? No, it was another individual of medium height in horn-rimmed glasses who came up to him, stood for a while as if awestruck, then shyly handed him an offprint of an article of his. The title was something like "The Liberals in the Politburo." He had then introduced himself and said in passable Russian that he wanted to discuss the restoration of socialist legality in the Soviet Union.

"Ever since the Revolution we have observed socialist legality in our country," Kondratiev replied. Or something to that effect, and added that he must excuse himself, but that his deputy, Mr. Tabaridze, would undoubtedly be glad to enlarge on this subject. He also now remembered that the article, which he never bothered to read, caused considerable merriment among his aides. Gorbunov tried to tell him about it, but they were very busy at the time and he reminded his secretary that they had more important things to do, and that the government had special institutes with hundreds of people whose sole business was to read, digest, and comment on all that claptrap that foreigners were writing about the USSR.

"I thought it might amuse you."

"Some other time. Now hurry up with a précis of the reports on Poland. That is not likely to be amusing."

And so it must have been around September–October 1980, when he and his colleagues were worried sick about the news from Warsaw. To the best of his recollection, he had never seen or heard about the professor since. The gall of the man saying, "I flatter myself that my writings on your country are not unknown to you." The letter went on, expressing the writer's satisfaction that the supremely important task of negotiating on behalf of the Soviet Union about strategic arms reductions had been entrusted to a man of his caliber and knowledge of the West. Then the usual stuff about how a war would mean the end of civilization, possibly of mankind. Kerner assured the addressee that he and "I dare to say the majority of the American people" had considerable reservations about the current administration's policies and the provocative language in which it addressed the USSR. Having spent a year on university exchange in Russia, he himself knew only too well how the Soviet people abhorred the mere idea of another war. "But I presume upon our acquaintance, dear Mr. Kondratiev [idiot], to point out that your own government is not entirely blameless when it comes to certain misconceptions current among the Americans about your country. You yourself, having been in your youth an innocent victim of repression, can understand the effect your treatment of dissidents must have on our public opinion, and how certain unfortunate incidents (which I am sure are deplored by forward-looking people such as yourself) serve our reactionaries to try to whip up anti-Soviet hysteria." The rest was quite banal: "Whatever the ideological differences . . . , the cause of peace . . . , memories of our common struggle against . . . , what a thrill it was for the writer to meet even briefly one whom he had studied and written about . . . , were he fortunate to have another opportunity to meet and talk at some length, Kerner could tell him some concrete suggestions about how the present deplorable state of Soviet-American relations could be ameliorated."

"Having been an innocent victim of repression." Well, an attentive foreign student of Soviet affairs could have gleaned that Kondratiev had gotten into some minor trouble in the thirties. At the height of his assault upon Stalinism, Khrushchev did see fit to say before the entire Central Committee: "And how widely and shamelessly those vicious slanderers operated in those years is also illustrated by the case of our own Mikhail Alexandrovich Kondratiev. Imagine, comrades, this man whom we all know and admire as an exemplary Leninist and outstanding activist in the highest Party and state organs was, because of some baseless accusation, excluded from the Party in 1936 and not restored to it until four years later. This faithful son of the Soviet people, who both in peace and war has rendered such great services to the Fatherland and the cause of socialism, was allowed to suffer an indignity all on account of the criminal negligence of those who then lorded over us." The statement, the *Pravda* report went on (it was one of Nikita Sergeievich's more unfortunate innovations to have accounts of such meetings published), led to great commotion and shouts of indignation in the hall, the members of the committee turning toward the slandered hero and applauding him tumultuously. Kondratiev, not without misgivings, had given his approval for the touching scene. "It will show that some of us also suffered under the old bastard," Khrushchev had told him, and seeing his skeptical expression added, "Also, it would counteract the talk of your being one of Stalin's favorites. I will change the dates somewhat. No one will be able to tell what it was really about."

In retrospect it now seemed not such a good idea. After Khrushchev's removal, Kondratiev's official biography omitted any reference to the matter, stating simply: "entrusted by the Party with important industrial tasks, 1934–41." But how could temporary exclusion from the Party be described as "having been a victim of repression"? Foreigners always exaggerated. Besides, there was no conceivable way for Kerner to know even part of what had really happened. All the relevant documents had long been destroyed. If, by a miracle, any KGB officer involved in the business had managed to survive (by 1939, practically all of them had been shot), he now would only crave to be able to live out his life in obscurity. His older colleagues? They were not prone to communicating Party secrets to foreigners, and this was not the method they would choose if one of them wanted to stab him in the back.

His initial apprehension was groundless and absurd. He finished the drink, undressed, and was soon asleep.

He awakened at dawn and almost immediately experienced an acute feeling of discomfort. Why? He had drunk temperately, the evening on the whole had been successful, his mind had been relieved. There were still several hours before the departure. Kondratiev got up, put on a dressing gown, and despite his longstanding resolution about not smoking before breakfast, pulled out a packet of cigarettes. Years before, he had thought it advisable to delve into Western psychoanalytical literature. He had concluded that the bulk of it was even more nonsensical than those appalling, dull treatises on Marxism he had to read in his student and Komsomol (Young Communist League) days. Still, there was an occasional insight into the human psyche here and there. Take the alleged inability to forget and overcome the traumas of one's past. On the face of it, absolutely ridiculous. Which Russian of his age, especially someone like himself, could have retained his sanity and ability to function normally if he constantly relived and agonized over the horrors he had witnessed: the sight of starving children in a Ukrainian village close to the dacha where the Kondratievs lived in full comfort during the spring of 1932; his mother's tearless face as she told him how his father had been taken away by the secret police and how his father's superior, when she pleaded with him, told her, "I cannot do anything. Thank your lucky stars that you and your sons are still free. No, don't write to the commissar. Go to your hometown and avoid drawing any attention to yourself"; the sight of his closest wartime friend eviscerated by a shell fragment and begging Kondratiev to finish him off. Had people not been able to put such and even much worse memories behind them, the whole country would be one vast madhouse.

What was it, then, about those experiences in December 1934 that periodically, as yesterday, aroused in him feelings of fear and shame? He was then young and foolish, had been coerced or victimized. Did he feel guilty? But for what? Had he behaved heroically rather than cravenly, it still would not have changed things or saved a single human life. There were several subsequent occasions on which he was responsible—no, instrumental—in sending quite a few people to their deaths. He could think without any inner revulsion about that day in January 1957 when he had to tell the Hungarian leaders, "You, comrades, are the best judges of your internal affairs. But I must tell you emphatically that the Politburo of the Central Committee of the Communist Party of the USSR feels that life sentences for those troublemakers of last fall would be inadequate; they ought to be subjected to the supreme penalty. Otherwise you will soon have another rebellion on your hands." It went without saying: better to have a few executions than anarchy and widespread bloodshed. Look at Hungary now! And he could think about the few other times when he had to make a similar calculation. But for some strange reason, what he did and did not do when he was a frightened twenty-two-year-old somehow always stayed in the back of his mind. He suddenly felt the cigarette stub burning his fingers and realized that with his other hand he had for some time been rubbing the left side of his face. Slowly, he allowed himself to be transported back half a century, to the Leningrad of his youth.

CHAPTER 2

LENINGRAD, DECEMBER 1934

The commotion, shouts, and noise of people rushing, then marching along the corridor subsided by seven o'clock in the evening. Misha Kondratiev sat in the little room into which he had been pushed some hours before after running downstairs at the sound of the shot, and a minute or so later catching a glimpse of Comrade Kirov being carried out, obviously unconscious, from his office. The man who grabbed and stopped him from following the carriers was one of the guards at the Smolny, with whom he had been quite friendly. The guard could hardly get a few words out, "Sergei Mironovich . . . stay there and don't budge," and then he was gone. Misha's solitude did not last long. Two men in security force uniforms thrust into the room a fellow Komsomol secretary and sat down themselves on the two remaining chairs. Before either of the two bewildered young men could open his mouth, they were told that no conversation was permitted. An hour later the room was inspected by a captain in NKVD uniform. He took down the detained men's names, ignored the obvious questions, and repeated the injunction against talking. When one of them had to go to the toilet, he was accompanied by a guard with a drawn gun.

Evening turned into night. Kostya Molchanov asked whether he could stretch out on the floor, and received a negative shake. All that Kondratiev would subsequently recall of that night was that one of the guards could not suppress his yawns and that he himself, when able to think coherently at all, kept reverting stupidly to the work interrupted by the shot: balancing the financial accounts of the Leningrad city Komsomol. But he was twenty-two and despite the discomfort and oppressive closeness of four men in a small room, he finally fell asleep. In the morning Molchanov was taken out. One hour later, Kondratiev was escorted to the lavatory and told to wash and refresh himself. On returning to what he now thought of as his cell, he found there two different guards, as well as the most welcome sight of a tray with a glass of tea and pieces of buttered bread. Only then he remembered that he had not eaten for almost twenty-four hours, and after devouring the breakfast he began to experience real pangs of hunger. Another hour passed. The NKVD captain reappeared; at a sign from him the guards stripped Kondratiev of his clothes, which they then inspected meticulously (quite superfluously, since he had been searched the previous afternoon). Dressed again, he was told by the officer to accompany him. Once outside the accursed room, the security man said unexpectedly, "Don't be too much upset, young man, at the way you've been treated. There has been a great tragedy. We cannot take any chances." Misha suddenly felt great warmth toward the officer. Those few soothing words appeared to him as an act of great generosity, a reintroduction to the normal world. He now recalled the beginning of the nightmare.

"Is Comrade Kirov—"

"Dead," said the captain. "No more questions."

Armed guards were stationed every few steps along the corridor down which he was led. They finally entered a large hall. This, he realized as his mind was now beginning to function normally, was a ballroom in tsarist times when the Smolny had been a finishing school for noble-born girls, and of late was the meeting place for the Leningrad Party Committee. It was here that Kirov had been scheduled to deliver his report last evening. Now the place was filled with officers, both from the NKVD and the regular army. His guide turned him over to a colonel, saying simply, "Mikhail Kondratiev."

The colonel knocked on one of the doors, and when it was opened led Kondratiev into the room where the bureau of the committee usually held its sessions. He had been there before on a few occasions, reporting on Komsomol business.

For a moment he thought he might be dreaming. The familiar, long oblong table was there, but only the seats facing the entrance had been occupied. There were also several people standing around, but at first he did not even notice them. His eyes were riveted on the faces across the table, faces he had seen on countless posters and in newspapers, but which seemed unreal because all those people were in the same room and so close to him.

Ages later, when he was a Party leader and Voroshilov was a senile and discredited has-been, Kondratiev still retained a mixture of compassion and gratitude toward the old man, an inveterate intriguer, as Kondratiev by then knew him to have always been. For on that occasion the marshal alone of the semidivinities grouped behind the table saw fit to give the young and frightened man an encouraging smile. The others, with one exception, sat stiffly, their expressions sending a new chill into his heart. Molotov barely raised his eyes at the newcomer, while continuing to scribble something on the pad in front of him. Even in his state of mixed stupefaction and agitation, Misha could not help perceiving something odd in Molotov's appearance—with his coat and tie and pince-nez, he looked incongruously bourgeois amid the others, who, except for Voroshilov with his uniform, were accoutred in workers' blouses, though obviously tailored ones. He did not dare lower his eyes, but he was certain that the chairman of the Council of the People's Commissars was also the only one to sport shoes rather than boots.

The man seated in the middle of the table and seemingly presiding over the gathering was the commissar himself—Yagoda. There were red blotches on his pallid face. A stranger noting his haughty look and arrogant manner would assume that the General Commissar of State Security (his other title) was the most powerful man among these notables. But this would clearly be a mistake. After a few minutes it became obvious that though the others tried hard not to show special deference to the short stocky man with a pockmarked face who occupied a seat at the right end of the table as Kondratiev faced it, it was clear who exuded real power. The other men were only partially paying attention to the proceedings, finding it difficult not to steal an occasional anxious glance at the dictator. He, though somber, appeared completely at ease, drawing slowly on his pipe.

These impressions coursed through Kondratiev's mind during

the brief interval that Yagoda allowed him to take in the scene before identifying himself and beginning the interrogation. The commissar had to repeat the question before he found his voice and answered. "Mikhail Alexandrovich Kondratiev. Twenty-two years old. Party member since 1930. Secretary of the city Komsomol committee. Profession, engineer."

Stalin raised his head. "Is Corps Commander Alexander Nikolayevich Kondratiev a relative of yours?"

"He is my father."

"And one of our best artillery experts," interjected Voroshilov.

At that moment the war commissar was undoubtedly the noblest, kindest person he had ever met.

Yagoda continued, but now in a much softer tone of voice. Did Kondratiev know what brought the Party and state leaders to Leningrad and why he was being questioned?

Yes, he understood Comrade Kirov had met with an accident. He saw him, unconscious—but before he could complete the sentence and say "being carried out of his office," the commissar interrupted.

"Comrade Kirov was murdered by a class enemy. Do you know the identity of his murderer?"

Kondratiev shook his head. Yagoda turned and whispered into the ear of the man standing behind his chair. The latter nodded and hurried out of the room. There were a few minutes of absolute silence. Stalin continued puffing on his pipe. Molotov went on scribbling. Others looked at the papers in front of them. The only man behind the table whom Kondratiev had met in person, the head of the All-Union Komsomol, Kosarev, looked furtively to his left and then poured himself a glass of water. His hand was shaking.

Then the door was thrown open. Yagoda's messenger came back, followed by two NKVD guards who were escorting, or rather dragging, in a tall man in his early thirties. He looked as if he had just come from an operating table. The top and sides of his head were covered by bandages, but his hands were manacled behind his back. He was pushed against the wall so he was standing sideways to the table, only a few feet from Kondratiev.

"Look at him and tell us if you recognize this man," ordered Yagoda.

For all his ravaged appearance, Kondratiev did recognize Nikolayev and was about to say so, when the latter broke away from his guards, tottered a few steps toward the table, and fell on his knees before Stalin. He was immediately seized again and at a gesture from the commissar carried out, sobbing and screaming, the only recognizable words, "I swear . . . I never did."

None of the others as much as changed their expressions, but Stalin laid aside his pipe and said sharply, "How does it help the investigation to have a man beaten into that condition?"

"Comrade Kirov's bodyguards said that they could not help themselves. They are under arrest. The culprit was quite lucid during his interrogation."

There was an uneasy pause, and then Yagoda turned again to Misha. "Well?"

"I know him. He is Leonid Nikolayev. Some years ago he was an instructor of a Komsomol discussion group that I attended."

"Be precise in your answers. Tell us everything you know about the assassin." There was special stress on the last word.

"I believe it was three years ago, the winter before I went abroad—" Seeing the raised eyebrows, Kondratiev added hastily, "I was one of fifteen apprentice engineers sent by the ministry to America to learn the latest production techniques."

"What do you recall about Nikolayev's lessons? Did he say anything against the Party or socialism?"

"How could he? He was instructing us about dialectical materialism, explaining the classics of Marxism and the writings and speeches of Comrade Stalin."

"But wasn't there a digression, a turn of phrase that, now that you know what he did, you recall as suggesting his criminal tendencies, and hatred of Soviet power? Think carefully before you answer."

"No, nothing could indicate that. He praised the Five Year Plan, eulogized Comrade Stalin."

"A clever criminal always tries to convey his treasonous message in roundabout ways. Did he talk about any incidents connected with the history of our Party, its struggles to purge itself of undesirable elements, of leaders who strayed off the path prescribed by great Lenin?"

"Not really. Except . . ."

"Go on."

"Well, he did mention that leaders like Trotsky and Zinoviev had wrongly opposed the Party line and Comrade Stalin. But he said they had done good work in their time and their punishment was too severe."

Yagoda looked around to see if the last sentence had sunk in and how the others reacted to his masterful way of eliciting the truth. The only one who reacted was Molotov, who for once stopped writing, raised his head, and said with a mixture of surprise and indignation, "P-Punished too severely? The capitalists are supporting Trotsky in great style in Turkey, from where he continues his venomous anti-Soviet activity. Zinoviev, for all his pharisaic and deceitful ways, was not only allowed to stay in our country, but was given a well-paying job. No wonder some of the riffraff that follow them grow more insolent. This Nikolayev—"

He was cut short by Stalin: "Vyacheslav, we are here to investigate, not to judge. Save your oratory for another occasion. [To Yagoda] Go on."

"You were not too young to comprehend that those seemingly innocent words of Nikolayev's constituted in fact a vicious attack on the Party, and on its leadership with Comrade Stalin at its head. Did you report those hypocritical remarks to an appropriate authority?"

The length of time he had been on his feet answering questions, the obvious tendentiousness of the last comments, and, finally, youth's defiant temperament, all combined to free Misha's mind of much of that awe he experienced on first entering the room and seeing the assembled great. He answered almost defiantly, "I did not have to. Shortly afterward, Nikolayev ceased being our instructor, and later we learned he had been excluded from the Party. Probably some member of our group was more clever than I and saw the treacherous intent in the words that to me sounded quite banal." He thought he caught something that looked like the shadow of a smile passing over Stalin's face.

"And have you seen Nikolayev between then and this morning?"

"Only once. I met him on my way to the Smolny—oh, it must have been two weeks ago. He told me he had been reinstated in the Party and was looking for a job."

"Did you have any intimation that he was planning this atrocious crime?"

The monstrousness of the implication struck Misha like a blow in the face. It did not matter who it was who had asked the question or who the people in front of him were. He steadied himself and raised his voice: "How could I have? I am a Communist. Comrade Kirov—"

"You are here not to ask, but to answer questions," shouted Yagoda.

But before either of them could continue, Stalin got up, walked from behind the table, and stopped directly in front of Kondratiev, looking him in the face. Though he suddenly felt as if the walls and floor began to heave, Misha did not lower his eyes.

"Alexander Nikolayevich Kondratiev," began Stalin slowly, as if reading a lecture, "despite his class origins, was one of the first to exchange his tsarist uniform for the Red Army's. He served wholeheartedly the cause of the Revolution and the proletarian state and contributed significantly to our victories over Denikin and the Polish bourgeoisie. He is one of the men on whom we depend to keep our armed forces in constant readiness to teach Hitler and Japanese militarists a lesson should they try to put their threats into action and dare attack our socialist Fatherland. I firmly believe," he turned away from Misha and toward the others, "that the son of such a man will give us an honest and full accounting of what he knows about the background of this dastardly crime." He walked back to his seat and addressed Yagoda, who was shuffling disconcertedly through papers in front of him. "We are all working under great strain, Genrikh Grigorievich, all anxious to get to the bottom of the plot that took away from us our dear Mironovich. But it would be better if you vented your wrath and frustration on your own security people who seem to have displayed singular lack of vigilance, rather than on a young man who lacks the experience to recognize a double-faced scoundrel when he sees him. Won't you let him be examined in accordance with socialist law by the proper authorities?"

"Most certainly, Comrade Stalin." There was just a touch of tremor in his voice. The commissar gave Kondratiev a look that, except for what Stalin had just said, would have chilled the blood in his veins, but then his face contracted into a grimace that was evidently intended to be a good-natured smile. "You may go. Comrade Agranov will take care of you."

What was the protocol on such an occasion? flashed through Kondratiev's mind. Could one say "good-bye comrades," "au revoir," or what? But with Yagoda's last words they all stopped paying the slightest attention to him. Agranov, the same man who had brought Nikolayev in and who, he soon would learn, was as of this morning the head of the Leningrad NKVD, took him by the arm.

"Let us go."

When the door closed behind them, Misha had a momentary and foolish thought that "you may go" was synonymous with being freed. He would return to his usual activities, and just be required to pay a visit to the local procurator's office, as he was some weeks ago when the Komsomol's automobile was stolen. This notion was immediately dispelled when Agranov whispered something in the ear of the captain who had originally brought him in and the latter said in turn, "Come with me," beckoning to two guards to follow them. They did not go into his original place of incarceration, but down into the courtyard. Here Kondratiev was told to get into an old Ford next to the driver; the officer and the guards sat in the back. There was another moment of hope when the car stopped in front of his apartment house. But his guardians followed him upstairs and into the room he shared with Molchanov. Kostya was not around. He would not see him until 1946, on Molchanov's release from the camps where he had spent the intervening years. Kondratiev, then a minister, asked what he could do for one of the closest friends of his youth.

"Leave me alone. You have already done enough."

It was at first impossible to convince him that Kondratiev was not primarily responsible for his calvary. "You see," said Kostya, with a ghastly smile, "they finally forced me to name you as one of the plotters. So how couldn't *you* have?"

He finally managed to convince him and procured a pension, for though only forty-two, Molchanov was physically and mentally incapable of any sustained work. He died two years later.

The search of the tiny apartment took four hours. The security men showed great interest in his collection of foreign language books and technical journals, and exchanged significant looks on discovering his American-made camera.

"Look at that," one of them exclaimed on pulling a photograph from beneath a pile of soiled laundry in a drawer. It was a picture of a bearded middle-aged man in a bemedaled uniform, looking sternly from behind an old-fashioned desk.

"Who is that?"

"That is my grandfather," explained Misha, his face reddening from rage and shame.

"Is he a White Guardist?"

"The picture was taken in 1888. He died in 1918."

After World War II the likeness of Actual State Councillor Nikolai Kondratiev came to occupy a place of honor on the mantelpiece of his grandson's living room.

"Yes, this photograph has quite a history," he would tell his colleagues and subordinates, who could not refrain from an exclamation of surprise on first seeing the picture.

After the search, he was led back to the automobile. A half hour's drive brought them in front of a huge structure that seemed quite familiar. The museum! Yes, it was such when he had gone on a tour of it some years before to see, in what had been a tsarist jail, the cells once occupied by V. I. Lenin and other famous revolutionaries. Now, the building had evidently been reconverted to its old use. The cell into which he was thrust, after the appropriate formalities had been transacted, once housed, he remembered vaguely, some nineteenth-century hero of the terrorist organization, People's Will. But it was no longer adorned with his portrait and nameplate, and it seemed much smaller. It gradually dawned on him that the old cells must have been partitioned into smaller units. Instead of a window giving out on the courtyard, there was now a narrow slit in the wall near the ceiling, unreachable from the floor. When had it been done? Building materials, he knew, were in desperately short supply, new factories were springing up every month, and they constantly heard in the Smolny piteous stories of people from the villages who came to Leningrad to work being unable to find living quarters, of men on the night shift doubling up with daytime workers to share a bed, and of similar hardships. Imagine wasting precious resources on reconditioning an old prison!

His civic concerns quickly receded. For the first time in twenty-four hours he was alone and could reflect on what had happened. Will reality return? Stalin's words, Voroshilov's smile, encouraged the hope. But then he had been locked up. For the first time he thought of his mother. Has she, will she be notified? Hopefully, he would be examined by a magistrate and freed before the news reached her. His deposition in the prosecutor's office after the car was stolen took only a few minutes. But it was idiotic to think that a case like this was at all comparable. Should he tell all he knew? Even though a young, disciplined Communist, and in utter distress, Kondratiev was shrewd enough to recognize that there was one thing he must not tell to anybody who might examine him. He had promised. And then, how could he be sure? Something that he already suspected as being the instinct of self-preservation had kept him from blurting it out during the questioning; now when he could think rationally, Kondratiev decided that it would be sheer folly to tell an investigator what was at best just his own theory about what had happened. During his brief acquaintance with Nikolayev, the latter did strike him as appearing quite unbalanced.

Years later when recalling his experience in jail, Kondratiev would often marvel at the relative amateurishness of the police methods then, as compared with the sophistication they reached by 1936 and kept up well beyond Stalin's time. As chairman of the secret commission set up in 1961 to investigate violations of socialist legality in the period of the "cult of personality" (its labors were abruptly terminated in 1964 upon Khrushchev's dismissal), he had occasion to review countless cases of arrests of "the people's enemies," "wreckers," and such. In comparison with them, his own treatment by the security organs during those December days in 1934 appeared not so much lenient as grossly unprofessional.

After 1936, the first commandment for dealing with persons arrested for alleged (that is, in the vast majority of cases, nonexistent) political crimes was: never give the prisoner time to compose his (or her) thoughts, never let the initial shock wear off, but on the contrary, let it be succeeded by a series of even sharper ones. It was considered advisable to put the freshly arrested into communal cells. The newcomer, on hearing his cellmates' horror stories, on being exposed to frightful overcrowding and overpowering stench and the screams of the demented, would soon crave an interview with an investigator; whatever might happen, it promised, illusorily, to be a reprieve from the hell into which he had been thrust. Those who for special reasons were incarcerated in one-man cells were usually compelled to keep walking during their waking hours; their sleep was frequently interrupted even when they were not called in for an examination, which as a rule took place at night. Prisoners in both categories were regularly beaten.

Restraint in physical torture was observed mainly toward those few who had been selected for public show trials and thus had to be in presentable shape for the benefit of the court audience. Some broke down after a few days, exceptional individuals struggled for months, but sooner or later practically all of them signed, and if required to do so recited in an open hearing their avowals of the most heinous crimes committed at the bidding of Trotsky, the German and Japanese general staffs, the British intelligence. Reading those often insane and fantastic tales, Kondratiev also felt shame at his naïveté during the years of the Terror. Despite his own previous ordeal, he had come at least to half believe that many of those confessing and condemned were in fact guilty. How else could they have spun such detailed accounts of their spying, wrecking, and murderous activities?

Unashamedly self-centered, he also came to appreciate his own good fortune in having been merely a pioneer victim of the Terror, and having gotten off so easily. He suspected, but could not be sure, that Stalin must have told Agranov something like, "Don't be too rough with Kondratiev's boy." But even if so, it was almost unbelievable that during the first days of his imprisonment he was not subjected to any special chicaneries. He slept when he wanted, since his bed was not chained to the wall in the daytime; the guard did not disturb him at night; the food was not too execrable. If this was supposed to be ordeal by loneliness, it did not work. Remembering accounts of prison life from the old revolutionaries, he set for himself a daily regimen of physical exercises, recited Russian poetry that he knew by heart, and then translated it, but this time silently, into English, French, and German. He tried to think systematically about what had befallen him and what was likely to happen when he would be summoned for an examination.

In his mind he went over again and again his encounter with Stalin and the others. Were there some additional details of the scene that he could now review and analyze? He identified two others who had sat behind the table and whose faces looked familiar, but whom he could not place at the time. The corpulent man with a round face was Andrei Zhdanov. The sickly looking individual, almost a dwarf, on Stalin's right must have been Nikolai Yezhov. He recalled seeing them in the group picture of the new members of the Central Committee elected at the Seventeenth Party Congress last January. Kirov? Kondratiev had never felt close to the man, who was a hard taskmaster and, at least since Misha's return from abroad, often gave the impression of being preoccupied and irritable. He was popular with the older Party members, but only in the sense (he never heard it said, but detected it from their tone) that they disliked and feared other of Stalin's closer lieutenants, such as Kaganovich and Molotov. Who was going to succeed Kirov as the boss of Leningrad? No, he himself could not hope to retain his job in the Komsomol after showing what obviously was felt to be lack of vigilance on his part in not reporting Nikolayev's words. It would be hard to give up the idea of making a career in the Party, but then he had his profession. He was going to be a brilliant engineer, and one day he would be director of a large plant, and then, who knows, a minister.

For all his fervent Communist faith, Misha Kondratiev never felt that it should inhibit a young man's ambitions to rise above the multitude. Hadn't Comrade Stalin said that egalitarianism was a "petty bourgeois superstition"? What was it that Maxim Gorky wrote about the Russian peasants? They were "half savage, and stupid." In his earliest, most idealistic phase, Kondratiev was shocked when he read those words of the great proletarian writer and long-time fighter (to be sure, mostly with his pen) for the liberation of the Russian people. But lately, especially after his stay in America, he had come to realize that it was naive to attribute great virtues and wisdom to the masses. In Russia, at least, the masses had to be steered and disciplined before they could understand what socialism was all about (even though the way it was done under collectivization was, perhaps, too hasty and cruel). In any case, Misha Kondratiev was more eager to serve socialism and his country as one of the leaders than among the rank and file.

His ruminations were interrupted in the evening of the fourth day—December 6—by the summons to the investigator's office. It was again a long walk, corridors, staircases. Whenever they heard sounds of approaching steps, Misha's guard made him stop and face the wall, so that he would not catch a glimpse of a fellow inmate. He was surprised, on entering a large office, to see that the man behind the desk was not a civilian but an officer of the security force, a man in his middle forties with an intelligent face.

"I am Major Nikiforov," said the officer. "Please sit down, Citizen Kondratiev."

Not "Comrade." Had he been expelled from the Party? But how, without a hearing?

Nikiforov, as if reading his mind, smiled. "As with other people who have had the misfortune to find themselves in your situation, your membership has been suspended. You will have every opportunity to state your case to the Party committee. That is, if your case will turn out the way I hope it will."

The next two hours partook more of a friendly conversation than of an interrogation. Nikiforov steered the talk towards seemingly innocuous subjects: Misha's background, his professional and Komsomol training.

"I am sorry that this has to be done while you are being detained. We've got to get to know each other before going into that ghastly business."

Nikiforov volunteered some information about himself. He had received his master of philosophy degree before the war, but was then imprisoned for revolutionary propaganda, and released from jail only to be conscripted into the tsarist army. He had come over to the Bolsheviks after joining the Party in October 1918.

"After the Civil War I decided I could best serve the cause of socialism by joining the ranks of those who stand guard against the enemy from within. This is a hard and not very pleasant job, but as vital as a soldier's guarding our borders. That is why I abandoned my earlier plans to continue with my studies and become a teacher."

The would-be-teacher-turned-secret-policeman then handed Misha a letter from his father, and asked him whether he had any special requests or complaints. Would he like something to read?

"Perhaps some technical books?"

"It will be taken care of," assured Nikiforov.

Back in his cell, Misha tore impatiently at the resealed envelope of his father's letter. Alexander Kondratiev expressed his confidence that the unfortunate misunderstanding would soon be cleared up and his son released. The war commissar, Voroshilov, had called him personally and had assured him that the extreme gravity of the crime constrained the authorities to place in detention all persons who might have any knowledge of the circumstances under which it took place, this being done mainly for their own protection. He, Voroshilov, had seen the lad and was sure that he could not conceivably have been involved in any wrongdoing. "This message greatly cheered your mother, who, to be truthful, has been much distressed by the news." His brother was doing very well in his flying school and was soon to be commissioned.

Against all logic, the letter threw him into the deepest depression since he had found himself in prison. His mother, he knew, though usually silent on the subject, loathed everything about the Soviet system even though, unlike his father, she came from a family of intelligentsia with pronounced radical sympathies. She was in virtual despair when he joined the Young Communists and then the Party, and tried to convince him that he would do better to concentrate on his professional career. This led to one of the few disagreements he ever witnessed between his parents.

"Maria," said his father, severely, "nowadays one has to be a Party member in order to get ahead and serve the country. I myself would be hardly in favor of it if we were still ruled by the Jews, like Trotsky and Zinoviev. But Stalin, though a Georgian, cares for the Russian people. I trust Stalin. Remember what your liberal and socialist friends did to Russia during the war."

"We never thought it would end up like this," said Maria Andreyevna, and casting a last imploring look at Misha, stopped arguing.

He felt embarrassed both by his father's anti-Jewish remarks (though on occasion, Alexander Kondratiev admitted that some of his Jewish comrades-at-arms had fought well and that Trotsky himself, for all his unbearable vanity and arrogance, had proved a better administrator than those asinine war ministers of the tsar's or Kerensky's) and by his mother's general attitude. Well, the Revolution did not deal kindly with many of their relatives, and they could not be expected to understand the new order of things. For the last few years, his visits home (his father was currently chief of artillery for the Kiev military district) had been infrequent and brief, and he usually felt relieved on getting back to his own world. But now he was overpowered by nostalgia. When he saw his parents again, he would no longer be so impatient listening to his father's stories about his military service, and his mother's reminiscences about life in what was then St. Petersburg.

The next morning a box filled with books was delivered to his cell. In addition to scientific texts, they included two recent novels in English by progressive American writers. This buoyed his spirits. The impression that he woke up at night and cried must have been a hallucination. Yet left to himself for another two days, his good feeling began to wear off. At times he heard what sounded like screams coming from other cells. At the next interview with the kindly investigator, he was going to ask point-blank what it was they wanted from him and when he would be released.

But it was not Nikiforov alone whom Kondratiev faced when summoned for an interrogation. Sitting at the major's side was Agranov, and the guard who had brought him this time stayed in the room. The proceedings were more formal and brusque than on the first occasion. Misha was asked questions probing his opinions on several issues of domestic and international politics. What were his views on collectivization? Was the Soviet government, faced with the Japanese and Hitlerite threats, right in taking *extraordinary* (special stress was put on the word) measures for its protection, the security of the country and its leaders? Did he think it conceivable that people who on the surface appeared loyal and devoted Communists still could harbor treacherous designs against the state? He answered all these in accordance with the Party catechism. But his face reddened and he loudly said no when asked whether something in the behavior of his associates, or anyone else he knew, could lead him to suspect that the given person might in fact be a double-faced creature, doing good work while waiting for an opportune moment to strike at Soviet power.

"And yet," intervened Agranov, hitherto silent, "several people whom you have already confessed to knowing have been involved in the plot against Comrade Kirov." The guard put his hand on Misha's shoulder, otherwise he would have tumbled off his stool. "Think again, think hard," said Agranov, and with a nod to Nikiforov left the room.

The major's face again assumed an expression of benevolence and solicitude. "I told Comrade Agranov that a man of your age who had been out of the country for two years does not have the training and sophistication to recognize what the eye of an experienced Party member would readily spot as a sign of evil intentions or guilty conscience. Perhaps it would be best if you wrote down in your own words all you know about the discussion group as well as a detailed account of your activities since you came back from abroad."

"But who was it who confessed?" asked Misha rather stupidly.

"That I am not allowed to tell you," said Nikiforov, getting up. "Make sure that Kondratiev has all the necessary writing materials," he instructed the guard. "And yes," he added as they were at the door, "you will be provided with a list of all the Party, Komsomol, and municipal officials in Leningrad during the last four years, in case you need it to jog your memory."

Once by himself, Misha lay down, still feeling dizzy. But soon he sprang to his feet, ran to the door, and only by great effort of will restrained himself from banging on it and yelling. He was furious. Only a fool could have missed the implications of what had just been said. He had heard rumors before about the sinister activities of the secret police, but never put any credence in them. The CHEKA, which then was renamed the OGPU and now was called NKVD, had been founded by Lenin and that revolutionary saint, Felix Dzerzhinsky. How was it conceivable that it would operate in the ways of the infamous tsarist OKHRANA with its use of provocateurs and forged evidence? But recently scoundrels and class enemies must have infiltrated the "organs," as his father with an undertone of distaste referred to the secret police. He recalled Stalin's words, "in strict accordance with socialist legality." Why not write to Comrade Stalin? The mere idea of taking such a momentous step sobered him up. No, he had first to make sure that the events of the last few days had not deranged his mind and that he was not imagining things.

During the next two days Misha kept writing and rewriting the report. Despite what common sense urged, some incidents he had witnessed seemed now to take on a suspicious coloration. Was it just the instructor's awkward phrasing when he told his night class at the university, "Even V. I. Lenin could not detect then anything anti-Marxist in Trotsky's writings"? How about those of his fellow committee members who argued that it was not quite fitting that they should have Kirov's picture adorning the wall in their committee room along with those of Lenin and Stalin, or that if it must remain it should be of smaller size? On second thought, such suspicions appeared ridiculous. He tore up the pages containing what might be taken as insinuation and flushed them away on his trips to the water closet. The final version of his report was strictly factual.

Nikiforov read it attentively, then looked at Misha for a while. "This will not do."

"I wrote down everything I knew and remember."

"Then you must have a very short or very selective memory." The major pulled out a sheaf of notes from a drawer and shuffled through them. "We have signed statements from other members of the discussion group to which Nikolayev lectured, and they all agree that he went in his treasonous remarks quite beyond what you recorded. He discussed ways and means of how the present leadership of the Party—'whose policies brought us to the brink of disaster,' those were his very words—should be changed. Several of those present expressed approval of his ideas. One, Dmitri Varennikov, exclaimed, 'We remember how the revolutionaries dealt with tyrannical officials in tsarist times.' What do you have to say to that?"

"Whoever said it must have been hallucinating."

"And your description of what happened after the shot," continued Nikiforov, disregarding the last statement. "Again, witnesses testify that when they arrived at the scene of the crime, they saw you among those staring at Nikolayev, who had just been seized and disarmed. Comrade Kirov was being lifted where he fell in the corridor, and not carried out from his office as you assert."

"Why should I be lying about that?"

Nikiforov looked at him reflectively. "Let us say the shock at what happened made you unable to remember the exact details. As to the other matter, there may also be an explanation. Not infrequently when we hear or see something that seems incredible and monstrous, we push it out of our minds. You, a good Communist, could not believe your ears when you heard what Nikolayev and his future accomplices, among them your close associates, were saying. That is why you have been trying to forget." He lowered his eyes and again started shuffling papers in front of him. After a few minutes of silence he raised his head. "Well?"

"I want to write to Comrade Stalin," blurted out Misha.

"That is your privilege, indeed duty, if there is some *further* detail with which you feel you cannot trust us. But our duty is to get to the bottom of this heinous conspiracy." He paused. "And my particular duty is to try to determine whether you were an innocent bystander, as I still tend to believe you were, or whether, for some reason, you have chosen to lie. If the latter, you are an accomplice in the crime, and I don't have to tell you what the consequences of such findings will be. I'll tell you what: I shall prepare a statement describing what in view of the already established facts we think you *ought* to have seen and heard. You will be free to correct any inexactitudes in . . . in the deposition, to sign it or not. Believe me, we are trying to help you." He indicated the session was over and that Misha would be summoned back within a few days.

During the interlude, Kondratiev's mood varied between heroic and what might be described as prudential. The heroic urged defiance. Surely he would be exonerated at the trial and leave the court with his head held high having lived up to the high ideals of communism and having shown up the shameless investigators. Prudence urged that anything in the nature of a public trial was most unlikely. He would be putting his head into a noose or disappear into some jail or to Siberia without anyone being apprised of his heroism. What about his parents, his brother? Misha's (though somewhat eroded) idealism notwithstanding, he had few illusions about what could happen to the relatives of one condemned as an accomplice in a crime such as this. But he was young and stubborn enough to recoil at the idea of implicating people who he was sure were completely innocent, some of them close friends. How could they have signed the lying deposition?

He finally arrived at what seemed like a sensible compromise between heroism and prudence. He *was* going to write to Stalin. And since he could not expect the letter to bring immediate results, he would try to temporize and negotiate with the investigator.

When duly summoned to the office, he immediately spotted that the erstwhile student of philosophy was in a bad mood. ["Good God," Nikiforov had been upbraided by a fellow investigator, "what is wrong with your man? All the others have confessed." "I had it conveyed to me from very high quarters that physical pressure was not to be used on Kondratiev." "What do they think this is, tsarist Russia, where children of noblemen had special privileges? Well, lean on him a little bit, no one is likely to raise much fuss about that."] He smoked one cigarette after another while Misha was perusing "his" deposition. It read much worse than the major's words at the last session had led him to expect. After a completely false account of Nikolayev's talk, the paper went on to allege that half of the many members of the discussion group had stopped attending its meetings. On meeting Varennikov, a few weeks later,

Kondratiev was supposed to have asked him why he and some others had been absenting themselves. "Varennikov, with an air of mystery in his voice, said that they had something much more important to do than to go over the old stuff about dialectic, the history of the revolutionary movement, and such. Pressed on what it was, he swore me to secrecy and confided that Nikolayev and himself, some other Komsomols, and a few older people had formed what they called 'the Leningrad Center.' The center's purpose was to bring about radical changes in the leadership of the Party and the state." The December 1 scene remained as previously outlined by Nikiforov.

"Sign it and let us be done with the whole business," said the major.

"We . . ." began Kondratiev cautiously, "I admit I may have been in error about what happened after I heard the shot and ran downstairs. But that other business is all false."

"What other business?"

"What Nikolayev and Varennikov allegedly said and how I met with Varennikov afterwards. I could not have talked with Varennikov a few weeks later. After that meeting where Nikolayev spoke, which I described in my own statement, I left almost immediately for America."

Nikiforov got out of his chair and walked up and down the room. Suddenly he approached Misha and smashed his fist into the left side of his face, sending him to the floor. Misha was up in seconds, spitting out blood and a couple of teeth, and was about to throw himself at the major when a huge guard who must have been hidden behind the curtain grabbed him from behind and forced him back onto the stool. Nikiforov resumed his seat behind the desk. He was sweating profusely. "Will you sign it if we change the date?"

Misha was astounded to hear the sound of his own laughter. The guard tightened the grip on his arms.

"Go away . . . no, bring a towel and some bandages," Nikiforov ordered the man.

After Misha's appearance was somewhat repaired, the guard was told again to leave the room. "But Comrade Major—"

"Go."

The two men sat for a while looking at each other. Finally, Nikiforov broke the silence. "Any other investigator would have had you thrown into an isolator with no heat or light a long time ago, and let you rot until you signed. Why are you torturing me?"

"I will write to Comrade Stalin."

"Do so. But you will have only one more chance to sign this deposition. If you don't, you will not be allowed much time to reflect on your stupidity and obstinacy."

In 1952, after his first election to the Politburo, Kondratiev had received a piteous letter from a Siberian *lager*—Nikiforov was begging him to procure his release. He had been through a number of camps, each worse than the preceding one, was now quite ill, and begged that during the few years or perhaps months left for him he could be allowed to be reunited with his family whom he had not seen since his imprisonment in 1937. "I swear, Mikhail Alexandrovich, that against strict instructions I had received, I tried to treat you then as gently as was possible. No one could have been more glad when you got out of that mess as well as you did. Forgive me and take pity on an old and broken man." Kondratiev's first impulse had been to let him rot. But after reflecting for a while, he had picked up the phone and called the new minister of state security, Ignatiev.

"But Comrade Kondratiev, I simply couldn't. You know what kind of people are among those who are 'sitting'—Molotov's wife, Mikoyan's son, and others close to the highest personages in the state. So how could I do anything for your man? This Nikiforov is a relative of yours?"

When Kondratiev had explained, with the necessary circumlocutions, the reason for his request, there was an explosion of laughter on the other end of the wire. "But this is capital, Mikhail Alexandrovich. It makes my day. I haven't had many occasions to laugh since I got this job. Say, if you are really serious, I shall relate your story to the Boss next time I see him. He might be so amused that he would authorize me to let the old scoundrel free. On the other hand . . ."

"Yes, on the other hand. Please forget my request, Comrade Ignatiev." Shortly afterwards the rush of political developments at home and abroad had absorbed all of Kondratiev's time and attention, and the general atmosphere was certainly not propitious for indulging in humanitarian gestures. Then had come Stalin's death and new kinds of problems. In January 1954, Kondratiev addressed an inquiry to the General Administration of Special Labor Camps.

Prisoner Nikiforov, he was informed, had died two months before.

On being dismissed from the investigator's office, Misha fully expected that something really awful would follow—possibly the kind of punishment cell he had just heard described. But no, he was escorted along the familiar corridors, locked up in the same cell. His jaw was throbbing with pain, but he set out immediately to compose the letter. They might come at any minute and remove the writing materials. Somehow he came now to believe that the letter, once written, would have to be delivered to the addressee. Writing frantically, he described to Comrade Stalin the indignities to which he had been subjected, and swore on his honor as a Communist and the son of a Red Army man that what he was saying was true. He then hesitated—no, they would not dare to unseal the letter. Nikiforov's expression whenever he said "Stalin" appeared to be a sufficient guarantee. Thus Misha found the courage to add that for reasons he had just elucidated, he had chosen not to mention to the investigator an incident he had witnessed the night before Comrade Kirov's death. Was it a huge presumption on his part to beg Comrade Stalin to have him brought before a member of the Central Committee, to whom he would readily confide the story that might throw new light on this frightful affair? He thrust the letter beneath his blouse and fought off the doubts that assailed him: of course he would be searched again, sooner or later. Scoundrels like that, would they hesitate to open the letter and try to beat the secret out of him?

Nothing unusual happened during the next three days. And then, most surprisingly, in the morning the guard announced with—was it his imagination?—special solemnity that he was being summoned.

This time Nikiforov was not alone behind the big desk. On his right sat a man in a regular army uniform. But the insignia on his lapel were unfamiliar, giving no clues as to his rank or branch of service.

"Accused Kondratiev," said Nikiforov, for the first time using this term, "This is Senior Military Jurist Matulevich, charged with reporting your case to the Military Collegium of the Supreme Court of the USSR, currently holding its session in Leningrad."

Misha nodded and without sitting down pulled out the letter. "I have written to Comrade Stalin."

Both men behind the desk stood up, Nikiforov visibly paled.

Matulevich took the letter and turned to a man whom Kondratiev had not previously noticed, also in a regular army uniform, sitting behind a small table in the far corner of the room. "Have it dispatched immediately. And, oh, don't come back unless I ring for you."

All three sat down. From solemn, Matulevich's expression changed to a half benevolent and half ironic smile. "So you are the impetuous young man who has given Comrade Nikiforov so much trouble."

"I want to cooperate to the best of my ability, but—"

"I know. You will not sign any statement that appears to you at variance with the facts as you recall them. Well, I have to report on your case to the collegium this nightfall. So, please tell me whether *this* represents an objective version of your recollection, and if so, sign it."

He handed Kondratiev a sheaf of, this time typed, notes. Compared with the previous version, the "deposition" had been tightened up, its gist less melodramatic and sinister. The 1933 episode with Varennikov was completely omitted. But in its place was inserted a fresh fabrication: on his return from America, Misha had supposedly encountered those seven members of his old Komsomol who in the previous version had been identified with the Leningrad Center, and they all expressed their dissatisfaction with the way things were in the USSR, and hinted at some changes that might soon take place.

"But I have hardly seen them since my return, and certainly have not talked politics with any of them."

"You see, Comrade Matulevich," burst out Nikiforov, "this man is—"

But the former raised his hand. "No, give me a few minutes." And to Kondratiev: "This afternoon I shall have to submit a recommendation to the procurator general on how to dispose of your case: whether you are to be tried as an accomplice in a terrorist plot, or whether you were misguided and naive enough to overlook or misunderstand the treasonous hints in what the plotters were saying. I don't have to tell you what is implied by the first alternative. Such is the widespread outrage at the foul murder of Comrade Kirov that our courts are under enormous pressure from the people to pass death sentences on those even remotely connected with the crime. If my report finds you were guilty of just lack of vigilance and are trying to make up for it by sincerely and contritely helping the investigation, your case will be referred to an ordinary court, and the charge will be one of misdemeanor. Of course, I could not predict what the verdict would be, but I strongly suspect that you'll soon be leaving this place as a free man."

"And what would be happening to Nikolayev and the seven people I would have—incorrectly—involved?" asked Kondratiev in a choking voice.

Instead of answering, Matulevich pulled out of his briefcase a copy of *Leningrad Pravda* and handed it to him. Not since he had read the announcement of V. I. Lenin's death as a boy had Kondratiev seen a newspaper headline printed in such huge letters. THE COURT'S VERDICT DOOMS ENEMIES OF THE PEOPLE. At first he did not even notice the introductory paragraphs. His eyes instantly riveted to a column of names beginning with Nikolayev and including the seven he had just asked about. At the bottom of the column, again in large letters, was printed TO BE SHOT, and the final words announced THE SENTENCES HAVE BEEN CARRIED OUT. He forced himself to read the piece from the beginning. It stated that the Military Collegium of the Supreme Court of the USSR had reached the verdict in the case of the Leningrad Center, the name adopted by a gang of the people's enemies and foreign agents who had plotted to assassinate a number of leading Party and state officials and who had planned and executed the dastardly murder of Comrade Kirov. In accordance with the decree of the Presidium of the Supreme Soviet of December 1, 1934, and under paragraphs 8 and 11 of Article 58 of the Soviet criminal code, the following sentences were reached, and the following condemned. There were some twenty names on the list, and in addition to the eight by now all too familiar, he recognized those of a few past and older officials of the Leningrad Party.

Not all of the first page was preempted by the story of the verdict and the execution. A side column announced that the investigation of the ramifications of the plot was far from completed and that new sentences might be expected.

He looked up.

"I know what you are going to say," Matulevich anticipated his question. "If the guilt of those eight has been established and they were executed, why is your statement needed? You are aware, perhaps more than others, being a son of a Red Army man, that our country is in imminent danger of being attacked by the Fascists. At a time like this, we cannot delay in disposing of the internal enemy who would stab us in the back as the Japanese and the Germans attack our borders. The treasonous activities of those condemned are beyond doubt. But we need desperately to raise the level of vigilance of our people to demonstrate how seemingly innocuous remarks may contain hints of sinister plots, how not only the organs of security, but every Soviet citizen, must be on guard at all times. If this lesson does not sink in, we stand in mortal danger. You will not be testifying to anything that *objectively* is not true, as you stated, quite correctly, last time." Here Matulevich could not help casting a withering look at Nikiforov. "You were not in this country in 1933, and you could not know that those few mild criticisms of the Soviet regime by your former, er, associates, had hardened into a criminal design. Now you know. If you need further proof, I can show you sworn statements of other members of the Komsomol discussion group—"

"I shall sign," cut in Misha.

Matulevich rang the bell. "You will witness," he said to his assistant, "how the Accused Kondratiev, entirely uncoerced and by his free choice, signed the statement."

His trial took place one week later. Despite what he thought Matulevich had implied, the proceedings did not take place in a civilian court. He was brought to a hall in the building housing the Leningrad offices of the National Commissariat of the Interior. Here he found himself among some fifty prisoners, a few among them his acquaintances from the Komsomol. Presently they all were summoned and ushered through a side door into what was supposed to be a kind of courtroom. There were just a couple of benches facing a podium with a table, behind which were seated three NKVD officers, and to the side of them a man in civilian clothes. Several soldiers with rifles stood against the wall. The presiding officer doubled as the clerk of the court, calling out the names of those to be sentenced. At each name the civilian would intone one of two formulas: "The facts speak for themselves, Comrade Judges," or "We have his signed confession." The presiding officer talked in low tones to his colleagues for a minute or two, then, looking at the paper in front of him, pronounced the verdict: guilty and, invariably, ten or twenty years at hard labor. Of the two fellow members of that disastrous discussion group who found themselves in the same batch of accused with Misha, Mitin was sentenced to ten, and Kaplan to twenty years. Misha had no time to reflect what could account for the difference in length.

"Kondratiev, Mikhail Alexandrovich."

He stood up. The presiding officer looked at him incredulously, then consulted again the document in front of him and beckoned to the prosecutor, with whom he held a few minutes' whispered conference.

"The Judicial Collegium of the NKVD, operating under the decree of December 1, 1934, finds you not guilty."

Misha would never remember what happened thereafter until he was back in his cell, where he threw himself on the cot and, as if drugged, fell instantly asleep. He still was not quite able to reconstruct the previous day's events, when his acute anxiety returned as he was driven under guard to the very same building in which he had found himself the day before. But this time, and without any preliminaries, Misha was ushered into an enormous and elegantly appointed office. It was none other than Agranov who took him by the arm and led him not to a stool, but to a comfortable chair, sitting down himself on a sofa next to it.

"You are an extremely lucky young man." The chief of the Leningrad NKVD was all smiles, but the tone of his voice did not quite fit his expression. There was just a touch of disappointment about it. "There are a few formalities to be attended to. You must sign a statement pledging never to discuss what happened during your detention." Agranov paused and again with a smile added, "But you now can see for yourself that we are not the man-eaters some people take us for."

"Let me sign it."

Agranov got up and picked up some papers from his desk. "Here it is. There is another thing. You will leave Leningrad within twenty-four hours. It has all been arranged. You have the same job, the same salary, in the Tula automobile plant. Here is the ticket and the authorization for your transfer and for living space in Tula. Any questions?"

"What about my Komsomol job?"

"I am sorry to say that your Party card has been lifted. But in a year or two you can apply for readmission. Your identity papers and personal belongings will be handed to you as soon as you leave this office. Go to your room and pack."

He walked Misha to the door and shook his hand. "Let me wish you a very happy New Year." It was January 1, 1935.

At the station he bought a copy of *Pravda*. It carried the news of further trials of those linked with the Leningrad Center, whose depositions provided fresh evidence of its connection with foreign powers. All of the accused were found guilty, it was stated, but no names or sentences were mentioned this time. The depot and the train were very crowded; the passengers, quite atypically for Russians when traveling, uniformly silent.

Even when he rose to become one of his country's leaders, Kondratiev, unless his duties absolutely required him, would avoid visiting Leningrad, the city he had once loved.

CHAPTER 3

MOSCOW, JULY 1982

Once *Tupolev 134* lifted off the ground, its cabin resounded with loud talk and laughter; Slavic sociability was reasserting itself. It had been a long six weeks. Especially for a junior official, this had meant that one had to be constantly on guard—foreigners were watching. The couple at the next table in a restaurant or nightclub might be CIA agents. Hotel rooms, despite emphatic assurances by the Swiss officials and a meticulous inspection by your own people, were still probably bugged. Now, one could relax.

Ivanenko, one of the official interpreters, and the *Izvestia* correspondent, Kuzmin, engaged in a spirited argument as to which capitalist country enjoyed primacy when it came to the ingenuity and boldness of pictorial representation of sex in films and magazines.

"When it comes to this, the Swiss are certainly very backward," opined Ivanenko.

"You are both disgusting," protested Natalia Demidova, while trying hard to keep from laughing. She was the only woman attached to the delegation. Having just been promoted from the Intourist to the translator corps of the Foreign Ministry, this had been her first trip abroad. "And the Swiss," she added with conviction, "are really disgusting."

"But what did you expect, Natasha? Hotel elevators that work, restaurants where the waiters are actually polite, spotlessly clean streets and parks—what true Soviet woman would not be repelled by such bourgeois decadence?" Kuzmin sounded rather different than one would expect from reading his newspaper columns with their vivid descriptions of life under capitalism: growing unemployment, widespread drug addiction, moral degeneracy permeating the entire society.

"They are not just bourgeois, they are practically feudal. I was told that until a few years ago women were not allowed to vote in the elections for their parliament, and they still cannot in some cantons."

"We will put you up for a deputy in the next Supreme Soviet. We do need more advocates of women's rights. Look at the composition of this delegation."

"Let's have less noise, please," commanded Kondratiev, emerging from his separate compartment. But he was smiling as he passed down the aisle, stopping occasionally to exchange a few words with some of his aides.

"Perhaps you will settle this dispute between Ivanenko and myself, Comrade Kondratiev," pleaded Kuzmin. "I say Denmark; he holds out for the United States."

"I lack entirely the kind of expertise on this subject that you two evidently possess. But guided entirely by what I know of the general ideologico-social condition of the capitalist world, I would opt for West Germany."

He ignored Pluyev, who raised his eyes beseechingly as Kondratiev passed his seat, and entered what was in effect the first-class section reserved for senior members of the delegation. Here the atmosphere was more subdued. Savitsky was trying to convince Feldman that the next war, as in the past, would be fought and decided mainly by infantry and tanks.

"Do you really think, Professor, that anybody would resort to those infernal rockets?"

"I believe that our government knows what it is doing," replied Feldman, cautiously.

"I am not questioning that," continued the general, "but our leaders occasionally do change their minds. Remember how Khrushchev had the illumination all of a sudden that we did not need such a big standing army? Quite a few first-class officers, many still relatively young, were sent into retirement. And how could they live on their meager pensions? So you had generals and colonels taking jobs as bookkeepers, librarians, and such. Ah, Nikita Sergeievich, a good man but once in a while something would happen to him and he would come forth with—" He turned to Kondratiev who had sat down next to them. "What was it that the Central Committee called it after they sent *him* into retirement?"

"'Harebrained schemes.' I do not want to break up this conversation, but perhaps we all should go over our notes. We may have to hold a preliminary consultation right at the airport."

This was most unlikely, he thought, but he did not want to have Savitsky go on prattling and embarrassing Feldman.

"Is the Chief himself going to meet us, Comrade Kondratiev?" asked the Foreign Ministry man.

"Quite possibly." Another mild lie. Leontiev, he knew, had not been well. "And I must go back and review my own report."

Back in his own compartment, he stretched out on the sofa. His tiredness subsided as he felt a surge of exhilaration, which he invariably experienced when returning from abroad. Travel in foreign parts was pleasurable, but Moscow was home, and also the stage for an intriguing drama in which he enjoyed playing a leading part: decisions affecting millions of lives, the exciting game of intra-Politburo politics, the discipline and sense of purpose pervading the entire political structure. He knew that within a few days a certain disenchantment would set in. It was exasperating to try to change anything in the cumbersome system of government. His elderly colleagues in the Kremlin constantly and senselessly plotted behind each other's backs. Fresh tales of inefficiency and corruption circulated within the bureaucracy. Still, the Russians, for all their faults, were the world's greatest people, and Moscow was now the political center of the world—previous contenders for that title, Paris, London, Washington, all watching anxiously and with trepidation what was being decided here. And he was one of the decision makers.

How much better things are now than they used to be! (He himself had had quite a hand in effecting the improvements.) Could one imagine a scene like the one he had just witnessed taking place in Stalin's time, or even twenty years ago, people chatting and laughing gaily, unawed by the presence of a Politburo member? He savored the knowledge that one sharp word from him would have brought instant silence. That barbarous servility, and the great fear that periodically gripped the entire society, were, thank God, gone. In their place now was proper and healthy respect for authority, the people recognizing that those wielding power may be severe but are not unreasonable. How senseless and even criminal of the Solzhenitsyns and Sakharovs to attempt to undermine society's inner discipline and trust in its rulers, the very qualities that had enabled the Russians to emerge from the ravages of war and terror and become the greatest nation on earth. Were they ever to lose those traits, they would quickly tumble into decadence and anarchy, even worse than that of the contemporary West.

The plane began its descent. Kondratiev's thoughts turned to more prosaic concerns. What present was he bringing for Irina? It would be silly to start now rummaging through his suitcases or to ask Gorbunov what it was he had asked him to buy for his wife. Probably a suitably expensive watch. What other luxury goods was Switzerland renowned for? For Pavel, he himself had selected a rare edition of a French translation of Pushkin's poems. Nikolai, his elder son, could have one of the bottles of old brandy he was bringing.

The engines stopped and the cabin door was thrown open. Kondratiev came down two steps and then paused for the photographers. His expression was solemn ("In spite of all our efforts, the conference broke down in view of the Americans' unreasonable demands." "The Soviet leader's somber expression may herald a heightening of the crisis in East-West relations."), yet confident ("The Soviet Union will know how to safeguard its interests and rebuff any imperialist provocation." "The Kremlin is likely to intensify its arms race.").

Once on the ground there followed the usual ritual.

"Thanks for your efforts on behalf of peace," said Lunin, loud enough to be heard by the correspondents, and then embraced him with a grip that belied his seventy-six years. There was no way of avoiding embracing other members of the Politburo who formed the welcoming party.

"You could not get a bigger reception if you were coming back from a successful conference," said Smirnov with an unpleasant smile. He and Kondratiev often found themselves on opposite sides of an argument, and Smirnov had opposed the whole idea of even pretending to negotiate with the Americans at this point.

Kuliabko, irrepressible as always, whispered as he hugged him,

"I thought, Misha, you would defect so as not to have to kiss Smirnov."

In the lounge, Kondratiev inquired about the general secretary.

"Konstantin Leonidovich is much better and he would be here, but the doctors insisted that he save his strength for tomorrow's meeting. There is a lot to discuss in addition to your report. You know we don't send the agenda abroad, so you might want to come to the Central Committee now and avoid being surprised at what we shall have to take up." Lunin smiled with the last words.

"I shall have to contain my curiosity until later. Right now, there is urgent business I must attend to at the Council of Ministers."

The oligarchs disappeared to their limousines. Kondratiev persuaded Kuliabko to share a ride with him. His driver had been his orderly during the war and was one of the few human beings whom he trusted without any reservations.

"Well," he said after the car moved out, "I do not see how the Chief can carry on much longer."

Kuliabko answered his unspoken question. "Maybe a year, maybe less. Smirnov is getting anxious, and he has had a mild stroke—you know, that supposed bout with the flu he had just as you left. But if it becomes widely known, there could be great pressure from below, and we might end up with Kubiak. I know how you feel about Smirnov, but Kubiak . . . good God."

"We must get some younger people on the Politburo and the Secretariat."

"Or an older but vigorous person in the latter. You must have guessed what that surprise is of which Lunin hinted," said Kuliabko, squeezing Kondratiev's knee.

"What? Oh, yes."

In fact the idea had not occurred to him, preoccupied as he was with the urgency of calling Andronnikov.

"But really, Mykola. This is too farfetched." And, to change the subject: "I must stop at the Council. Will you, too?"

"And what would I do there, Misha? Unlike you, I am one of those deputy prime ministers who has no real job."

Kondratiev picked up the tube: "Drop me at the Presidium, Trofim, then take Comrade Kuliabko to wherever he is going. Come back in an hour."

"As ordered, Comrade Kondratiev." Trofim retained the military form of address.

In the office he disregarded the pile of documents on the desk and picked up the phone marked INTERNAL. Andronnikov was not at the KGB, and the call was transferred to his home.

"Welcome, Mikhail Alexandrovich. I would have been there, but I am in bed with a fever. Must be catching, or haven't you heard? I think I know what is on your mind. We've started to make inquiries."

"I don't think we should talk about it now. Will you be able to make tomorrow's meeting?"

"I must, even if they have to carry me. But I will not stay until the end. We of the lower orders have to leave when Your Excellencies take up the really important business." Though he joked about it, Andronnikov could not conceal his bitterness at not having been promoted to full Politburo membership, having been an alternate for twelve years. "Summon me whenever you're finished, and I will come with all the information we've gathered."

"Oh, no, you must not go traipsing back and forth in your condition. When the general meeting ends, why don't you go to my office right there? You could lie down. The closed session will not last too long."

After putting down the receiver, Kondratiev deliberated for a few minutes whether he should not go now to the Central Committee and look at the agenda. No, better to relish the surprise more fully tomorrow. He personally dialed his home number.

The housekeeper who answered his call greeted him effusively. He had inherited Marfa, so to speak, from his parents. She, then a sixteen-year-old peasant girl, became Kondratiev's maid in 1933, coming back to help bring up his children after the war and now presiding over a household that consisted, rather modestly for a Politburo member, of a cook, maid, and, in his suburban dacha, gardener. When vacationing in their villa on the Black Sea, they usually resorted to local help.

According to Marfa, things had gone on normally in his absence. Irina Ivanovna had been very busy with her work at the Arts Council. She had to go this afternoon to an official reception—film directors from Poland, or was it Hungary?—but she had left word that she would be home for supper. Pavel Mikhailovich just telephoned—he would call again. If his father would not be coming in too late, he would like to see him. No, she had not seen his elder son during the entire period, but he did call a couple of times.

"Tell Pavel I do want to see him and to come to supper if he can. And, oh, Marfa, I hope you will like the little thing I have brought for you from Switzerland."

"What does an old woman like me need? And you should be saving your money, Mikhail Alexandrovich." Marfa's experiences in the thirties and forties had left her with an indelible impression of the precariousness of high Soviet officials' fortunes. Wasn't Maria Kondratieva, after the arrest of her husband, evicted from her luxurious apartment to live in poverty until her son became a minister?

After he hung up, Kondratiev's mood brightened. He and Irina had a peaceful marriage. It was simply that after the initial exchange about what had been happening during the last few weeks, there would be those awkward silences that usually characterized their rather infrequent dinners together, she being almost totally disinterested in politics, he abhorring modern art and music, the only common conversational ground between them being gossip about her old friends from the theatrical world and her friends' past or present liaisons with various Party and government personalities. By the same token, whenever he was alone with Pavel, they would sooner or later get into a political argument. Since Irina was interested in her younger stepson's work and vice versa, he might avoid both dilemmas and actually have a pleasant evening if Pavel came tonight. A quick glance at the papers on his desk—nothing that had to be attended to right now. Anyway, if tomorrow's "surprise" turned out to be what he confidently expected, his career as a deputy prime minister was rapidly coming to an end.

During the ride home he sat next to the driver. Trofim, and in a different way, Marfa, were Kondratiev's main unofficial sources of information about the public mood. He disliked those contrived occasions (fortunately the nature of his duties spared him from too many of them) when one had to go among and interact with the "masses": factory workers, collective farm peasants, and the like. There was a dreadful artificiality about such encounters, a mutual, silent understanding that neither party—the government potentate on the one hand and his audience on the other—was really interested in what was going on, since both had said and heard it before on innumerable occasions. "Comrade Kondratiev was warmly greeted by the workers of ———. They listened with great attention to his exposé of the international and domestic situation, and the steps being taken by the Party and the government to safeguard peace and promote ever higher standards of living for the Soviet people. After the speech there ensued a lively discussion, the workers questioning the honored guest about various points of his talk, he in turn displaying vivid interest in their working and living conditions. 'I was much heartened by what I've seen and heard here,' said Comrade Kondratiev, before departing. 'And you may be sure that your concerns and suggestions will be communicated to the proper authorities and acted on.' In talking with our correspondent, Matvei Lutovinov, a foundry worker and Hero of Socialist Labor, said, 'It is only in a socialist country such as ours that . . .' "

When, ages ago, he himself worked in industry, he did have a real rapport with the workers and was a solicitous, if strict, boss. As minister, he took it to be part of his job to visit the workers' housing and to try to ameliorate their then pitiful living conditions. Now he had responsibilities of a different kind. In the early days of Soviet power there was some sense to the rituals—the middle-class intellectuals who emerged as rulers in the wake of the Revolution needed contact with real workers, and the latter were curious to see the leaders and to hear about their wonderful future under socialism. But now, sixty-five years later, such charades were ridiculous. The people expected those whose business it was to rule them efficiently and justly. The top leaders had more important things to do than to ape the democratic politicians and their even more farcical electoral campaigns.

He remembered Pavel's "But Father, how do you know how the people really live and what they really want?"

"I've had more contact with people of all sorts than you and your dissident friends put together."

"But Father, that was many, many years ago."

"And I also spent some time in jail, an experience that gives one the kind of insight into human nature that I sincerely hope you'll be spared."

This reference to the family secret (of course, none of them knew the full story) usually served to appease Pavel, for whom the fact that his father had once been imprisoned mitigated the embarrassment felt over his present status as a member of the ruling elite.

Trofim's family was doing well: one daughter a doctor, another a schoolteacher, and his only son a major in the air force. It was concerning the last that he expressed anxiety. "He might be transferred to somewhere in Asia. I hope it is not Afghanistan. They say that those bandits there kill all our men they can get their hands on. Even the Germans did not do that. I don't see how those barbarians can hold out for so long with the majority of their own people against them and with us helping the government."

"It is a very difficult terrain for regular military operations, and the rebels get all kinds of help from abroad, the most up-to-date weapons from America, China. Is there much talk about Afghanistan?"

"Only from such as myself whose children might be sent there. But people do worry about the Americans and the Chinese ganging up on us. I can't understand how anyone who even read about the last war could ever think of starting a new one."

"People often exaggerate. And we are now strong enough to crush anybody who would try to pick on us."

Trofim felt close enough to Kondratiev to occasionally question his statements: "Comrade Leontiev said that a new big war would be terrible for everybody. And how could it be otherwise, with those awful new weapons?"

You try too hard to scare the others, and you end up by frightening your own people, thought Kondratiev. "I am sure that Comrade Leontiev meant that no one would dare to attack us, because the punishment meted out to the aggressor would be so terrible."

Trofim nodded his head to indicate that he now understood what Comrade Leontiev had really meant, but his expression remained somber, as if he could not quite rid his mind of the vision of the apocalypse.

The evening turned out quite well. Just as Trofim began to unpack his suitcase, Kondratiev recalled happily that following Gorbunov's delicate hints, he had asked him to buy a Swiss watch for Marfa—Irina Ivanovna already had one, and she would probably appreciate an album of drawings by Picasso.

"Mikhail, how thoughtful of you," his wife said, kissing him.

"All those important conferences did not make you forget what I really wanted."

In fact, the Bulgarian minister of culture had presented her with the very same album on his visit to Moscow two weeks before. But wives of Politburo members were not supposed to accept presents from foreigners, especially if they were officials from the "fraternal countries," and so she had already given the album to one of her painter friends.

"I suppose these conferences were like any of the others. You must have read how newspapers here were full of your speeches and statements. Were any of the Americans amusing, or just stubborn and irritating? Why was the whole thing so important if in the end nothing came of it?"

"It would really take too long to explain, but in brief, many more Europeans now understand that the Americans don't negotiate in good faith."

His wife sighed. She had begun her affair with Kondratiev thirty years ago—she was then only half his age—not only because she believed he would help her theatrical career but because she was fascinated by him. He could talk about politics, a subject she had hitherto believed too dangerous and depressing to discuss, in such an interesting and amusing way. But after they married, this lighthearted chatter about the tantalizing doings on the Soviet Olympus stopped, and was replaced by her husband's rather tiresome disquisitions on the international and domestic political scene.

"You sound increasingly like the front page of *Pravda*," she once told him, incautiously precipitating a very disagreeable scene. After that she took refuge in affecting, and in time it became real, disinterest in the whole subject. Once a member of the Politburo, Mikhail declared that it was unthinkable that she should continue on stage. Yet there were compensations besides the obvious ones: her husband, unlike so many of *them*, neither drank excessively nor wenched. (Or, if he did, he was extremely discreet about it.) Her job in arranging cultural exchanges enabled Irina to meet all sorts of interesting people, and once in a while it took her abroad. All in all, a sensible marriage arrangement.

"Why don't you mix cocktails, Mikhail? Pavel should be here any moment." For all their diverse views on many subjects, the Kondratievs were united in their preference for the Western style of dining, even though Irina occasionally capitulated to Marfa's stratagems to sneak in a typically Russian meal, featuring borscht or cabbage soup and heavy meat dishes.

Kondratiev rang the bell and the maid wheeled in a cart with an array of bottles bearing British and French labels. His wife took Pernod; he mixed martinis for himself and Pavel.

"Pasha's will get warm," said Irina to break the silence. But almost immediately Pavel Kondratiev entered the room. He had on a suit and tie, in contrast to his usual somewhat disorderly appearance.

"Your security system must be breaking down, Papa," he announced after kissing them. "Those people in civilian clothes who walk so casually back and forth in front of the house hardly gave me a glance. How can they be so careless in protecting the building that shelters six ministers and a Politburo member?"

"The love and trust of the people of Moscow is our surest protection," replied Kondratiev in the same bantering vein, handing him a drink. "Besides, dressed as you are tonight, who would take you for a suspicious character?"

Pavel had given him a lot of worries, but he could not help a feeling of exasperated affection as he looked at his handsome son, tall and blond like his mother. Even when smiling, as now, there was a pensive cast to his expression that reminded his father of pictures of nineteenth-century revolutionaries; thank God, up to now he had not passed over the line that separated what might be called passive dissent from active troublemaking. At thirty, his younger son was a lecturer on French literature at the university. He had written a treatise on the sociopolitical roots of modern existentialism, which those who knew about such things assured Kondratiev was brilliant, but which could not be published without some revisions and additions suggested by the official literary watchdogs. Kondratiev had hinted at a sensible compromise: excision of a couple of particularly objectionable paragraphs and insertion of a quotation or two from Lenin, but his son would not hear of it. As it was, Pavel's academic career appeared to have come to a dead end, and were his father not who he was, he undoubtedly would have been fired some time ago.

"You visited Paris, Papa?" The year he spent at the Sorbonne was the high point of Pavel's life, and for the past three years he found it impossible to obtain permission for even a brief trip abroad.

"I took two weekends off. One was entirely unofficial; the other involved lunch with the president and dinner at our embassy. But I found time to wander through some bookstores, even though the French police were extremely nervous about it. "Here," he handed him two volumes of Pushkin.

This turned the conversation to literature and France: the quality of various foreign translations of the Russian classics, how Paris had changed since Irina and Pavel had last seen it, the Delacroix exhibition that Kondratiev did visit since the museum was opened especially for him after the public hours.

"But you could have gotten away from the conference more often," expostulated Pavel, who for a brief moment experienced a sinful pang of envy for all those children of high officials who "behaved" and were rewarded by frequent trips abroad—his own brother, for instance.

"The other weekends I had to work, and besides, Paris in the summer . . . many places closed, crowds of tourists, Americans, Japanese, Germans, especially the last."

"It is still Paris," insisted Pavel disconsolately.

"Of course it would not even have entered your head to go and see the Beckett play," said his wife.

Kondratiev laughed. "How could you think they would have let me go see any play? You have no idea how they guard even their own officials, and for good reasons. Several of their diplomats told me how they prayed for a tour of duty in a socialist country. They feel safer sitting here in Moscow than anywhere else, including their own ministry. You must have read how a week or two ago, someone tried to blow up a government building in Paris."

"Couldn't the French have done for you what they did some years ago when Leontiev was about to visit France? The police rounded up several thousand exiles—our own, Czechs, Poles—and sent them out of Paris. I was a student at the Sorbonne then, and I had some difficulty persuading the authorities not to pack me off to Corsica for a week's free and supervised vacation."

"My dear Pavel, I am hardly that important. Frankly, I think the French were overanxious, at least insofar as our *émigrés* [he stressed the word] were concerned. They are too busy scribbling and squabbling with each other. They are just a nuisance, more to their hosts than to us. No, most of those terrorists are home-grown products of a sick society. Just as ours were before the Revolution."

Irina made one of her rare interventions in the father-son dialogue. "I feel as if I were back on stage. Turgenev—rebellious youth confronting the stern voice of authority. Come, let us eat." And she added, "Pavel, remember you are dining with your father and me, not with the government of the Soviet Union."

During dinner she was unusually talkative and discussed her problems in arranging the Festival of Film of the Socialist Countries—the Ministry of Culture was so straitlaced, and suspicious of anything that smacked of the new. Kondratiev agreed, not because he felt any sympathy for modern trends in the cinema, but because he wanted to please his wife, and also out of a genuine conviction that it was ridiculous for those responsible for cultural controls to view an occasional nude scene or anything that departed from the simplistic canons of socialist realism as a threat to the Soviet regime. On the contrary, a bit of broad-mindedness in these matters might wean the youth from unhealthy craving for the forbidden Western fruit and keep them from channeling their intellectual and aesthetic frustration into political dissent.

"Some of our people have not grown up," he declared, "even though they are in their fifties and sixties. Speaking of growing up, how is Kolya?"

"Nikolai has a new girl," announced his wife and Pavel at the same time.

This was indeed the most frequent item of news about his older son. If he worried about Pavel, then his most frequent reaction to Nikolai was irritation. Kolya was . . . well, a careerist. Life was like a bad novel, one son completely impractical, almost a rebel, the other one eager to reach a high position and enjoy all its appurtenances and privileges. Nikolai had been quite abashed when his father had told him, after he finished the university, that an unwritten rule precluded children of Politburo members from advancing up the Party ladder. Kolya's ambition was not helped by his indolence and strong aversion to discipline. Thus the career of a professional army officer was out of the question. He chose the diplomatic service. But there his amatory propensities proved a stumbling block to advancement. While a secretary of the embassy in Athens, he got involved with a Greek girl suspected of being a CIA agent. Recalled and chastened, he married a general's daughter and found a comfortable niche in the Ministry of Foreign Trade. Now, he was divorced, and his father, only too aware that contacts with foreigners exposed high officials of that ministry to temptation, and not only when it came to women, had another cause for apprehension. Nikolai's new girl was an employee of the ministry, which was not particularly reassuring.

Over coffee and brandy, Kondratiev's mood mellowed. Suddenly, and surprisingly to himself, he was enjoying domesticity. The discordant events and impressions of the last twenty-four hours yielded to a pleasant feeling that he was at home with his wife and son, that for all the initial tension, all three had managed to steer clear of the shoals of controversy, they exhibiting genuine pleasure in his company, he in theirs. Was he ready to retire from the tumult and noise of politics? Certainly not. Part of his contentment derived from the anticipation of what was going to happen at the Politburo meeting the next day. Much of the warmth he felt toward his wife and son reflected his gratitude that this domestic interlude took his mind off the awful memories—December 1934 seemed to have happened to another man in another life. Tomorrow he would take the plunge again into the political fray, and might also have to confront the past. Tonight he was on leave, a family man.

At times like this he liked to dwell on the Kondratiev family's history—his only symptom of aging. His wife and son had heard the stories before. "My grandfather's unsmiling expression," he pointed at the photograph of the state councillor on the mantelpiece, "is very likely due to the mortification he felt over his older brother's fortunes. Andrei Kondratiev as a young idealist official denounced his minister for taking bribes. His boss, the protégé of a grand duke, managed not only to clear himself but to send Andrei to jail for slander. He emerged from prison a convinced revolutionary, participated in some plots, and was caught and sentenced to hard labor. After being released from the camp, he set himself up in the fur business in Siberia and became a millionaire. In his old age, Andrei supported every conceivable reactionary cause, was received at the imperial court, and achieved notoriety for his harsh treatment of his employees."

"Russian history in a capsule," whispered Pavel to Irina.

His father pretended not to hear, and proceeded to tell about another family black sheep, a mid-nineteenth-century officer who was decorated for extraordinary bravery in the Crimean War, but then fell prey to the usual temptations of peacetime garrison life and ended up embezzling his regiment's funds. "He had to flee abroad. Years later, one of his old acquaintances traveling in America was shocked to discover that great-granduncle Pyotr had become a Protestant pastor and leader of a religious community in Kansas."

Irina begged to be excused. She had an early morning appointment. Pavel got up to go, hesitated a bit, and asked whether his father could do anything for a colleague of his who was being pestered by the KGB.

"Kulagin, Dmitri. He has done nothing illegal, but because he is seen occasionally with foreigners, he has been summoned and grilled several times by the security people. And the other night he was roughed up by some alleged hooligans."

"I'll see what I can do." Kondratiev took down the name. "But take care of yourself, Pavel."

Rather unusual and possibly encouraging for Pavel to ask him for help—perhaps he was finally getting some sense in his head, thought Kondratiev while undressing. Sleep would not come, and even trying to read the latest issue of a literary journal noted for strictly toeing the Party line failed to have the usual effect of inducing drowsiness. There was still a light on in his wife's room. How long had it been? He put on a dressing gown and knocked on her door. Irina did not appear surprised, and her smile was encouraging.

"I had a feeling that you would come tonight."

"Foreign travel stimulates passion even in a man of my age," he tried to joke awkwardly.

"Don't be silly. But you were so . . .," she searched for the word, "amiable this evening, and at the same time one sensed your mind was preoccupied with something. What is it, Misha?"

"A thing in the past and something that might happen tomorrow."

"It could not be the old Leningrad business about which you used to have nightmares? But of what importance would it be now, after all those years?"

"I'll tell you about it later [but not everything]."

"As for tomorrow, Nina said she had heard that you might get a new, important position."

Nina was Irina's friend from her acting days. Once a mistress of Leontiev's, their relationship for the past few years had for obvious reasons assumed a thoroughly innocent character: he would visit her every Friday evening to chat and play gin rummy. The old man must really be getting gaga to mention Party matters to that birdbrain!

"You know I don't meddle in your affairs, Mikhail, but is it wise for you to take on new responsibilities when already—"

"I may have no choice. In this business you either keep moving or end up an emeritus. And frankly, I am not ready to confine myself to puttering around our dacha and garden or to writing memoirs that some hack in the Institute of Party History would, while 'preparing' them for publication, turn into the usual trash."

Tenderness now mixed with irritation: couldn't he get into bed with his wife without discussing politics, and why did Irina have to talk about things she did not understand? He got up. "Good night, my dear."

▪

The long room resounded with chatter and was already impregnated with tobacco smoke. Soon it would reek with it. Himself a four- or five-cigarette-a-day man, Kondratiev detested the fumes and stale air that would envelop the session after the first hour or so. Many of the members suffered from cardiac and circulatory troubles, and still continued smoking cigarettes, or worse, pipes and cigars. It did not help to remind them that Lenin, whose picture on the wall looked on sternly at the scene, had while its chairman banned smoking at the Council of Commissars, and that the Ministry of Health kept publishing those frightening statistics. At one time he and the only two nonsmokers on the Politburo had proposed that those seized by an irresistible urge should be segregated near an open window, but the "antismoking faction," as it was promptly dubbed, was hooted down.

"I cannot concentrate on the proper ideological solution of any problem unless I keep puffing on my pipe," declared Kuliabko, speaking for once for the majority. "Would you want us to stray from the Marxist and Leninist path, just because you have such a delicate sense of smell?"

"Mao did, and he was a chain-smoker," replied Kondratiev in the same vein.

"Ah, but he smoked imperialist American cigarettes. And, pray, let us not go into the consequences of Stalin's always fiddling with his Dunhill pipe."

Such banter was quite common before the formal sessions. The average Soviet citizen would be amazed to watch those demigods, known to him mainly from the stiffly official portraits or as photographed earnestly listening to or delivering those stilted speeches, behaving here like any group of middle-aged and elderly men. They inquired about each other's families, compared their ailments, described recent travels and vacations.

Only an insider could have sensed the tension beneath this easygoing mood. Who else would have guessed that Kuliabko and Vishnevsky, now talking so amiably, were in fact bitter enemies? For years the latter, when prime minister of the Ukraine, had kept insinuating that Kuliabko, then the first secretary of the republic's Party, was scandalously lax in dealing with nationalist and anti-Russian tendencies sprouting up within the Ukrainian intellectual circles. Kuliabko reciprocated by spreading malicious tales about Vishnevsky's social background and private life. For one, that he falsified the data about his class and ethnic background. Instead of having been a bookkeeper, as Vishnevsky's official biography stated, his father had been the chief steward of Count Potocki's vast estates before the Revolution. As this fact suggested, the family was of Polish origin. The prime minister's Polishness explained his inability to conceive how pride in one's Ukrainian heritage could be combined with irreproachable loyalty to the Soviet power, and also why his lifestyle was more appropriate to Polish nobility, rather than to Soviet socialism. The quarrel was finally resolved by advancing Vishnevsky to Kuliabko's post. Kuliabko was transferred to Moscow, bitterly resenting the demotion—from a virtual viceroy over a nation of forty million, he had become a supernumerary deputy prime minister.

Smirnov, his status as the heir apparent now seriously in doubt, was loudly complaining of how the doctors always exaggerated: he now felt perfectly well and yet they insisted that he take a month's vacation on the Black Sea.

"Do what your wife tells you," suggested Viktorov. "I have always followed my wife's advice, rather than that of the doctors, and look at me, eighty and haven't had a day's illness for the past fifteen years."

Alexander Ivanovich Viktorov, chairman of the Council of Ministers and the oldest member of the Politburo, did in fact look a picture of health, the only visible sign of age being the proneness to doze off whenever the discussion turned to subjects that did not interest him. His was an unusual story, even for a member of the Politburo. Then a young statistician, he was made minister of finance in 1938 after the three previous incumbents had been dismissed within a brief period (two of them were subsequently shot). To everyone's amazement, he not only held on to the job for several years but then continued in a number of other important positions, becoming a permanent and indispensable member of the government. The secret lay in Viktorov's amazing ability for mastering and retaining the most minute details and figures pertaining to the economy and administration. At the time when industrial and agricultural production data were being distorted and falsified at both the central and local levels, he was the only official capable of keeping up with this fantastic system of double and triple bookkeeping and of making sense of what was really happening in the Soviet economy.

"Let us see," he would say, without resorting to notes, "the Likhachev factory will never fulfill this year's plan. At the most, 75 percent. And productivity per worker did rise by 11 percent while Boldyrev was manager." Within a few days, Boldyrev, recently arrested for "wrecking," would be released and back at his job. Viktorov's phenomenal gifts made him virtually the only official in Stalin's Russia who could feel reasonably secure. Even so, his fellow ministers could not believe their ears when on one occasion he interrupted a tirade by the Boss, saying in a matter-of-fact voice, "I am afraid, Comrade Stalin, that the data you have just cited are incorrect."

This was the only time Kondratiev saw Stalin close to losing his self-control. He cursed and half rose as if to throw himself at Viktorov, but then sat down again, breathing heavily. Two days later, Tatiana Viktorova was arrested. But unlike other high officials who found themselves in a similar situation, her husband declared emphatically that they could put him away, too, but he would not go back to work while his wife was in prison. Shortly afterward, Mrs. Viktorova was freed.

It was in no small part due to this stubborn man that Russia's industry made such a phenomenal recovery after the war. But as years went by, Viktorov, while retaining his unique skills, became more and more averse to any changes and innovations in the existing system. This used to infuriate Khrushchev.

"You and your shitty statistics," bellowed the first secretary when Viktorov objected to one of Khrushchev's proposed reorganizations of industrial management, and pointed out that it had been tried before and resulted in the economy sustaining more than a 20-billion-ruble loss. "We may have to replace you by a computer."

But shortly afterward, it was Khrushchev who was replaced, Leontiev taking over as the first (soon renamed "general") secretary, Viktorov inheriting chairmanship of the Council of Ministers. As such, Viktorov continued to be a stumbling block to internal reforms, and a critic of any foreign policy initiatives that promised to be expensive.

"It hasn't worked too badly until now. Why tamper with it?" and "What do we get out of those beggarly Cubans for all the money we spend on them?" were his typical refrains.

"Why not make Tatiana Maximovna minister of health?" asked Kubiak, who had been listening with what appeared to be excessive solicitude to Smirnov's description of his medical problems. Kondratiev smiled inwardly, but then felt a sense of guilt. He was among those who had strongly supported Kubiak's candidacy for the Politburo, and then his secretaryship. As Party boss of the North Caucasus region, the man had shown himself to be a capable and vigorous administrator — there was no major farm in the area that he had not personally inspected, straightening out local troubles, chastening incompetent officials, helping to raise the district's grain production to new heights. He had seemed to be just the person to bring a new spirit into the mess that was Soviet agriculture. Alas, once in Moscow he appeared to undergo a change of personality. The exemplary administrator turned into a political operator of a kind unusual for a member of the Politburo. At fifty-eight its youngest member, he was not above surreptitiously insinuating to the more influential members of the Central Committee that some new blood was needed at the top, and also that the Committee should recover some of its old functions rather than being just a rubber stamp for its elders' decisions. In the meantime, he neglected his proper job, the sequence of disastrous harvests being blamed by him on the weather or, if that excuse could not be used, on the negligence of the minister of agriculture, though the latter was just an executor of Kubiak's directives, with no power to make independent decisions.

The chatter stopped as the door of the inner cabinet opened. Walking slowly and somewhat unsteadily, Konstantin Leonidovich Leontiev, General Secretary of the Central Committee and Chairman of the Presidium of the Supreme Soviet of the USSR, Marshal of the Soviet Union, entered the room.

"Sorry not to have been able to greet you at the airport, Misha," he said, shaking hands with Kondratiev. He looked around as if trying to recall who some of those present were—in addition to the Politburo members, the first part of the session was being attended by a number of ministers and other officials involved in the business to be discussed—and lowered himself heavily into an armchair. Viktorov on his left, and Lunin, the senior member from the point of service, on his right. Only the full members, and those alternates who were also Central Committee secretaries, occupied seats around the table. The others sat in chairs lined against the wall. There was a brief moment of suspense—at times within the last year Leontiev had felt unable to proceed, turning over the chairmanship to Lunin or Smirnov. On one occasion he had started a meeting under the impression that it was the Presidium of the Supreme Soviet rather than the Politburo that he was chairing. But this time, as if reading his colleagues' minds, he started briskly.

"I am glad to see you back and well, Dmitri." He smiled at Smirnov. "Let us go ahead with the agenda. The international situation—Comrades Kondratiev and Filimonov."

Kondratiev launched on his report: As the government of the USSR had decided (*we* in connection with such decisions would have been in bad taste), the time was not yet ripe for reaching an agreement with the United States on either strategic or tactical nuclear weapons. The conference had amply demonstrated that the Americans as usual were responding to pressures—on the part of their allies, from public opinion at home—and were ready on several points to come down from their original position. The abrupt termination of the negotiations by our delegation undoubtedly gave Washington a salutary shock—soon they will be begging us to renew the talks. The Soviet government, Kondratiev smiled, might then astound the world by its magnanimity in agreeing to go back to the negotiating table. Perhaps the Politburo would think it timely to hint at some political offerings on the Americans' side in return for this . . . concession by the Soviets—say, a pledge not to sell arms and modern technology to China, or recognition of the Soviet Union's legitimate role in helping establish a just peace in the Middle East.

"Let me emphasize, Comrades, that the widespread acclaim with which world public opinion greeted the constructive proposals of the government of the USSR and, by the same token, the crushing rebuff dealt to Washington's duplicitous tactics that were aimed at securing nuclear superiority for the United States, have been mainly due to our delegation's adhering to the wise directive laid down by this body and personally by Comrade Leontiev."

"And a great deal of credit must go to our skillful negotiators, so ably guided by our Mikhail Alexandrovich," said Leontiev generously. "An outstanding job of diplomatic leadership," chimed in Filimonov. Kondratiev modestly lowered his head as the others applauded.

As foreign minister, Filimonov would present the general prospectus of the international situation. Unlike the public pronouncements of the Soviet leaders on the subject, this inside report was remarkably free of ideological jargon and propagandistic touches; insofar as its tone was concerned, it might have been delivered by a nineteenth-century tsarist minister. The outstanding feature of international relations, Filimonov unsurprisingly declared, was Soviet-American rivalry. Some comrades minimized the American danger, maintaining that the government makes our people unnecessarily apprehensive about the possibility of a nuclear war initiated by Washington. But we know that whereas the Americans are too much in awe of our power to attack directly, they spare no effort to damage our interests and prestige throughout the world. They try to exploit our vulnerabilities in Eastern Europe, they connive against us with China, they openly encourage subversion in our and other socialist countries. To be sure, in most cases the United States has failed because of our resolute response. But the minute Washington begins to doubt our resolve and stops being afraid of our power, it would start pushing and threatening us, even more insistently than it has done up to now.

It is therefore in our interest to make sure that the Americans have plenty of troubles of their own. In this respect, Latin America has increasingly become a very promising area. The Persian Gulf as well, though there we must proceed with the utmost caution and avoid a direct confrontation. He would also respectfully disagree with Comrade Kondratiev's hint that we might eventually compromise on tactical nuclear weapons, agreeing to let NATO have a token force of cruise missiles and intermediate rockets deployed in West Germany. Suppose East Germany experiences an upheaval similar to Hungary's in 1956 and Poland's in 1980, and the only way of preventing the counterrevolutionary forces there from overthrowing socialism is through a timely intervention of the military forces of the fraternal countries? What then if Washington and Bonn say to the Soviet government, You must not send your troops in or we might have to use our tactical weapons?

Kondratiev shrugged his shoulders. "Better to have NATO deploy a few of those weapons and allow the Americans to save face. We would still preserve a crushing superiority in conventional and nuclear forces. This is preferable to pushing them against the wall when they might grow really ugly, as in 1962."

Filimonov liked to take an occasional dig at him. He believed, and not unjustifiably, that Kondratiev was largely responsible for keeping him from becoming a full Politburo member, his fourteen years as an alternate notwithstanding. For his part, Kondratiev viewed the foreign minister as an ignoramus and toady. After forty-five years in foreign service including twenty as minister, Filimonov still could not speak any foreign language and had but the most superficial knowledge of the politics of major countries. Filimonov held on to his job partly because his sarcastic manner and bilious expression were believed to impress foreigners, especially the Americans, and also because of his servility to whoever was on top at the time.

"Doesn't Filimonov's face remind you of Nixon's?" Khrushchev had asked Kennedy during one of the lighter moments of their encounter in Vienna, while the hapless foreign minister listened with a wan smile.

Another time, when Nixon had suggested to Leontiev that the next summit be preceded by a foreign ministers' conference, the Russian roared, "Foreign ministers cannot decide anything by themselves. Take Filimonov here—do you think you are a policymaker, Andrei Andreyevich?"

"Certainly not, Comrade Leontiev. I am but an executor of the policies laid down by the government under your leadership."

"But he is very good at that," observed one of the Americans present, charitably.

"Bah, we have plenty of others who could do the job just as well," said Leontiev, who at the time was trying to imitate some of Stalin's ways of letting his subordinates know where they stood.

As a way of compensating, Filimonov was rude and overbearing with his subordinates and, when he thought he could afford to be, with foreign statesmen as well.

His suggestions to put additional pressure on the U.S. met with a generally skeptical response.

"As things are going now, we are getting stronger; they are growing weaker. Why try to push them too hard, when as Comrade Kondratiev quite rightly warned, they might do something desperate?" wondered Marshal Vorontsov, the minister of defense.

"Let us not exaggerate, Comrade Filimonov." Lunin's was often the voice of common sense in such matters. "You talk of their evil designs in East Europe, Iran, and elsewhere. But, good God, they cannot even handle a few pip-squeak Central American republics. Everywhere you look they are getting ever deeper into messes of their own making—attempting to make peace between the Arabs and Israelis: it's like trying to square a circle. And will the Americans' democratic virtue allow them to help South Africa, when its blacks erupt in a rebellion? Time is definitely on our side. Why incur risks by being in too much of a hurry?"

"I am definitely of Comrade Lunin's opinion," Leontiev delivered the final verdict. "After a suitable delay, we shall indicate our willingness to reopen talks on nuclear and conventional arms control. In the meantime we have to negotiate with the Americans, and the West, about economic issues. How about grain? How much shall we have to buy abroad, or has a miracle occurred so that we shall not have to import any this year?"

"Not a miracle, but improved methods of management and hard work by our collective and state farmers should give us a bumper crop, something like 230 million tons," declared Kubiak proudly.

Mention of numbers brought Viktorov out of his slumber. "Actually, we shall be lucky if we collect as much as 200 to 205 million."

The general secretary's face reddened as he practically shouted,

"So it is the old story again. Crops rotting in the field or disappearing, God knows where. What is happening this time?"

Kubiak motioned to the minister of agriculture, who in a faltering voice began a complicated exposé as to the reasons for the shortfall: the state committee on building materials had not come through on the additional silos and granaries, the Ministries of Automotive Industry and Agricultural Machinery had also failed to provide for the increased harvest. . . .

Leontiev kept tapping with his fingers during the recital and finally banged his fist on the table. "Let the procurator general's office draft forthwith a law providing criminal penalties for ministers and other officials whose neglect of their duties causes serious damage to the national economy."

"We already have such a law on our statute book, Konstantin Leonidovich," said Smirnov quietly. "What we really need is not new laws, but for Comrade Kubiak here to knock those various ministers' heads together and come out with a synchronized plan of action."

Kubiak must really be getting under his skin, thought Kondratiev. Such face-to-face criticism of fellow members of the supreme body were rather unusual.

Leontiev remained silent for a while and then said, this time wearily, "Let us have a committee prepare a report on agricultural management, Comrades Viktorov, Kubiak, and Remizov . . . within one month."

Since Kondratiev had rejoined the body in 1957, there must have been twenty-six or twenty-seven such committees, but none had been able to come up with a real solution.

The next items on the agenda, improvement of industrial discipline and changes in the organization of the higher institutions of learning and the Ministry of Culture, were dealt with expeditiously and without giving rise to controversy. Not so the final item, measures to curtail anti-Soviet activities and hostile ideological influences.

"I do feel that our excellent security forces display at times excessive zeal," Arkadi Remizov began the discussion. "Quite a few of our younger people are indeed irresponsible and fall prey to undesirable influences. It is so easy here in Moscow, with all the foreigners milling around. But how many of them do actual harm? Let them sow their wild oats, or if they are really incorrigible, face the courts. But why harass or molest some young fool for an incautious word, or for having a drink with a foreigner?"

Remizov was hardly a liberal. As a matter of fact, he began his career as a security officer. But now, as the Party boss of Moscow, he was both solicitous of the reputation of his city and resentful of the KGB's arresting and beating up real or alleged dissidents without prior clearance from his office.

Andronnikov spread his hands in a gesture of helplessness. "We are just servants of the Party, and if I am so instructed by this body I shall indeed order the security forces to check with the proper Party organ prior to interrogating any suspects, though I am afraid this procedure would take most of our Party officials' time. As it is now, a young person after one visit to our office is quite often . . . impressed enough to mend his ways. I doubt whether a conference with a local Party man would have as speedy and salutary a result."

"We have more important jobs than to try to reeducate parasites, speculators, slanderers of Soviet society," said Smirnov irritably. "You are a Muscovite patriot, Arkadi. It hurts you to admit that the capital draws to it like a magnet the riffraff from all over Russia, whether they have a residence permit here or not, and that they must be dealt with severely or the plague will spread all over the city, and then elsewhere."

"I wish we had fewer Jews here. They are the main source of the contagion." This was Pavel Lisogor, an alternate member and secretary of the Central Committee.

Kondratiev could barely keep from smiling. Lisogor had been touted by the foreign press not only as the rising star on the Soviet firmament but also, presumably because of his youth, at age fifty, as a leading representative of the liberal tendency within the highest Party organs.

"Then why not let those who want to emigrate go?" asked Kuliabko impishly, reinforcing the general impression that his days on the Politburo were numbered.

"Speaking seriously," said Kondratiev, "I have always been opposed to the Americans or any other foreigners pressuring us to let this or that group emigrate. But why keep those who loudly proclaim their alienation from our society? As for the rest, let us treat them just like any other loyal Soviet citizens."

"There is no point in going over the ground we have covered

many times," declared Leontiev, whose powers of attention and endurance were obviously waning. "I think we'd better hear Comrade Andronnikov's report next time. The general session is closed."

As others began to leave, Kondratiev caught Andronnikov's eye and received an acknowledging nod.

Not counting Leontiev's assistant who doubled as recording secretary, the room was now emptied of all but eleven full Politburo members. There was a subtle but quite discernible change in the atmosphere. Superficially, this was still a group of politicians carrying on with their business, but you could also sense the presence behind them of the concentrated might of the Soviet Union, 260 million people strong, with its terrifying military machinery and vast economic power. Should the eleven so decide, the world would be plunged into a nuclear war, or the conditions of life and work of every Soviet citizen could be altered drastically overnight. How vainglorious in comparison was Louis XIV's boast, "I am the state." The monarch's power had been subject to a whole maze of dynastic, feudal, and religious rules and constraints. But these eleven people *were* the Soviet state: who or what could stop them if they were united and determined on a course of action?

Looking around, Kondratiev felt that similar thoughts had been going through the heads of the others. Those elderly and middle-aged men seemed suddenly transformed and rejuvenated by the awareness of their role and responsibility. Even old Viktorov straightened up in his chair and looked alert.

To be sure, there were considerable differences in the extent of the individual members' influence within the supreme body as a whole. Usually, though frequently of late, Leontiev had the last word. Few of his colleagues would choose to directly contradict Lunin, whose tenure on the Politburo went back to Stalin's last years. But whatever their individual standing, and their often sharp differences of opinion and personal rivalries, all eleven were bound to and usually did present a united front against any outsiders who would presume to encroach on their collective power and superior status. This had been the situation ever since the overthrow of Khrushchev, whose cardinal sin lay precisely in attempting to bring the Central Committee into play so as to curb his fellow oligarchs. But now with the Leontiev era drawing to a close and a new struggle for succession in the offing, this collective solidarity might well be put again to a test. Witness Kubiak and his machinations.

The closed meeting began its deliberations. Lunin in his capacity as head of the propaganda department raised the issue of the five high officials of the Ministries of Food and Foreign Trade found guilty of taking bribes and otherwise using their offices for corrupt practices. The lower courts had passed sentences ranging from five to ten years at hard labor, as prescribed by the penal code. But in view of the rising tide of corruption and the consequent need to set an example, he felt this body should instruct the Supreme Court of the USSR to heed the procurator general's appeal and sentence the culprits to death.

"Why not have public executions for those scoundrels!" exclaimed Vishnevsky.

That, especially coming from a man widely known for his own luxurious style of living, was really too much, thought Kondratiev.

And even Leontiev, not given to humanitarian scruples, could not refrain from expressing distaste. "Would you have us imitate the barbarous spectacles that Mao and his gang used to put on in China?"

It was agreed without dissent that the five should be executed in a normal and civilized way.

Next on the agenda was another routine matter. Smirnov, the secretary for personnel, presented the list of nominees for various intermediate Party and government offices. Since the list had been previously vetted by the Secretariat, insofar as the Party was involved, and by the Presidium of the Council of Ministers, where the state positions were concerned, there should have been a unanimous "Approved" heard after each name. But when Smirnov recited, "Kuleshov, Mikhail Dmitrievich, to be first secretary of the Tambov Party District Committee," Viktorov perked up his ears.

"Is this the same Kuleshov who in 1955 was discharged as director of the Lvov electric plant after the discovery of irregularities in its accounts?"

"He was cleared of any personal responsibility in the matter," responded Smirnov, irritably.

"He was the son-in-law of the then minister of power industry, and was in fact as guilty of corrupt practices as those five we just decided should be sent to the gallows," continued Viktorov, relentlessly.

For a minute Smirnov sat silently glowering at the old man.

It was hardly a boost to his standing to have overlooked the fact that a man he was recommending for a responsible Party position had a crooked past. "We shall review his case," he finally said. And, trying to make light of the incident, "I do hope, Alexander Ivanovich, that there is nothing in *my* past to which you object."

"You have always been an exemplary Communist, Dmitri Pavlovich," replied Viktorov affably.

The remaining appointments were confirmed without any trouble.

The recording secretary now paused, as if to endow what would follow with appropriate solemnity, then at a nod from Leontiev read, pronouncing each word with special care, "Changes in the personnel of the leading Party organs."

The General Secretary lit his first cigarette of the session. "As you comrades know," he began, "I have not been in particularly good health of late."

"But you look marvelous, Konstantin Leonidovich," interjected Gabayev, the boss of Uzbekistan, and the only Asian on the body.

Kondratiev bit his lip; why did people of Gabayev's ilk feel the need to indulge in such silly ass kissing when it was no longer in fashion?

Leontiev gave Gabayev a long look. "I am very grateful for the compliment, Rashid Gafarovich, but we are among ourselves, not at a public meeting." He stopped, then continued. "As you know, I have requested more than once to be relieved of my duties as General Secretary. It was your judgment that I should continue at my post. But if so, we must have additional strength in the Secretariat. I cannot continue to pay as much attention to both the domestic and international fronts as I used to. And our old friend . . ." he put his arm around Lunin's shoulder—there was genuine affection between the two men, "also finds it difficult to attend simultaneously to the propaganda department, foreign fraternal parties, and all those other responsibilities that he has handled so well for so many years. We need another secretary of the Central Committee to relieve us of some, at least, of our responsibilities in the international sphere."

In a way, it was moving to see the old man recognizing that time was running out for him and that he would have to give up part of that power for which he had fought so long and so ruthlessly.

"All the other secretaries have their hands full already. Consequently, I propose the creation of a new general department of the Secretariat, and it is my opinion that Comrade Kondratiev would, in view of his talents and experience, be the person most qualified to head it. What is your pleasure, Comrades?"

"Personally, I don't believe that any discussion is needed," said Smirnov, and no one who did not know him could have detected the slightest trace of insincerity in his voice. "We have known Mikhail Alexandrovich for a long time. We have come to trust his judgment and recognize his enormous capacity for work."

"His appointment will be warmly greeted by the rank and file of the Party," added Kubiak.

The motion passed by ten votes to none, with Kondratiev abstaining.

"Let this be the first order of business at next week's meeting of the Central Committee," ordered Leontiev. "But Mikhail Alexandrovich, you will assume your new duties at once and will organize your staff. Turn your present jobs over to your deputies. We will think of permanent replacements after the formalities at the Central Committee are done with." He went around the table and embraced Kondratiev. The others hastened to shake the hand of the new secretary.

Kondratiev was now very close to the top of the precarious ladder leading to supreme power. Of the now four secretaries of the Central Committee who were simultaneously full Politburo members, Lunin was of the same age as Leontiev, and in any case would not dream of aspiring to the general secretaryship. Smirnov had had a stroke. Kubiak was not particularly trusted by his colleagues. As for himself, Kondratiev had no illusions; he was respected but not particularly liked. With the international situation figuring ever more importantly in the overall scheme of things, however, his unique experience in the field might well outweigh other considerations. Of course he would enjoy it—not in the way the others did, by collecting titles, prizes, decorations, by drowning in the sea of insipid flattery. He had five or six active years left before him, at least; enough to get the Party and the government out of the mess into which Leontiev's slumbering leadership had plunged it of late, to raise Russia's power to new heights, to leave as his legacy a more civilized and vigorous society. One could not expect supreme power to drop in his lap; one had to fight for it, and the first test was to come right away.

After a brief recess to enable Leontiev to lie down and rest, the leaders reconvened to consider the next and last point on the agenda. This was the ticklish business of whether to expand the size of the Politburo, and if so, deciding who would be the most suitable newcomers to the Soviet Olympus.

"Personally," said Leontiev, "I do not see any imperative need of enlarging full membership. We've gotten to know and work with one another very well. I realize that some of us [he glanced at Kubiak] . . . feel that we are getting too old and set in our ways. But the Soviet people understand and appreciate the continuity and stability of our leadership. Yet I would not object to adding a tried and judicious person to our body. Twelve is a good number."

Kubiak's face dropped; he had hoped to suggest two or three younger men, but that possibility was now precluded. Leontiev evidently had in mind another oldster from the roster of alternate members.

"There are, of course, several worthy candidates among the people who for years have shared our deliberations."

Smirnov also divined the sense of Leontiev's statement. "Comrade Filimonov, for one."

"At seventy-three, he would hardly bring the breath of youth into our midst," said Kuliabko, who knew Kondratiev's feelings about the foreign minister.

Viktorov was suddenly launched into reminiscences. "I remember Josif Vissarionovich saying that it is better *not* to have foreign ministers in the Politburo because a foreign minister once in a while has to tell foreigners . . . well, not the *exact* truth about what the Soviet government is about to do. And he would, some would call it, *lie* with greater conviction if in fact he did not know what the Politburo had decided. I also recall Molotov saying, 'But Josif, I am both a Politburo member and foreign minister.' " Here Viktorov chuckled. " 'Oh you, Vyacheslav,' said Stalin. 'You've never had any trouble being a convincing liar.' "

"Spare us such recollections, Alexander Ivanovich. We are discussing a serious matter." Leontiev hated being reminded of

Stalin. "I discern a certain lack of enthusiasm for Comrade Filimonov's candidacy. How about Andronnikov? He is next in seniority among our alternates."

That in turn met with reservations on the part of Smirnov and his allies. Kondratiev would not tip his hand as yet by openly supporting the man who had once been his private secretary.

"We need someone who has headed one of our large territorial organizations," suggested Lunin, finally. "Comrade Georgadze has done a splendid job of clearing up that mess in Georgia."

And so the jovial Georgian, not identified with any particular faction, was unanimously voted in as one of the twelve supreme rulers of the Soviet Union.

Two new alternate members were also appointed, without much discussion this time: Viktor Berg, head of the State Planning Commission — "Wouldn't some think he was Jewish?" wondered Vishnevsky. "So much the better for our reputation abroad," said Kondratiev, lightly. The man was, in fact, of Finnish extraction, Russian born and bred — and Yakov Malyshev, the Party satrap in Leningrad and one-time personal assistant of Lunin's. Against the protocol, it was the latter who terminated the meeting.

"You must be tired, Konstantin." He turned solicitously to Leontiev. "We have done enough business for one session." The others stood up as the two old men, arm in arm, left the conference room.

Kondratiev found Andronnikov in his office, stretched out on the couch. "You will now have to get a much larger suite," he said, sitting up. "May I offer my congratulations? Any other secrets?" Kondratiev told him about Georgadze. "But you will be there soon, Sasha, believe me."

"I do hope to be of help when the time comes, Mikhail Alexandrovich. And it cannot be much longer. We have our own doctors who keep tabs on the precious health of our leaders. Rather scandalous, but you would not give me away, would you?"

Kondratiev laughed. The word *trust* did not belong in the lexicon of politics, especially in this country, but he thought he had good reasons to count on Andronnikov. When he became minister he took Sasha, who in wartime had been a lieutenant in his regiment, as his personal assistant. Unlike some others, Andronnikov did not abandon him during his temporary eclipse after Stalin's death. In the late fifties, when Kondratiev had begun his comeback in the Party's council, he procured for his protégé a position in the Central Committee apparatus, then a regional secretaryship. And in 1967, when Leontiev sacked the security chief, Kondratiev was instrumental in persuading the Politburo that Andronnikov was just the man to head the KGB: the right combination of toughness and discretion, a good organizer, likely to keep firm control on the Party's behalf over the organization that could so easily get out of hand. The two men now had to be somewhat circumspect in their relationship; the Politburo would not look kindly at the head of the KGB being especially partial to one of its members, other than the Chief himself, and among Andronnikov's deputies was a son-in-law of Lunin's. Even so, on several occasions, the security chief had, in a discreet way, rendered Kondratiev important services.

Andronnikov now sat across the desk from his patron, pulling out notes from his briefcase. "Let us start with the less important matters, Mikhail Alexandrovich. This idiot Pluyev. I propose to demote him to captain and assign him to duty in one of the corrective penal camps in Siberia. He might be put to use censoring the prisoners' mail. Hah, hah."

"Oh, to hell with him," said Kondratiev impatiently.

"I would, of course, punish him more severely if you so wished. And my assistant, Smorogdin, who chose this moron for the mission will be given a severe reprimand and transferred to a local post. From now on, I shall personally select security personnel for our delegations abroad."

"Sasha, I could not care less what you do with these people. How about the letter, its author?"

"We do have some data." Andronnikov turned to another document. "Valentin Kerner, born in Budapest in 1931, brought to the United States in 1939. No, not a Jew." He anticipated Kondratiev's question. "His father, a lawyer with a socialist background, felt that the war was coming and sent his little son to live with his uncle, a businessman in America. Educated in public schools in New York. Bachelor, master of arts, and doctor of philosophy from Columbia. Instructor there, 1960–1966. From then on has taught Soviet and East European politics at Midland University in Indianapolis. Visited our country under an exchange program in 1962. Then, in 1978–79, spent a year studying the archives of the Imperial Ministry of Justice, 1900–1910. A rather strange subject, considering he is a political scientist, not a historian. Then was here at the International Political Science Association meeting in 1980. That is when you met him, is it not?"

"Yes. You must have more."

"To be sure. Wonderful things, these computers. Our people made some surreptitious approaches during his year here, but decided he was not a promising subject for . . . well, you know what. Drinks in moderation. Awkward with women, not interested in boys. He simply did not seem important enough to make any effort. Don't get impatient. I am coming to it. His books and articles — the usual nonsense they write about us in the West. He sees the rising liberal tendency within our regime represented by people like yourself and younger leaders like Lisogor who are combating the sinister influence of old Stalinists, among whom he lists none other than Viktorov and myself! He is quite complimentary about you. I began to wonder whether I should not place you and those 'younger, forward-looking men,' as he calls them, under surveillance."

Kondratiev could hardly conceal his growing irritation. Andronnikov was being flippant; instead of getting to the point, was he pretending, or didn't he catch on to the importance of one phrase in that otherwise idiotic letter?

The security chief read his thoughts. "Mikhail Alexandrovich, the wretched professor undoubtedly got hold of your official biography from 1962, which stated that you were between 1936 and 1940 unjustly, and in violation of the legal norms, excluded from the Party. Surely that's what he means by 'innocent victim of repression.' What else could it be? It is only the highest Party personages who know the unfortunate story of your troubles in 1934, how in the hysteria following Kirov's assassination you were arrested, and how even in the atmosphere that then prevailed, you convinced the authorities that they had made an outrageous mistake. But how could *he* have heard of that?"

"You know, Sasha," said Kondratiev softly, looking Andronnikov straight in the eye, "that the way things happened in December 1934 was not exactly the way you described."

"I know it as your friend, not as head of the KGB. Whatever it was, there is no way for the American to have learned about it. We are now running a thorough check on everybody he might have met, any materials he might have seen during his year here.

But I don't think we'll find anything beyond what I've already said." He paused, and then added, "In any case, what is unusual about the story? The man is obviously a fool — one of those alleged Western experts on our country who want to ingratiate themselves with us and who dream of becoming politically important. In 1980, he was on the advisory group of one of the candidates for the Democratic presidential nomination. You know yourself that hardly a week passes but an American businessman, professor, or occasional schoolboy writes a letter to one of our leaders presenting a plan for how our two countries could get together and live happily ever after. Leontiev has quite a collection of them. And speaking of Leontiev, you have more serious things to worry about than a silly letter from a silly man."

"I am not worried, just curious," said Kondratiev.

"Of course. I would be, too. Damn the Americans for always pestering us about this or that."

He did say "worry," noted Kondratiev mentally.

Both men felt relieved to shift to other topics: Andronnikov's problems with foreign correspondents prying into things that were none of their business, the persons Kondratiev might select for his branch of the Secretariat, his probable replacements as deputy premier and chairman of the Committee for Scientific and Cultural Relations with Non-Socialist Countries. The KGB chairman was about to take his leave, when Kondratiev remembered Pavel's request.

"This, as you might imagine, comes from my younger son. A colleague of his, Kulagin, has evidently become of great interest to your people."

"Let me make a call and ask. I am not familiar with the case."

As the KGB chairman listened to his subordinate on the other end of the line, he frowned several times and then sighed as he put down the receiver. "It is somewhat serious. Kulagin was first summoned to our offices about a year ago after being overheard saying to a foreign correspondent, 'How I wish we could be rid of the whole damn lot of them. We Russians have always been a nation of slaves ruled by a handful of scoundrels.' "

"Article 70 of the Penal Code."

"Precisely. And this was pointed out to him." Andronnikov recited, superfluously, the relevant portions of the statute: "Agitation or propaganda designed to undermine the Soviet state . . .

spreading of slanderous fabrications . . . punishable by imprisonment . . . up to seven years . . . followed by exile."

"Why wasn't his case then turned over to the prosecutor right away? Or did he sincerely repent? But if so, why have further interrogations?"

Andronnikov remained silent for a few moments. "It would not be proper for me to give you a direct answer, Mikhail Alexandrovich. But you can guess what it would be. I've known Pavel since his childhood, when he thought of me as a kind of uncle. But if he gets into real trouble, neither you nor I might be able to help. It was bad enough getting Nikolai out of his Greek mess, and that was just the usual stuff over a woman."

Kondratiev got up. "I understand, and I appreciate your staying so long when you should be in bed. Get well soon, Sasha."

After his visitor left, Kondratiev walked to the window through which one could see officials' cars going in and out of the Kremlin. He would have to get a larger office. But for the moment, he could not concentrate on the consequences of his elevation. What a fool Pavel was not to catch on to his friend's being a KGB informer. It was ironic that their father's prominence made his children all the more vulnerable, certainly insofar as political transgressions were concerned. Another thought flashed through his mind, that Andronnikov had been, as usual, cordial and ingratiating, and yet something about his manner—Kondratiev couldn't tell what or why—was disturbing. How bizarre: his real political education had begun about fifty years before, when, still a boy, he was being tossed to and fro by the secret police — and now, at the highest point yet in his career, with the most glittering prize of all within sight, a conversation with the head of the KGB, old friend and protégé though he was, could still make him feel puzzled and uneasy. Was it himself, or was it something about Russia that had not basically changed since a frightened and embittered youth boarded that train in Leningrad on New Year's Day in 1935?

CHAPTER 4

TULA AND KAZAN, JANUARY 1935–MARCH 1943

When he thought of them, which was not often, the four years spent in Tula were remembered by Kondratiev as in some ways more depressing than the terrible month in Leningrad that had preceded them. He was then in his middle twenties, when one is supposed to live and feel most intensely, and when physical vigor joins with a certain worldliness to make most people confident of the future—they no longer merely dream of but begin their active pursuit of life's prizes. Yet whatever career aspirations he had had before and would have in the future were stilled for those four years. He could not recall a single moment of exuberance. Youthful ambition lay dormant. It was the instinct of self-preservation that took precedence over and dominated all else in his mind. In the beginning, it was not so much fear as a kind of numbness that took over concerning everything that did not touch directly on his everyday existence and needs. Later on, his behavior took on the character of conscious simulation; he sought to lose his identity in the crowd, to eschew anything that might make him appear different or distinct among the two hundred thousand or so inhabitants of the city. And only toward the end of the Tula period did he begin to feel like a man who, having lost the use of a limb, suddenly notices that the organ is beginning to revive. With one part of his mind he was watching his own recuperation as if he were a dispassionate observer of another person. And it was only the war that made Kondratiev, as it did so many of his countrymen, rediscover in himself powers and emotions that he once believed would never return.

It came as no surprise to him to find, upon his arrival in Tula, that his living and working arrangements had been taken care of. The militia officer handling residence permits perfunctorily examined his personal documents and told him his living quarters were ready and waiting for him. The factory manager greeted him in a matter-of-fact way, as if there were nothing out of the ordinary about the new employee.

"We were told you are a good worker, Kondratiev. Ours is, as you probably know, a relatively small plant, not like those giant ones in Moscow and Gorky. We make and test experimental models of automobiles, trucks, and armored vehicles. We shall start you in the drafting shop where Perventsev here is the boss. He will fill you in on the details. Good luck."

Perventsev, in turn, gave him a tour of the factory and talked for a couple of hours about the specifics of the job, again without asking a single personal question or making any allusion to nonprofessional matters.

The administrator of the newly built housing complex to which Kondratiev had been assigned showed him immediately to his quarters: a large room all to himself and a private bathroom. Plaster was already peeling off the wall, and the elevators worked sporadically and whimsically. Still, under contemporary housing conditions, this would have been considered the height of luxury for a married couple in Leningrad or Moscow, not to mention for a single young person in a provincial town. Indeed, most of his fellow tenants turned out to be local bureaucrats and senior engineers from Tula industrial enterprises. Those he would run into coming in and out of the apartment exhibited no surprise at having a young bachelor enjoying the much coveted housing space. They were polite, but rather circumspect, in chatting with Kondratiev. Again, no personal questions, no invitations to drop in for a glass of tea or vodka to welcome a newcomer into their midst.

The same restraint was observed by his fellow workers. Some younger engineers would, after he had been at the factory for a while, give vent to their curiosity and start questioning him about his American experiences, but more often than not they would check themselves and shift the conversation to other topics: whether he had seen the historical monuments of Tula, how he liked provincial life after the splendors of Leningrad.

Had everybody he would come into contact with here been told about him and what had happened? This was early 1935. For all the shock of the Kirov business, Soviet society was still light-years away from the Great Fear that would engulf it in 1937–1939, when people would shun strangers like the plague, when even the most intimate friends, and husbands and wives would suspect each other of being informers. Yet already the mere inkling that the newcomer had had a brush with the dreaded NKVD was sufficient to make almost everyone he encountered desist—Slavic effusiveness and tradition of hospitality notwithstanding—from trying to relieve his loneliness in a city as yet completely strange to him.

To be sure, in his frame of mind, Kondratiev would have been suspicious of anyone unduly friendly or inquisitive about his past. It was with a certain unease that, three weeks after his arrival, he greeted the first breach in his isolation: an invitation to dine with the Perventsevs.

His hosts and their little daughter lived in quarters hardly more commodious than his own: two rooms and a kitchen that they shared with another family. Perventsev, taciturn and strictly business at work, turned out to be an amiable and tactful dinner companion. Not a word about the circumstances that brought Misha to Tula. In fact, divining his guest's mood, he was actually loquacious, talking about his own youth in prewar Moscow and then his military service, skipping nimbly over the Revolution and the Civil War. Later on, Kondratiev learned that Perventsev had served with the Whites, had been taken prisoner in 1919, and because he was an officer had been about to be shot. But when his Bolshevik captors learned that he had been an engineering student, they had given him the choice of being the equipment specialist in the Red Army's only armored car unit. Perventsev described his career under the Soviets. First, he had had to eke out his living as a cab driver.

"But I did it in Moscow, whereas my two cousins are still following the same profession in Paris. But then, they were born counts," he said with a grimace.

Valeria Perventseva gave her husband an anxious glance, the only one in the evening, at this reference to his family's social background. When it eventually became possible for a man with his class origins to enroll in the university, he completed his engineering degree, just as the infant Soviet automobile industry was launched on a huge expansion.

"But take our roads, and even city streets. How can the cars and trucks we produce—"

"No, don't," said Valeria Perventseva decisively, determined not to let her husband indulge in what Kondratiev was subsequently to learn was his pet peeve: how the various branches of the Soviet economy were being poorly coordinated in the haste to fulfill the targets of the Five Year Plans, and how the cars and trucks produced to Western specifications were largely unsuitable to the Soviet conditions. An attractive brunette, in her late thirties like her husband, Perventseva steered the conversation in Misha's direction, while still avoiding the ticklish aspects of his situation.

His lodgings were most comfortable, he assured her, and the food in the factory canteen where he took all his meals was not too bad. He hadn't had time yet to get to know the city and, no, he had not joined any clubs or circles.

"If you ever played before, why not try out for our soccer team?" said Perventsev. "We still don't think it shocking, as evidently they do in Moscow and Leningrad, to have our managerial personnel play alongside the workers. I personally believe that it is good for the men's morale."

Kondratiev promised to give it some thought once the soccer season approached, and rose to say good-bye.

"You will come again," said his hostess firmly. "We are usually at home in the evening. There are so few places to go anyway, and then there is our six-year-old."

But it would be a few weeks before Kondratiev would avail himself of this standing invitation. For all the liking he conceived for the Perventsevs, he sensed the conscious effort on their part to avoid anything that might remotely touch on his misadventure. It had been a pleasant, but not quite relaxing, evening.

Shortly afterward, another invitation came his way. In fact he had long half expected it, and was not shocked to receive a letter with the address of the local office of the NKVD on the envelope. He soon realized that the "invitation" was couched in a way to cause the least possible alarm to the recipient. He had not been summoned by a phone call at his place of work; the letter did not specify the time he had to appear. Captain Mazurov presented his compliments to Citizen Kondratiev, and asked him at his leisure to call his office, so they could meet at a mutually agreeable time.

He called immediately, and the next day Misha entered what was one of the most imposing public buildings in Tula. He felt neither trepidation nor anger, but something he could not have described, perhaps a mixture of weariness and curiosity. Captain Mazurov was all solicitude. He had been asked—he did not say by whom—to ascertain whether his visitor was beginning to feel at home in Tula, and whether there was anything he needed or that "they" could do for him.

"But surely a young man needs more than that," he said, on receiving reassuring answers about Kondratiev's living and working conditions.

Misha told him that he might join the factory soccer club.

The captain frowned. "Some might think that it is not conducive to factory discipline to have staff people and workers play alongside each other." Then, with a broad smile, he added that he had a personal interest in the question: "Last fall our own team was edged out by the factory's for the championship of the city. So we would not like them to get another good athlete."

Besides, one did not meet girls playing soccer. How about the skating club? But, he added, all these were his personal suggestions, and he would not want Kondratiev to feel that he was under any obligation to follow them. And the same also held in connection with what he was about to say.

"Many people," continued Mazurov, reciting what he must have said many times before, "have the mistaken notion that the NKVD deals just with police matters. In fact, one of its jobs, indeed the main one right now, is to assist in the fulfillment of the Five Year Plan, to help transform rural Russia into a mighty industrial power. As Comrade Stalin said, this must be done in a hurry, for otherwise we would face grave dangers of the imperialists and Fascists attacking the Socialist Fatherland. You read the papers, don't you?"

Kondratiev allowed that he did.

"Well, I don't have to tell you what Hitler is doing in Germany and how the Japanese imperialists, having ravaged China, are openly threatening our own country. You, as every patriotic citizen must, want to help in the struggle for industrialization to make our country so strong that if the Fascist scoundrels attack us, they would be crushed."

Of course he did, said Misha, and that was why he spent most of his free time studying to master his profession, so as to do as good a job as possible.

"But you can help in yet another way. One of our tasks is to keep the proper authorities informed about the morale of the working force and the technical staff of our burgeoning industry. You are an intelligent and well-educated man. Suppose you would report to us from time to time, in writing if you prefer, about what goes on in your enterprise, how the people feel about their work, about our social system, how well they tackle their jobs, how well the management personnel get along with the men. In brief, anything that strikes you as noteworthy."

It was as if listening to another man that Kondratiev heard himself replying in an even voice, without any pause or hesitation. He appreciated Mazurov's offer to entrust him with such an important responsibility. But he was new to the city and had just joined the plant's staff. He felt that, for the time being, he had to devote himself entirely to his job and studies. Under the circumstances, his reports would certainly be superficial or misleading. Later on, when he had familiarized himself with the conditions at his place of work, he would not hesitate to share his observations and, if need be, criticisms with the proper authority, which in this case was Comrade Artemyev, the director of the enterprise.

Mazurov raised his hand to cut him off, but Misha did not heed his warning and continued that he had read a recent speech given by Comrade Stalin in which he stated very clearly and emphatically that the full authority for the running of a factory lay with its manager. All employees, even the factory's union and Party secretaries, are subordinate to him and must communicate with other officials only through him. Were Comrade Artemyev to authorize him, Kondratiev, to share any information with the security organs, he of course would consider it his duty to do so instantly. Had Comrade Mazurov read the speech in question?

A momentary flicker of fury on the secret policeman's face gave way almost instantly to an expression of solemnity. "I read and reread it as I do everything our Leader says and writes. Yes, Comrade Stalin's precepts must guide us in all our actions."

The interview was over. Mazurov walked his guest to the door and shook his hand cordially.

"Remember, if there is anything you need, just let us know."

"Oh, how I would like to get my hands on him," Mazurov was saying a few minutes later in the office of the chief of the Tula NKVD. "The insolent brat, presuming to give me lessons about Comrade Stalin's speeches."

"I am afraid you will have to restrain your impulses," said his superior. "The message from Leningrad was explicit: 'Try him, but under no circumstances lean on him.' "

"How can we preserve respect for Soviet power when a young son of a bitch like that can mock an officer of the NKVD?"

"In our profession we cannot afford to hold personal grudges," observed his chief, philosophically. "But cheer up, Mazurov. I think that very soon there will be plenty of others on whom you will be able to get your hands."

What made him say the things he had? pondered Misha, once out in the street. How did he happen to come up with those quotations from Stalin's speech, which he now realized must have been given three or four years before? He felt no elation at besting the security man: all he knew at the moment was that he had been reprieved. Only much, much later would Kondratiev recognize the interview as the first manifestation of those powers and skills that had carried him to the Politburo, the first inkling of the determination to reach a position from where he could make the Mazurovs of this world tremble.

His Tula existence settled into an almost invariable pattern: factory in the daytime, solitary evenings reading Russian classics and whatever English and French novels one could procure from the limited library resources of a provincial town. After a bit of reflection he decided not to join either the soccer team or the skating club. The fewer associations one had, his instinct told him, the safer one was in the Russia of 1935. He felt no imminent danger; it was obvious that some powerful personage—was it Voroshilov or Stalin himself?—had spoken a word that so far had shielded him from the worst. Yet how long would this word protect him? Great men tended to forget Misha Kondratievs. They had so many other things on their minds. And recalling the expressions on Agranov's and Mazurov's faces, he knew that those people did *not* forget when a prospective prey had been snatched away from their clutches. Above all, nothing and nobody would protect him were he ever to blurt out, or as much as hint at, the secret he carried with him. How could he form a close friendship, go to bed with a woman, or get drunk, and yet trust himself not to babble out something that would make one suspect what was hidden in the recesses of his mind?

The burden of this knowledge seemed so insufferable that at times he was on the point of writing Comrade Stalin and this time telling him *all* he knew. But then immediately Kondratiev's mind was assailed by doubts. Did his letter written in prison in fact reach Stalin? And even if it did, would this one? There was little doubt that the local NKVD's solicitude extended to his correspondence: he could virtually see Mazurov or his like opening and avidly scrutinizing his letters. Besides, why should Comrade Stalin, even if it was his word that had saved Misha from the same fate as his friends, believe a fantastic sounding tale related by a twenty-two-year-old youth? How could he, with his genius-like insight into human nature, have permitted all those Leningrad horrors to take place, if he as much as suspected what the true story was?

It was again only in retrospect that Kondratiev recognized that his belief in Stalin's genius was yet another manifestation of that instinct for self-preservation that guided all his actions during those grim years. It enabled him to live at peace with himself, and fostered the delusion that he could understand the reasons for the terrible things that were happening in his native land. Like the medieval Christian who found no contradiction between his faith in the omnipotent deity and the obvious manifestations of evil in the world, so Misha devoutly believed both in Stalin's infallibility and in the existence of some dark forces bent on frustrating the Leader's wise and benevolent intentions. These dark forces had obviously penetrated various organs of the government itself, certainly the NKVD; their agents inflicted suffering on innocent men and women, so as to discredit the Soviet system in the eyes of the people and undermine their faith in Stalin. As to the final result of this struggle, there could be no doubt: light must prevail over darkness; Comrade Stalin would unmask and deal appropriately with the hostile elements, including those who may have managed to infiltrate his immediate entourage. But for the moment, one had to be wary and vigilant—one's neighbor, the man on the trolley trying to engage you in a conversation, might be one of them. . . .

This interpretation of Soviet reality worked out in solitary meditation proved to be of enormous relief to young Kondratiev. It lifted the burden of guilt and fear from his mind—no, nothing and nobody except Stalin could make him reveal the story of that incident in Leningrad. An element of youthful fantasy reentered Misha's thoughts: some spectacular achievement brings him to the attention and then into the presence of the Leader. There he would make a full avowal; let him be punished for the dereliction of not revealing information of such grave importance before, but in view of what had happened he felt he could not communicate through a third person or a letter. He had to tell it in strict privacy to Comrade Stalin himself. Stalin would understand and believe Misha, and then mete out stern justice to those who had abused his trust and sought to deceive the Soviet people. In his more sober moments he recognized such thoughts for what they were: daydreaming. Still, the vision of the audience with Stalin was a comforting one and helped to allay his anxiety. He was not concealing the truth; he was waiting for the only opportunity when he could tell all in good conscience. Until then, why think and worry about it excessively?

The test of the mental fortifications he had erected came during the August vacations when he visited his parents' home. He had both longed for and dreaded the visit. He wanted to be with his mother and father almost as badly as during his lowest moments when in the prison cell, but he was terrified at the thought that they might see through the answers he would have to give to their questions. It was then a great relief, though at the same time a bit strange, that they did not ask any questions touching on the details of his ordeal. He could not have known then that, coincidentally with his release, his father had received a letter from Voroshilov that concluded: "And so your boy is free and safe. Believe me, Alexander Nikolayevich, I write this as an old friend rather than as your superior: it would be best if you and dear Maria Andreyevna avoided any discussion of the dreadful business when you see him. This is important not only for his sake, but also yours."

His father, indeed, could not restrain himself when greeting him. "The scoundrels—but I knew that Stalin and Voroshilov would not let them harm an innocent Russian lad." But he immediately switched to questioning Misha about his new job and life in Tula. His parents were perspicacious people; they displayed no special solicitude toward Misha, conversation flowed easily, the visit passed almost the same way as any other time he had come down from Leningrad.

The "almost" touched on a single incident. They were sitting around the dinner table and laughing over some story of prewar regimental life related by the elder Kondratiev when his brother exclaimed, "But Misha, you lost some teeth! What happened?"

"I stumbled and fell while at work." He answered in a natural tone of voice, but at the same time realized that he was rubbing his cheek and must have done it before in moments of stress.

"Well, see our military dentist. I dread to think what the ones in Tula must be like," said his mother, a bit too lightheartedly.

His father's cheerful mood reflected not only his pleasure in seeing his two sons—Vladimir was on leave after graduating from the air academy—but also the recent developments in defense and foreign policy.

"We have done with . . ." he groped for the phrase, "old superstitions and are getting a professional, modern army. The rank of marshal has been restored. There is still some silly prejudice against reintroducing that of general, but it won't be long. The other day in Moscow, Tukhachevsky, now Marshal of the Soviet Union, said to me, 'Don't think you are dreaming, Sasha, when you are transformed from a corps commander into a colonel general and those unseemly insignia on the collar tabs are replaced by epaulets. Just like old times, eh?' Tukhachevsky will undoubtedly be commander in chief if the Fascists attack us. This shows again how farseeing and magnanimous Stalin is. He and Tukhachevsky were at sword points in 1920, and Stalin has never liked him. But with him the interests of the Fatherland come first. And Tukhachevsky is the best military mind we have."

"Oh, I do hope we get a crack at the Japanese and the Hitlerites!" exclaimed Vladimir.

His father slowly shook his head. "At your age I felt the same way you do, Volodya. But no one who has been through the Great War, and especially a soldier, could wish for another one. But if we must fight it will not be like the last one: I remember in 1915 our battery ran out of shells just when the Germans opened their offensive and half of the soldiers in our division had worn out their boots and could not find new ones. Why talk about war?" he added, seeing the unhappy expression on his wife's face. "We have just signed a military alliance with France. Hitler may be a madman, but his generals understand what it would mean to fight both us and what is still the best army in Europe. And in a few more years, with our industry growing by leaps and bounds, we should be so strong no one would dare to attack us."

"Then we should attack Hitler and liberate the German workers. They will surely rise once we cross the border," insisted Vladimir.

The elder Kondratievs exchanged half amused, half exasperated looks, but did not say anything.

The visit raised Misha's spirits. He had passed the test. And though not a Party member, he still felt himself to be a Communist and was greatly cheered by his father's confident outlook on the future. Maybe what had happened in Leningrad had been just a single terrible interlude, and that in general, as Comrade Stalin had said in 1934 and as countless posters still instructed the Soviet citizen, "Life has become better; life has become gayer."

A few days back in Tula were enough to dampen his mood. His loneliness was all the more oppressive after the warmth of the parental home. He remembered his brother's words, which at the time had indeed seemed puerile, but now the prospect of a war suddenly appeared to him almost alluring—the comradeship of military life would fill in that great void in his life. At the New Year's Eve party for the staff, he was greatly tempted when Filipov, the secretary of the factory's Party organization, approached him and asked whether he would not like to apply for readmission.

"We know you had some troubles in the past, but we all have come to know you as a loyal comrade and hard worker, and I am sure there would not be a single voice raised against you."

He was about to say, "I shall be glad to," when something inside him told him to wait and think. He answered that he was greatly honored, but would have to think it over. He did think hard during the next few days and recalled the NKVD chief in Leningrad telling him precisely one year before that in a "year or so" he would be able to rejoin the Party. He was still dangling at the end of a string manipulated by someone somewhere. He sought out Filipov and, after thanking him again, explained that after much reflection he had decided he was still not worthy or prepared for the honor and responsibilities of membership in the All-Union Communist Party.

"I was removed as a result of gross negligence, or, to put it otherwise, stupidity on my part, and my comrades justly felt that I was not mature enough for the high calling of Party member. Ever since then, I have tried to improve my theoretical and practical knowledge of what it means to be a Communist, but I feel my education is still not complete. When it is, you may be sure I shall reapply. Comrade Stalin, I recall, said, 'One does not have to be a Bolshevik to serve loyally the Soviet state and the working class.' "

Filipov was genuinely moved by such modesty. He cordially shook his hand and said, "Party card or not, I feel you are already one of us, Misha."

A few months later, Kondratiev had an occasion to thank his lucky stars. Filipov was arrested, the accusation/verdict stating that he was a Trotskyite who arranged for admission into the Party of hostile class elements, so as to organize a wrecking-sabotage group within the factory. Major (as he now was) Mazurov was especially commended in the official press communiqué for unmasking this nest of the people's enemies before it could embark on its wrecking activities. In 1939, Filipov, who in the meantime died in a camp, was fully rehabilitated. It turned out that he had never been a Trotskyite—the confusion arose from the unhappy man's having listed in his curriculum vitae as his residence in the early twenties Trotsk, the city then indeed named after the erstwhile great of the Revolution, but quickly renamed once he was identified as "the people's enemy and agent of the German general staff."

The tragic mistake was one of the many charges brought then against Colonel Mazurov, until 1939 head of Tula security, but eventually "unmasked as a wrecker, sentenced to suffer the supreme penalty, and shot for having, for careerist purposes, imprisoned and repressed many innocent people, using impermissible methods of investigation, and numerous other violations of socialist legality."

But that happy, in Kondratiev's memory, event (indeed the only occasion he recalled of having laughed at hearing of someone's death) still lay in the future. The years 1936 and 1937 were to be the years of people like Mazurov. Not since the great outbreaks of plague in the Middle Ages was there so much fear in the

Russian land. Not since then had everyone, whether high or low, from a Politburo member to the common laborer, had to live with the constant fear that this might be his last day of freedom. And as in the plague days, fear spawned not only hysteria but also obsessive craving for a faith that might explain all that was happening.

People watched out for the slightest symptom of possible contamination both in themselves and in those with whom they were in contact. Had they said or done anything—never mind when: yesterday, or before the Revolution—that might serve as evidence that they were carriers of the virus of Trotskyism or some other form of contagion, the sufferers were declared beyond the pale and branded as enemies of the people.

A strange kind of faith became a companion to the fear and hysteria. In later years Kondratiev found it impossible to explain to anyone not an adult in the thirties how it could have been possible to live through that period and yet retain one's faith in the Soviet system. In fact, never was the faith of the masses in that system as great, the worship of Stalin as intense, as in those times when practically every family in the land had been stricken by the purges, at least one of its members victim of a firing squad or an inmate of the Gulag. One could and did demonstrate that faith by assisting the organs in unmasking the enemies of the people, by denouncing neighbors, friends, relatives. Some did it out of baseness or fear, but many, many others because they really believed that by doing so they were helping the Leader and the Socialist Fatherland to prevail over the forces of darkness.

Other forms of propitiation of the offended deity included the mass meetings where thousands shouted themselves hoarse, applauding the Revolution, demanding the death penalty for the most recently unmasked batch of traitors and double-faced villains, going into ecstasy at the mention of Stalin's name, cheering tumultuously any reference to the "avenging sword of the Revolution"—the NKVD, the sword, many realized, that might one day descend on their own heads.

As with all of one's beliefs, one experienced occasional doubts. For every scoundrel or fanatic who denounced someone close to him or her, there were of course many who knew that their husbands, wives, or friends had been accused and repressed unjustly, and who bewailed their fate. Others, like Kondratiev, very early reached the conclusion that the scope of the purges had gone beyond all reason and need, and that vast numbers of innocent people were perishing because the secret police itself had been infiltrated by the likes of Nikiforov and Mazurov, sadists and as yet unrevealed enemies of the people. But almost nobody, including the victims themselves, could perceive the monstrous absurdity of the process as a whole. Yes, mistakes and crimes had marred the necessary task of purification of Soviet society, yet sooner or later *he* would see through his false servants, and would punish them in *his* ruthless yet just manner.

Had he not believed in Stalin in those days, Kondratiev reflected in later years, he would have gone mad or done away with himself. And for countless others, that belief was also their main anchor in sanity; without it the Russia of 1936–1939 would have become one vast lunatic asylum.

For a year and a half, Kirov's death and its sequel may have appeared to the Soviet people as a solitary thunderclap, the threatening clouds having then dispersed. Yet one felt that the air had not quite cleared. And in August 1936, a deluge started.

On the sixteenth of the month, Misha, on arriving at work, cast his usual cursory look at the pages of *Pravda*, plastered on the wall just inside the entrance to the factory. Suddenly he felt as if he had been dealt a blow between the eyes. A screaming front-page headline announced: THE INSTIGATORS OF THE FOUL MURDER OF COMRADE KIROV TO BE TRIED BY THE MILITARY COLLEGIUM OF THE SUPREME COURT OF THE USSR.

He could not go on reading. He staggered into the staff room and sat down. Fortunately, it was early and there was no one else in the room. After a few minutes he felt strong enough to get up. There were now a few people gathered in front of the announcement. No one was saying anything. People would read the story and then hurry away.

Misha experienced difficulty in making out the small print beneath the large-letter headline and the list of names, and he felt he must not linger. Somehow, he managed to get through the working day. After leaving the factory, Misha walked two blocks in the direction opposite from the one he usually took going home and bought a copy of the local newspaper. He folded it carefully so it would fit in his inside pocket and took the trolleybus to his apartment house. He read and reread the story several times before tearing up the paper and flushing it down the toilet.

His head was whirling, but he could have recited the communiqué word for word. The procurator general of the USSR announced the forthcoming trial of members of the "Trotskyite-Zinovievite Terrorist Center." Its accused members had plotted to assassinate the highest leaders of the Soviet state, beginning with Stalin himself. "One of these terrorist groups, consisting of Nikolayev, Rumyantsev, and others, who were convicted by the Military Collegium of the Supreme Court of the USSR on December 28–29, 1934, had carried out the foul murder of Comrade S. M. Kirov on December 1, 1934, on the direct orders of Zinoviev and L. Trotsky and under the direct guidance of the United Center."

For some reason Kondratiev could not fathom, the initial awe and silence that greeted the news was succeeded the very next day by widespread talk and agitation about the case.

"One has come to expect any kind of villainy from Trotsky," Misha heard one older worker and Party member say during the lunch break, "but imagine Kamenev and Zinoviev, the two people once closest to Lenin, descending to such depths."

"Be careful what you are saying, Firsov," the local Komsomol secretary sitting at the next table cut in. "Nobody was closer to Lenin before, during, and after the Revolution than Comrade Stalin. Those two have always been double-faced scoundrels."

Artemyev, who had been working in Leningrad when Zinoviev was its Party boss, listened distractedly when Misha asked him to clarify a technical problem connected with putting a new model into production, and finally interrupted him: "It is difficult to keep one's mind on the job when you think to what terrible dangers we have been exposed. Thank God for the vigilance of our Stalinist NKVD. I hope they hang them all, don't you?"

"There is no question they will be found guilty," replied Misha.

Yet, how could they be? he kept asking himself, as he feverishly followed the court proceedings and read the abject confessions of the two erstwhile companions of Lenin and the phantasmagoric tales of treason, murderous plots, and utter moral degradation readily admitted by the two main, as well as all the other, accused. One part of their confession he *knew* was false. But on further reflection, was it really so difficult to believe that unscrupulous and power-hungry men could have resorted to the lowest kind of intrigue and actual murder once they saw their ambitions frustrated and the Party casting them off?

As the reports of the trial continued, Misha experienced an enormous sense of relief. It became obvious that the name of Mikhail Kondratiev, or those of the other minor actors in the Leningrad drama, was not going to be brought in. In fact, the entire Kirov affair was referred to but infrequently in the court proceedings. Thus, no reference whatever was made to what must have been an enormous mass of depositions and confessions that had been collected by the security and judicial organs following the shot that rang out on the afternoon of December 1, 1934. Instead, what was unveiled at the trial was a vast panorama of conspiracy: Trotsky, from his exile abroad where he worked hand in hand with German intelligence, transmitting all sorts of treasonous instructions to Kamenev and Zinoviev, they in turn putting their heads together with some other former Party leaders to devise heinous plans to assassinate Stalin, Voroshilov, and others in the Leader's closest entourage, so as to weaken the Soviet state, make it an easy prey for the Fascist invader, and thus wreak vengeance for their rejection by the Soviet people.

As Kondratiev's personal fears abated, he found himself more and more willing to believe in the essential truthfulness of the horrendous tale. Otherwise, why did Zinoviev, Kamenev, and the others confess so readily and describe in such convincing detail the complex story of the conspiracy? He himself had signed a false confession, but he certainly could not and would not have repeated all those lies in open court. Above all, if Comrade Stalin permitted the dreadful spectacle to take place, he must have been convinced that the accusations were true. It undoubtedly cost him dearly to allow this story of moral degeneracy and criminality among the old Bolsheviks to become known to the nation, and to the whole world.

To be sure, the prosecutor, Andrei Vyshinsky, appeared to be laying it on too thick, and indeed his bullying manner with the accused reminded Misha of his own treatment at the hands of Major Nikiforov. Misha conceived a strong dislike toward the procurator general of the Soviet Union, a dislike that turned into physical revulsion when fate threw them together as fellow ministers during Stalin's last years.

On August 22, loudspeakers and notices hastily placed all around the factory announced that the staff, the workers, and even the cleaning crews were expected to attend a meeting to be held the next day at noon when "a subject of the highest importance to our Socialist Fatherland will be discussed."

On arriving in the morning, Misha was not particularly surprised that the guard in the booth at the entrance, usually half asleep and paying no attention to what was going on, was this time awake and alert and checked off his name on the list in front of him. There could be no doubt about what was to be discussed at the meeting.

In the dining hall where the workers took their meals in several shifts there was standing room only. The only ones sitting behind a little table on an improvised podium were the secretary of the Tula City Party Committee, Filipov, and the manager. Artemyev, who opened the meeting, looked pale and tense as he explained that the gathering was held at the initiative of the factory Party organization, which felt that at this crucial moment in the struggle against the counterrevolutionary forces, workers of the factory named after the great Lenin should have an opportunity to express their approval of the measures taken against the gang of traitors and degenerates who were currently being tried in Moscow.

He turned the meeting over to the city boss, Yegorin, who pulled out a sheaf of notes and in a tired voice (he had delivered the very same speech several times within the last twenty-four hours) began to describe the wonders of the new Soviet constitution drawn up under the personal direction of Comrade Stalin. Mention of the name provoked a storm of applause, but after it subsided Yegorin droned on, pointing out how the constitution bestowed on the Soviet workers and peasants rights and freedoms undreamed of in capitalist countries, whose constitutions were just scraps of paper, designed to conceal the ruthless exploitation of the mass of the people by a handful of bankers and manufacturers. The crowd was growing restless. The stifling August heat, combined with the closeness of perspiring bodies, made the air almost unbearable. Suddenly the speaker raised his voice and emitted what was intended to be a shout, but came out as a hoarse scream: "And those Trotskyite-Zinovievites tried to kill the man who bestowed these blessings on the Soviet people, the leader of all progressive mankind, our own Josif Vissarionovich Stalin!"

This led to pandemonium. Some people thought that they had to cheer the name of Stalin, others that they were being called upon to howl their execrations of the "fiends." Shouts rang out: "Long live our Father and Benefactor!" mixed with "Death to Trotsky and Zinoviev!" and "Kill the traitors!" One voice cried: "Death to our Father and Benefactor!" This temporarily sobered the crowd, and the tumult ceased. Fortunately for him, the victim of confusion was never identified, but Artemyev grew even paler and in a shaky voice announced that Comrade Filipov would now offer a resolution.

Filipov had his speech all prepared and, mercifully, it was brief. They all had read how this faithful Leninist and disciple of the great Stalin, the procurator general, Comrade Vyshinsky, had masterfully untangled the threads of the vile conspiracy undertaken by Zinoviev and Kamenev and fourteen other villains. He could not do better than to quote from the eloquent summing up before the court by this outstanding representative of justice.

"A contemptible, impotent group of traitors and murderers thought that by means of sordid crimes they could cause the heart of our great people to stop beating. This contemptible, insignificant group of adventurers tried with their mud-stained feet to trample upon the most fragrant flowers of our socialist garden."

Filipov paused. "Comrade Vyshinsky concluded, 'I demand that as you do to mad dogs, they be shot—every one of them.' "

This time there was no doubt that one could and must cheer. Kondratiev, while clapping not very vigorously, looked furtively around. No, no one was watching him; a strange exhilaration had seized the crowd. People laughed and screamed: "Well said," "Shooting is too good for them," "Hang them." It was only on the faces of a few, mostly older, people, that one could discern signs of inner turmoil. But they too clapped. Artemyev had to call for order several times before Filipov could read the resolution.

"We the members of the collective of the V. I. Lenin Automotive Works of Tula join our voices to those of millions of other Soviet citizens in demanding that you, Comrade Judges, show no mercy to the despicable band of traitors whom you are about to sentence, and that they all receive the supreme penalty."

"Who is for? Against? Adopted unanimously."

"The meeting is concluded," Artemyev hastily declared as a new round of applause had begun.

The rest of the working day passed uneventfully, but somehow the factory was quieter than usual. People did engage in small talk, but for some reason spoke in hushed voices. On getting home, Kondratiev took from the shelf a history of the Communist Party, published in 1925, and reread the pages about the Civil War, which extolled the services of Trotsky, Zinoviev, and Kamenev to the cause of the Revolution. He would have to get rid of the book. Though he seldom drank more than a tumbler or two of vodka, he now poured himself a full glass, and downed it in a few gulps.

It is uncertain whether the message of the Tula automotive works ever reached Comrade Ulrich, the presiding judge in this and the subsequent Moscow show trials. But the voice of the millions of righteously indignant Soviet citizens was certainly heeded: all the sixteen were sentenced to be shot and were duly executed. The trauma of August 22 was not to be repeated. Executions of once prestigious revolutionary leaders grew too commonplace and mass meetings to denounce them became too frequent to excite people. Above all, almost everyone became too concerned about his own safety and that of those close to him to pay much attention when this or that of Lenin's close collaborators or of Stalin's recent "comrades-in-arms" bit the dust.

One month after the trial, the chief of the security police, Genrikh Yagoda, was abruptly dismissed. This greatly cheered Kondratiev, who remembered the former commissar bullying him on that December night. But he had an uneasy feeling about Yagoda's replacement. Nikolai Yezhov he recognized from the newspaper pictures as the tiny, almost dwarflike man who had sat next to Stalin on the same memorable occasion. He now studied Yezhov's face: rather childish and not very intelligent. Hardly a man who would keep a tight rein on the NKVD, curb its excesses, and recognize and eliminate the scum that had infiltrated its ranks.

Kondratiev soon found out that he had been at least partly mistaken. The chief of the local security office was dismissed and then arrested on charges of criminal laxity in discharging his duties. Mazurov, his successor, on the contrary, demonstrated exemplary zeal in identifying and apprehending enemies of the people. One of his first victims was Yegorin. He was unmasked, a meeting of the factory Party members was informed, as "a double-faced wrecker who while pretending to denounce the Trotskyites and Zinovievites did in fact seek to lull the revolutionary vigilance of the masses by intentionally making long and incoherent speeches, thus distracting their attention from the traitors' crimes." Then it was Filipov's turn, and that of several men and women he had recently recruited into the Party who were identified as members of "the Filipov sabotage gang."

Early in 1937, Kondratiev was summoned to the office of the local procurator. On entering the waiting room, he found there Perventsev, two other engineers, and a foreman from his plant. Sitting in the corner were two men whom he did not recognize. They, unlike the others who kept silent and acknowledged Misha's greetings with just a nod, were chatting animatedly about the fortunes of the local soccer team. Though in civilian clothes, it was not difficult to guess their profession. In a little while the secretary asked all except the two soccer fans to come inside. This was rather encouraging, thought Misha—when they made up their minds to arrest someone, they usually questioned suspects and witnesses separately.

The procurator shook hands with each of his visitors (another encouraging sign) and launched immediately into the reason for their being summoned. There had come to his attention recently very perplexing facts concerning the director of their factory. It seems that while employed in Leningrad in the twenties, Comrade Artemyev had formed some unfortunate connections. What was more disturbing was that his appointment as director had been signed by the former deputy commissar of heavy industry, Pyatakov. And as they all must know, in last January's trial of members of the Anti-Soviet Trotskyite Center, Pyatakov was revealed as the man principally responsible, both himself and through his agents, for the wrecking activities in the industry. In addition, he had been informed—the procurator wiped off his pince-nez and looked at a letter in front of him—that one-third of the trucks produced by the plant broke down within one year of coming off the assembly line.

"Therefore, I must ask you," said the procurator, taking off his pince-nez and looking at them intently, "to tell me frankly whether any of you have noted anything untoward or suspicious in Artemyev's behavior or management of production. You are aware that withholding such information, whether on account of misguided personal loyalty or for other reasons, is itself a grave crime."

He evidently expected a moment of silence after such a solemn warning, but Perventsev spoke up immediately. He had absolute faith in Artemyev, both as a loyal Soviet citizen and a capable and conscientious administrator. The number of vehicles that broke down was one-fifth, not one-third, of the total, and it compared favorably with the corresponding figures for other automotive plants in the country. The main reason for the breakdowns was the poor quality of the pieces of machinery produced elsewhere, a fact noted several times by Artemyev in his reports to the Commissariat. And it was unfortunate, but a fact, that all appointments to higher managerial positions between 1931 and 1935 had been countersigned by Pyatakov. That was all he had to say.

The official looked inquiringly at the others. The foreman, a man in his sixties, mustered up his courage to say that the workers considered the director a strict but fair boss and a good Communist.

"Well, there is at least one person in Tula who does not think so." The procurator pointed at the letter in front of him. "It says here that Artemyev is a wrecker who sympathized with and protected the Filipov gang."

"I remember," Kondratiev broke in before anyone else could reply, "Comrade Stalin saying that one of the most vicious forms of anti-Soviet activity is carried out by those who often anonymously denounce honest and competent officials for fictitious crimes, and thus try to besmirch socialist justice and bring disarray into our economy."

"We are certainly on guard against such people, since all our actions are guided by Comrade Stalin's directives," replied the procurator, after staring for a while at Misha. "I thank you citizens for coming here. My secretary will usher you out."

The two young men were still there as the five of them passed through the receiving room and they raised their eyes expectantly. But the secretary shook her head as she held open the door.

"Where did you find that citation from Stalin?" asked Perventsev, as the two of them were walking back.

"Oh, somewhere. You don't like Artemyev, do you?"

"Not particularly. He did not as much as lift his little finger to try to help poor Filipov and those others. How ridiculous to think of this perpetually frightened man as a potential saboteur."

"Who is not frightened nowadays?" said Misha, and immediately regretted his remark.

Perventsev did not answer. They walked for some time in silence before he turned to Kondratiev. "Karpov, the foreman who defended the director while our two colleagues kept silent . . ."

"What about him?"

"Well, on at least two occasions Artemyev cursed him in front of all the men of his shop, and fined him for being drunk while at work. The average Russian is a decent human being. How then can one explain what is happening all around us?"

A different kind of puzzlement pervaded the local NKVD office when a call from the procurator informed its chief that the case against Artemyev was being dropped because of lack of evidence.

"The man is a goddamned pedant. With him around we shall never fulfill our quota for saboteurs," declared Mazurov irritably as he put down the phone.

"But why do we need him? Usually we first arrest and then get a warrant as a matter of course," his assistant observed with seemingly irrefutable logic.

"New instructions make our work more complicated. Cases against directors of large enterprises and some others are to be processed first through the procuracy. Never mind, we will get Artemyev somehow."

And so they did. A few weeks later the police discovered what had been widely rumored for some time, that a considerable proportion of meat allotted to the factory's dining hall never in fact reached the intended consumers. The manager of the food store and the dining hall supervisor were sentenced to death for theft of socialist property. Artemyev, though in no sense privy to the crime nor responsible for the factory's provisionment, received five years at hard labor.

He was succeeded by a man who had just completed his engineering studies in Moscow. Though Perventsev, not being a Party man, could not be appointed director, he in fact took over the plant's technical management.

And then came the supreme test of Kondratiev's self-control and defenses, one that he almost failed. On June 12, 1937, screaming headlines announced the executions by firing squad of yet another batch of traitors and people's enemies. But this time the culprits were not some discredited Party leaders, bureaucrats, or industrial managers. Shot by order of a military court as guilty of conspiring with foreign powers were eight outstanding commanders of the Red Army, headed by Marshal Tukhachevsky. Seeing Kondratiev's face on arriving in the drafting room, Perventsev took him aside.

"Go immediately to our medical office." And in a whisper, "Don't come back until you can control yourself."

Before following his directive, Misha ran into the lavatory where he was violently ill. Providentially, the medical assistant did discover high fever.

"I can excuse you from work for only forty-eight hours, Citizen Kondratiev. For a longer leave you need a certificate signed by two doctors and should go to the hospital."

He would be all right at home, he assured her. God only knew what he might babble or scream in his sleep.

Once in bed, his fever subsided and he could begin to think coherently. Tukhachevsky—a traitor? He remembered the debonair figure of the marshal in his father's living room, so vivacious and gay, growing solemn only when speaking of his devotion to communism and respect for Stalin.

"We have had our differences, you know, but he does not hold grudges," Misha heard him tell his parents, before Maria Andreyevna hastily sent her two teenage sons out of the room.

And the others, also heroes of the Civil War, traitors, too? One of them, Yona Yakir, had been his father's immediate superior as head of the Ukrainian Military District, and Alexander Nikolayevich, for all his anti-Jewish bias, held Yakir in high esteem. Here was another absurdity—three of the eight were Jewish. Aside from all other improbabilities, how could *they* have conspired with the Hitlerites against the Socialist Fatherland, the only country in the world that had given Jews real equality and where they themselves had reached the top of the military hierarchy, something unimaginable for a Jew anywhere else. The whole thing was sheer lunacy, or more likely part of a vicious plot to cripple the Red Army by destroying its most brilliant commanders, just when the threat of war loomed from both East and West. No, it was in the NKVD that one should look for Hitler's and Tokyo's agents.

Suddenly, and for the first time since he had been arrested,

Misha was seized by fear for someone other than himself: how about his father, a friend of Tukhachevsky's and a close collaborator of Yakir's? He groped for some way to persuade himself that it was inconceivable, recalling Stalin's words about Corps Commander Kondratiev. But a voice inside Misha kept insisting that it was fatuous in this terrible year of 1937 to base one's hopes on anything said or done three years before. "They" had obviously deceived Stalin about Tukhachevsky and the others; "they" would not relent in the campaign of slander and vilification against every patriotic and talented commander in the Red Army until Stalin saw through their dirty game. And by that time, it could be too late.

In the evening Valeria Perventseva arrived with some medications and soup, which she warmed up on Misha's electric plate. After he finished eating, she touched his forehead lightly:

"You no longer seem sick."

He hardly heard her words; his thoughts were still on his father. But the physical contact with an attractive woman, after years of abstinence, was too much; he found himself pulling Valeria onto the bed and kissing her. Feeling her completely inert in his arms, he let go. She was not visibly offended.

"On second thought, you are still feverish."

Misha indeed was quite red, feelings of shame and self-hatred having now replaced all other thoughts and worries. She stayed for a while, trying unsuccessfully to draw him into conversation about trifling matters, but finally gave up.

"I'll be back tomorrow, but you must behave."

Misha mumbled a few incoherent words, meant to be an apology.

▬

"Yes, Valeria was very fond of you," Perventsev was saying twenty-five years later as they sat in his apartment after returning from Valeria Petrovna's funeral. "She told me about that episode in Tula. Now, this is the first time I've seen a member of the Politburo blush," he added with a sad smile. "She also told me that she had gone there quite ready to sleep with you, if you wanted her to. She thought you were on the verge of doing away with yourself, and that was the only remedy . . . I knew, of course, what was on her mind, but I also knew that neither of you would go through with it."

"Pavel . . . ," Kondratiev had mastered his embarrassment and now felt only enormous gratitude and sadness. "How could you trust anybody in those times? You two were my only friends, but to be honest, I did not feel I could be entirely open and frank even with you . . . Yes, we all lived in fear, and in some ways *he* was more afraid than anyone else."

"That is the difference between your generation and mine: naturally, I was afraid, but I did not think for a moment that my wife or Misha Kondratiev were capable of denouncing me to the secret police. As for *him*, he should have been afraid, with the blood of millions on his hands. But perhaps I should not be saying this to a member of the Politburo?"

▬

Misha was both relieved and disappointed when, instead of Valeria, it was her husband who appeared in his room the next evening. Pavel's expression was grim as he handed him the newspaper.

"You would see it soon, in any case."

Kondratiev unfolded the paper with trembling hands. Nothing about his father, but the front page headlines announced further discoveries of nests of foreign agents among the military.

"Read the second page."

It was entirely devoted to resolutions passed by various schools, factories, and professional associations expressing approval of the June eleventh executions. Like the one passed by the mass meeting at their own plant, these offered profuse thanks "to the illustrious sons of our Socialist Fatherland, workers of the NKVD led by their fighting commissar N. I. Yezhov, so indefatigable and ruthless in unmasking the people's enemies"; pledged that "we shall all be faithful helpers of the NKVD"; and concluded, "Long live the famed and vigilant Soviet counterespionage with its iron commissar, Yezhov."

"You cannot stay out of work any longer. But when you go back tomorrow, make sure you act completely normally."

"Will I have to sign the resolution?"

"You must *volunteer* to sign it. I have. Is there any vodka around?"

Corps Commander Kondratiev's turn did not come until January 1938. Arrested along with him were his aide-de-camp and chauffeur. Despite the advice given her to go immediately to her native Saratov and to stay quietly there, Maria Andreyevna rushed to Moscow. Here, after several refusals—some of her husband's close friends would simply shut the door in her face—she was finally taken in by an elderly great aunt. For several weeks she tried unsuccessfully to be received by the commissar for war, Voroshilov. Written appeals to Stalin and some Party potentates with whom she had been personally acquainted remained unanswered. But perhaps they did have some effect, for one day in August the emaciated figure of Alexander Nikolayevich appeared in the room his wife was sharing with her aunt.

"I did not sign," were his first words, after embracing her. Two months of intense "investigation" failed to persuade the elder Kondratiev to confess that while the military attaché was in Tokyo during 1929–1930 he had been recruited as an agent by Japanese intelligence. After four months' stay in the prison hospital, he was released and told that his wife was in Moscow. This was the first news he had had of her since the arrest.

Misha rushed to see him, the first opportunity he had to obtain a leave. The great aunt had died, and his father and mother continued to live in her one-room apartment. The elder Kondratiev had been cleared of charges of espionage, but a special commission was still investigating whether he should be rehabilitated and restored to his previous rank, in view of his "close association with the convicted enemies of the people." The old soldier had regained most of his pre-arrest weight, but he was still spitting blood—his broken ribs had not been reset properly in the prison hospital. And his mind had been affected: occasionally, he spoke as if Nikolai II were still on the throne, and he were an artillery colonel enjoying his leave prior to the launching of the great Russian offensive against the Austrians in 1916. Yet it was almost worse when he was lucid.

"Misha, how could they have done this to me? How could Stalin have allowed it?"

And then, in moments of complete clarity, "No matter what, when the Germans attack, you and Vladimir must fight to defend Russia." Gradually his ravings grew more frequent, and the special commission decided that "in view of the former Corps Commander Kondratiev's state of health, no further investigation can be pursued concerning his culpability." He was confined to an asylum, and Maria Andreyevna had to subsist on whatever her two sons could save from their salaries. Alexander Kondratiev died on June 5, 1940, in a mental hospital. His son's first step on becoming a minister was to demand of the military procuracy a review of his father's case, and on September 1, 1943, the Presidium of the Supreme Soviet of the USSR decreed Alexander Kondratiev fully rehabilitated, and posthumously restored him to the rank of colonel general. His widow was awarded an appropriate pension.

The emotions aroused in Misha by his father's ordeal only strengthened his determination not to become, even in his own mind, a rebel: one day he must have the power to help restore the system to what Lenin and Stalin meant it to be, and to mete out justice to those who had tortured the old soldier and countless others. His faith in Stalin, to be sure, did waver momentarily on hearing about the blow that befell his family. But it was restored when, in the great purge trial of March 1938, the former NKVD chief Yagoda was revealed to have been an agent of foreign intelligence services, as well as a moral degenerate, and was sentenced to be shot. The Leader was finally catching on to the traitors and criminals who had infiltrated his entourage. Misha's hopes on that count were strengthened when in December the evil dwarf Yezhov was dismissed from his post as head of the secret police, and soon disappeared from the public eye. The erstwhile "iron commissar" was imprisoned, getting a taste of his own medicine. The personality of the new commissar, Beria, inspired confidence: a longtime confidant of Comrade Stalin, with his round face and pince-nez his photograph suggested an intellectual of an equable temper, not like those haughty and strained expressions of his predecessors. (What a fool I was in those days, would reflect Kondratiev in later years.) And indeed, arrests grew much less frequent. Sadists and murderers within the security forces were obviously being weeded out—yes, the forces of darkness have finally been overcome, or at least the process had begun.

In October 1939, Perventsev was summoned to Moscow. Even after the downfall of Yezhov, such invitations were not to be taken lightly. For two days his wife and Misha, who made it a point of visiting and staying with her on both evenings, had a hard time in concealing their anxiety from each other. On the third day, Valeria greeted him with more than her usual warmth.

"Pavel just called. Things are fine. He will be coming back soon with very good news."

So great was her relief that she grew quite flirtatious in the course of the evening, but Misha, though with an inward sigh, refused to yield to any illusions or temptations on that count.

"Kondratiev, come to my office at two o'clock sharp," commanded Perventsev the morning he returned from Moscow. This stern official manner of address was usually an indication of good humor on his part.

And indeed, Perventsev's face was radiant when Misha stepped into his study.

"I saw the new commissar of heavy industry, Viktorov, a remarkable man. He offered me the directorship of a new factory that is to make tanks and armored vehicles. It is in Kazan, and is slated to begin releasing the first series within a few months."

" 'Yes,' said Viktorov, 'we are currently great friends with the Germans, but between you and me, I think Hitler is bound to attack us within two to three years, maybe sooner. Some people live in a fool's paradise. My predecessor wanted to locate the plant in Lvov, which we recently liberated from the Poles and which is some one hundred kilometers from the new borders of the Greater Reich. I told them that it was sheer lunacy to locate defense industry where an invader could reach it on the second or third day of a war.' "

He was shocked, continued Perventsev, to hear such talk from a high dignitary and reminded him of Comrade Stalin's statement that if anyone dared to attack us, the second day of the war would find the Red Army fighting on the enemy's soil.

"Viktorov winced, and after looking hard at me said, 'Of course, but in any case, the factory is to be in Kazan. And I want you to be the director.' "

Perventsev could not believe his ears and reminded the commissar that he was not a Party member.

"Pavel Vladimirovich, I am not appointing you to be the head of the Marx-Lenin Institute, but to do something I believe you'll be good at. We need new, modern tanks. We know the Germans are way ahead of us in that respect. Unless we catch up with them in technology, and do it fast, God help us."

"He then asked me to write down the names of designers and engineers I would like to take with me, and, of course, I included yours. I spent the next three days familiarizing myself with the blueprints and production schedules. Then I had a call from Viktorov that all the names I proposed were approved. We leave for Kazan in one week."

Something else happened during those three days. Kondratiev learned of it from Viktorov when they became colleagues on the Politburo.

"I sent the names in for approval by the Secretariat of the Central Committee. The next day, a telephone call came from Beria himself. 'But Comrade Viktorov, you must be out of your mind: the director of the factory is to be a former tsarist officer, one of his chief assistants a man who was implicated in the Leningrad affair.' I told the son of a bitch that some of my best designers and engineers were sitting in his jails. If my appointments were again vetoed or if he started any funny business with the people on the list, I would go straight to the Boss and resign. Let the NKVD produce tanks. . . . There was a long pause and then he said, 'All right, Alexander Ivanovich, have it your own way this time. But I shall not forget it.' I hung up."

Perventsev's story and offer made Misha's head spin. Pavel was his friend. But it was more than friendship, it was something close to heroism to propose a man who had "sat"—and in connection with what a case!—and was under secret police surveillance to be an assistant manager of a munitions factory. He had been *sent* to Tula, now he was *going* to Kazan. For the first time in almost five years, Misha felt really free. This feeling would not last, and the nagging memories would come back. But now it was wonderful not to be afraid, to be twenty-seven and moving up in the world.

"So why are you standing there without saying anything? Are you despondent at the prospect of leaving this wonderful metropolis?"

"Pavel, of course I shall come. I cannot tell you how—"

"Get back to work, Kondratiev. We have a lot to do in one week." Perventsev resumed his official manner.

Kazan was later dimly remembered by Misha. Tula had been boredom punctuated by periods of intense anxiety; on his solitary wanderings he had walked all over the city and forty years later still could name all its streets and main buildings. But Kazan was a whirl of constant and absorbing activity. For the life of him he could not recall the topography of the ancient Tatar capital. Work took twelve to thirteen hours a day; not infrequently he would spend the night on a cot in his office to be up with the first shift, which began at six o'clock in the morning. A few of the older engineers collapsed and had to be hospitalized, but Misha thrived on this feverish style of life. Somehow he found the time to join the local hunting club, entertain girls, and go boating on the Volga.

Nothing was allowed to interfere with the production, though there was one jarring episode. In April 1940, Balabanov, head of the engine department, was arrested. As soon as he could, Perventsev hastened to Moscow. It was ten o'clock at night when he was received by the commissar, who himself had just flown in from inspecting new factories in the Urals. Viktorov listened to the news impassively, did not ask any questions, and pulled out a telephone from a drawer in his desk.

"The Kremlin. Give me Poskryobishev . . . Yes, this is Viktorov, Alexander Ivanovich. When could I see Comrade Stalin? It is urgent . . . No, I don't think Comrade Malenkov would do. I must talk to the Boss."

After some further exchanges, he put down the receiver and replaced the phone.

"Wait here. I should be back in an hour or so. If I am not, it means you have another commissar, and good luck."

Perventsev waited with growing apprehension. More than two hours passed and he was about to go back to his hotel when the commissar reappeared. His usually placid face was red. He threw himself into a chair.

"What is this nonsense about revealing state secrets?"

"Balabanov was in Germany with our trade delegation last December. He was *instructed* to boast about our progress in military technology, in fact to exaggerate and tell fibs, so as to impress the Nazis in case they have some funny ideas—"

"That is what I thought and told the Boss. You will have Balabanov back. Go easy on him at first. He would not confess and is not likely to be in good shape."

Two days later, Balabanov, his head shorn of its usually unruly mop of hair, his features drawn, was back at his desk.

In May the first T-34s, the tanks that were to be the mainstay of Soviet armor, began to roll off the assembly line. But on June 23, 1940, France capitulated. Hitler stood master of the continent.

What would happen after he finished off England, as everyone expected him to within two or three months?

Despite serious misgivings, Misha went to the district army office, presented the certificate of his military training while in the Komsomol, and asked to enroll in the reserve officer corps.

"You are not in the Komsomol or the Party. We shall have to check with Leningrad where these papers were allegedly issued," said the military clerk, eyeing him suspiciously.

What a piece of monumental stupidity on his part, thought Misha. For a few days his Tula mood returned. But at the end of the week he was summoned back and sworn in as junior lieutenant in the armored corps reserve.

As were most other Sundays now in the armaments industry, that of June 22, 1941, was a regular working day. After fifteen continuous hours in the factory, Kondratiev felt entitled around noon to go out for fresh air and a stroll along the river. But precisely at that moment, the sirens wailed and the loudspeakers began broadcasting a speech by Molotov: War. Stuttering more than usual, Stalin's closest "comrade-in-arms" announced that the Germans had "perfidiously" broken the Non-Aggression Pact. As of three o'clock in the morning, Hitler's and his satellites' armies were attacking all along the border from the Black Sea to the Baltic. The Luftwaffe was bombing Soviet cities.

"It must come; it will come sooner than most people think," Misha remembered Perventsev saying at dinner Saturday evening, "and as of now, we are still far from being prepared for an all-out war."

The next week was one of complete confusion. In the midst of Russia, no one could tell what was happening. The enemy was obviously fighting on the country's soil, but the official communiqués exuded fatuous optimism and plain lies. No one except the region's highest officials was privy to the appalling facts: the Germans had already seized large parts of the western USSR, and were advancing at lightning speed. Most of the Soviet military planes had been destroyed *on the ground* in the first few hours of the war. Misha thought of his brother Vladimir, captain in the air force. The last time he heard from him he was in the Far East, he had downed two Japanese planes in border skirmishes. But no doubt he would be rushed to the front. How long could Volodya last?—he knew that the German planes were faster and more maneuverable than most of the Soviet models. What must his mother feel? It was hopeless to try to get in touch with her. The telephone service and mails, like everything else during that terrible summer, were in total disarray. The war itself seemed as yet distant, here in Kazan. One could and did suppress anxiety by working during all one's waking hours. Still, a pall of fear hung over the people: where was Stalin? Why didn't he speak to his people at this supreme hour of danger?

"The old bastard completely panicked," Kondratiev would later hear Khrushchev reminisce irritably among his intimates. "He sat in his villa drinking and taking tranquilizers. Once in a while, he would call the Kremlin and ask for Molotov or Malenkov and say 'Have we stopped them yet?' If Timoshenko [the commander in chief during the first week] had had any guts, he would have had him shot. Some leader—left the country unprepared, had butchered the officer corps."

Fortunately, very few knew about the actual condition of the "Genius-Leader." Had it become public knowledge, all of the Soviet Union, not only the regions in the path of the advancing Wehrmacht but all the way to the Pacific Ocean, would have dissolved into a vast sea of anarchy. And that was probably why Timoshenko and the others covered up for him.

On July 3, he finally spoke. It was a very human Stalin, thought Kondratiev, as, along with the millions, he listened to the radio. There was this startling beginning: not "Comrades," but "Brothers, Sisters, I turn to you, my friends . . ." There were long pauses, audible heavy breathing. His hands were obviously trembling, for at one time there was the sound of a glass clanging against the microphone as he stopped to drink water. Yet unmistakable signs of the old, masterful Stalin were coming back. He scorned the official lies and let his people know the appalling truth: Lithuania, Latvia, Byelorussia, and large parts of the Ukraine were already in the enemy's hands. (More territory than the Germans had conquered in two and a half years of World War I, which had led to the Revolution, flashed through Misha's mind.) And who else, in view of such news, would have had the fortitude, verging on supreme effrontery, to call on the people "to unite around the Party of Lenin and Stalin"? The speech was grim, yet also touching, and in a strange way, reassuring.

The next day Kondratiev, as did thousands of others, applied for readmission to the Party. There was no probationary period this time, no prolonged formalities: in two weeks he received his Party card. Perventsev grimaced when he told him about it, but said nothing.

In November, he finally heard from his mother: Vladimir had been rescued from a burning plane. His left hand had to be amputated. There was an undertone of relief in the otherwise sorrowful letter: fighting was over for Volodya. He would be assigned to a training school; he would live. The news helped Kondratiev make up his mind.

Perventsev was poring over blueprints and did not even raise his eyes as Misha entered his office.

"Whatever it is, be brief. I am frightfully busy. One of the plants being evacuated from Moscow is to be located here and merged with ours. The Germans may be there any day now."

"I have been called up and will be leaving for the front, I hope, tomorrow."

"I don't have time for nonsense," said Perventsev irritably, without taking his eyes off the papers on his desk.

"My brother has been incapacitated for active service . . . There has always been a Kondratiev fighting in Russia's wars."

"And what do you think you are doing here? This is not the eighteenth century. Anyone can carry a rifle or learn to drive a tank." He was practically shouting, still not looking at Misha.

"I am not that essential, Pavel. A lot of engineers and other specialists have recently been freed. You can easily replace me."

Perventsev now raised his head. "I will not sign your release," he said firmly.

"Then they will have to arrest me and send me to a penal military unit or a camp, for I shall not report to work."

Pavel kept looking at him for what seemed a very long time and then lowered his eyes. "All right, I'll sign. Go away!"

Misha was at the door when he heard the command, "Wait." Perventsev rose slowly from behind the desk, came over, and embraced him. "May the Almighty watch over you and bring you back safely." It was the first intimation Misha had that his friend was a believer.

Fifteen months later, Major Kondratiev stood in the Great Hall of the Kremlin, one of a hundred or so other officers summoned from the front for the ceremony, in itself an indication that the tide of the war had swung in Soviet favor after the great victory at Stalingrad. Previously, they could not have been spared and would be issued decorations right there on the battlefield. He heard his name and stepped forward. A frail little man with completely white hair and beard was facing him. Mikhail Kalinin, the titular head of the Soviet Union, looked much older than his sixty-odd years would warrant and official portraits suggested. He appeared distracted, and his hands shook as he picked up an order from the tray. No one on this festive occasion could have guessed the reason for the old Bolshevik veteran's preoccupied air. His wife had been arrested four years before, and her repeated appeals to Stalin to be allowed to rejoin her husband, going through the first stages of a fatal illness, were being ignored.

"Congratulations, Major." Kalinin managed a smile, but eschewed the traditional embrace, as if afraid of too strenuous a hug from one of those vigorous young men.

There was loud chatter and laughter in the adjoining banquet room to which they adjourned after the ceremony, but Kondratiev, having exchanged pleasantries with a few acquaintances, picked up a plate of *zakuski* and a glass of beer and sat down alone at a little table. His was far from a festive mood, as he nibbled at the delicacies he had not tasted since the beginning of the war.

He thought of Xenia, the doctor attached to his regiment, with whom he had struck up a romance almost immediately on his arrival at the front. Xenia was probably pregnant, and, apart from everything else, he hated the prospect of a scene with his division commander, essentially a decent man but whose every second word was an obscenity.

"You can screw the nurses and other broads as much as you want, as long as it does not interfere with your or their duties," Panfyorov kept telling his officers.

His mother, Maria Andreyevna, lived in one unheated room with her old servant Marfa, who somehow had made her way to Moscow in the beginning of the war, fleeing, often on foot, just ahead of the Germans. Both women had been subsisting mainly on bread and potatoes, and had looked incredulously at the American conserves and chocolates he had brought them from the front. Mother was not well and terribly worried, as much about his brother as about himself. Volodya could not stand being grounded, and his drinking brought him repeated reprimands and even a threat of court-martial from the commandant of the flight school where he was an instructor.

He stood up—one more day of leave. He had previously noticed an officer pushing his way through the crowd, obviously looking for somebody. He now stopped in front of Misha.

"Kondratiev, Mikhail? Aksyonov of the general staff. Will you please accompany me, Comrade Major? A high military personage desires to see you."

Misha was startled, but immediately dismissed the thought from his mind: certainly not here, not on an occasion such as this.

He could have sworn that his elegant guide had never smelled powder. But as they passed the long corridors and across a couple of courtyards, the colonel chatted about the battle before Moscow, where he had been seriously wounded.

"And you haven't even been scratched. Except for your four orders, one would have thought you were one of those political watchdogs who usually take good care to stick to the headquarters when the fighting actually begins."

Such a scathing remark about the dreaded arm of the NKVD within the armed forces would have normally astounded Kondratiev, but he was too preoccupied by the mystery of their errand.

Prior to the award-giving ceremony, his credentials had already been examined at four checkpoints, and he had to deposit his service revolver on first entering the Kremlin. But they were stopped twice more, their documents and photographs carefully scrutinized, the names and serial numbers being passed on over the intercom. There could be little doubt now about whom he was going to see, and the colonel himself grew silent and tense as they came to an inconspicuous little building. Again armed guards, who this time gave them but a passing glance and saluted as they ascended to the second floor.

The small office that Kondratiev and his escort entered was presided over by a portly figure with glasses, ensconced behind a desk with several phones on it. Two men, one in colonel general's uniform, another a civilian, were sitting in plain chairs set against the wall, both in an almost identical rigid posture, with bulging briefcases on their knees. Such was their absorption, or more likely, trepidation about the forthcoming audience, that they hardly noticed the two officers, and the general did not return their salute.

Poskryobishev got up, his jowly face wreathed in a smile. "It is a pleasure to meet you, Comrade Kondratiev. Please go right in."

"And here is the young man I have just started telling you about, Lavrenti. Three Orders of the Red Banner, Hero of the Soviet Union," said Stalin as he got up and vigorously shook Misha's hand.

His hair was grayer and thinner, but otherwise he did not look to have aged since that night. The marshal's uniform, with its gold epaulets and broad red stripes running down the trousers, seemed a bit incongruous on the short, stocky figure. Beria, who in turn greeted Misha, did indeed remind one of a schoolteacher, but the official photographs did not catch the sardonic glint behind the pince-nez, which seldom left his face. There was no one else in the large room that, as the long table covered with green cloth suggested, must have served as the meeting place for the Politburo as well as Stalin's working study. The walls were hung with portraits of the commanders and heroes of Russia's past wars, and only Lenin's marble death mask on a special panel suggested that this was also the office of the leader of the world proletariat.

"You are still in the old uniform," observed Stalin reproachfully as he sat Kondratiev down across the table from himself.

"The quartermaster corps has not as yet provided us in the field with the new ones, Comrade Stalin, but as long as they send us enough tanks, shells, and artillery to keep pushing the Germans back—"

"Ah, that is precisely why you are here," said Stalin, smiling mischievously at Beria, who on hearing this straightened up in his chair. "Major Kondratiev, we are appointing you Assistant Commissar of Munitions."

Without waiting for a reply, he pressed a button. Before Misha could collect his thoughts and say something, an aide entered through a door he hitherto had not noticed and sat down, ready for dictation.

"Decree of the State Defense Council: One, Zaytsev, M. V., to be relieved as Assistant Commissar of Munitions because of health reasons. Two, Kondratiev, M. A., to be Assistant Commissar of Munitions."

The door had hardly closed behind the aide when Beria began to talk agitatedly in what had to be Georgian. Stalin raised his hand.

"Our young friend, I understand, is a talented linguist, but I don't think he knows the language of our youth. Repeat it in Russian, Lavrenti."

"As I was saying, in view of his youth and an unfortunate incident in Comrade Kondratiev's past—" He stopped abruptly at another warning sign from the dictator.

For a while Stalin kept cleaning his pipe, then he placed it in the ashtray and lighted a cigarette. He got up slowly, walked around the table, and sat down again, this time across from the commissar.

"He has worked at producing tanks, and fought in them, and because he is young he is not likely to collapse from fatigue as did poor Zaytsev." And then, lowering his voice and speaking very slowly, "As for the other thing, you, Lavrenti Pavlovich, better than most people, must know that sometimes it is not wise to probe too deeply into a person's past."

He had watched a few boxing bouts when in America, and for a few seconds the sudden shock in the commissar's face reminded Misha of a fighter's just before he crumbles to the floor. Then the little smile returned.

Stalin pulled out a watch from his pocket. "As I told you, I shall not be attending this afternoon's meeting of the State Defense Council. Will you be kind enough, Lavrenti, to present the decree for its approval?"

Beria got up. "Of course, Josif Vissarionovich." And to Kondratiev, "Once again, and this time on both counts, my heartiest congratulations . . . Mikhail Alexandrovich."

Kondratiev, somewhat startled by this unexpected familiarity, also stood up, but when the commissar left the dictator turned to him with a twinkle in his eyes.

"We haven't talked yet. Sit down."

"I am honored by your trust in me, Comrade Stalin, and shall work hard to justify it. But I must not take any more of your time."

Stalin's face broke into a smile, the familiar smile of the Father of the People lifting up and kissing the little girl who had handed him a bouquet at the May Day celebrations, or joking with a delegation of collective farmers.

"Oh, those," he waved his pipe at the door. "I don't think they will get impatient and leave." And then, no longer smiling and out of the blue, "We meet under different circumstances than we did the other time."

Those greenish eyes were looking with strange intensity into Misha's, but he replied in an even voice. "Quite different, Comrade Stalin. I was then very much afraid."

"You had a good reason to be. We share a secret, but we shall never so much as allude to it."

"I understand."

They talked for another thirty minutes about Misha's responsibilities as assistant minister—"Yes, *minister*; we are going to change the titles. Never liked *commissar*. Trotsky had thought it up"—and his impression of the battle performance of the various types of tanks and artillery. Finally Stalin looked at his watch.

"Poskryobishev will be after me for keeping those people waiting. And then the American and British ambassadors are coming, I suppose with yet another excuse why there could be no second front this year . . . You will assume your duties as of tomorrow morning. If there are any personal matters connected with the regiment you've commanded, bring them if you wish, here to Moscow . . . We do try to obtain full information about the people we appoint to responsible positions," he added with mock seriousness, noting the young man's confusion.

Once on the slushy street, the new assistant commissar felt a pleasant glow of pride and ambition enveloping him. It was a great opportunity to serve his country. He would be able to secure decent living conditions for his mother. Xenia might work in one of the local hospitals. But why was Mikhail Kondratiev chosen when there were undoubtedly others more qualified for the job than a thirty-year-old major? Was it because of what had happened to his father? No, it would be absurd to think that. *He* was hardly the sentimental type.

Something clicked in his head and he stopped sharply, right in the middle of a deep puddle. "You had a good reason to be afraid." Had Stalin known all along what really transpired in the Smolny on December 1, 1934? If so, quite an actor! All of a sudden, Misha felt much older than his years; he had been robbed of his youth and its illusions. The faith that had sustained him during the darkest moments was melting away just like Moscow's snow under the rays of the April sun.

CHAPTER 5

MOSCOW, LATE JULY 1982

The news of Kondratiev's elevation created quite a stir in international circles. A spokesman for the Foreign Office in London, who refused to be identified, expressed satisfaction that the new secretary of the Central Committee, and thus one of the likeliest successors to Leontiev, was a man who knew and understood the West, and who while a staunch exponent of official Soviet policies, had always impressed foreign diplomats with whom he had come into contact as being reasonable and flexible. A Paris journalist dwelt at length on the Russian potentate's obvious liking for things French, his almost perfect command of the language, and the fact that he seldom let a visit to the city on the Seine pass by without attending some nineteenth-century art exhibition and dining in one of its famous restaurants. On his last trip there, it was noted he spent just twenty minutes in a conference with the head of the French Communist party, but took more than two hours viewing the Delacroix collection in the Louvre.

There were other and less optimistic assessments of the personality and political views of the new candidate for succession to one of the two most powerful offices in the world. One, under the title "Back to Stalin?" appeared in London's *Observer* and was authored by a recent Soviet defector. The writer drew attention to the disturbing, from the Western point of view, facts of Kondratiev's career. The man had been one of Stalin's favorites, picked by the dictator while still very young to become in rapid succession an assistant minister, then full minister, and finally a Politburo member. Demoted after Stalin's death, he then managed to ingratiate himself with Khrushchev, and again ascended to high Party and government posts, only, at a crucial point, to turn against and help overthrow his benefactor. Kondratiev's to be sure very extensive knowledge of the West was accompanied by neither the slightest sympathy for its institutions nor by liberal leanings. The article concluded, "Behind the polished veneer and manners reminiscent of the Russian gentleman of the old school, one can perceive a firm believer in the Communist orthodoxy and a man convinced that it is the Soviet Union's duty and destiny to achieve world mastery."

Equally disheartening was the portrait painted by Frankfurt's *Die Zeit*. Were Kondratiev to become general secretary, the Western world would find itself confronted by a ruthless enemy. The sketch recalled his mission to Budapest when, according to well-informed sources, he browbeat the Hungarian Communist leadership into executing the main figures in the uprising of 1956. And a member of the Czechoslovak delegation who participated in the talks with the Kremlin's representatives prior to the Soviet invasion in 1968 remembered Kondratiev as an uncompromising enemy of Dubcek's reforms: "No, Comrades," he was quoted as saying, "too many Soviet soldiers gave their lives to liberate your country, for us to let Czechoslovakia slip back into the capitalist camp. And look what is happening here—a complete breakdown of all social norms. You think you are promoting 'socialism with a human face.' In fact, you are opening the door to total anarchy. We shall never allow that."

"Well," said Kondratiev as he read the last item, "this represents fairly accurately what I felt at the moment, and still do, for that matter. But I certainly did not phrase my statement in such terms. If I had, Dubcek and those deluded colleagues of his would have been alerted to the imminence of our, er, intervention in Czechoslovakia, and that was furthest from our intentions. Anything from our American friends, Mitya?"

"Quite a lot," said Gorbunov, handing him yet another folder. He barely glanced at a number of items from the provincial press with headings such as "Changes in the Kremlin" and "New Candidate for Leontiev's throne." But one in the *Detroit News* arrested his attention: "Former Fellow Worker Talks About New Kremlin Bigwig." The person in question, John Hirniak, recalled for the paper's reporter his acquaintance with Kondratiev when they both worked at the Dearborn Ford plant in the early thirties. According to the article, the Russian, then an engineering student, was in this country to learn American production methods and was for a few months on the assembly line along with Hirniak. His English was at first quite rudimentary, but between Kondratiev's Russian and Hirniak's Ukrainian, they could communicate. Mike, as he was known, was initially quite diffident about closer contacts with his fellow employees, but as time went on he became more gregarious and talked quite freely about Russia, how they were doing great things there, and how in a few years the Soviets would have plants as big and efficient as American ones, and eventually would surpass the United States. "Most of us thought he was fibbing, but this was during the Great Depression, and quite a few of our fellows were impressed by his stories that there was no unemployment in the USSR and that the workers not only had their unions, something at the time we were not allowed at Ford, but also that they, and not the bosses, ran the factories." But in general, as Hirniak recalled, Mike avoided political arguments and would have absolutely nothing to do with the local Communists. "Eventually we became quite friendly, and I would have him to my house, where he could enjoy some of the dishes he had been used to at home. He left for Russia at the end of the summer of '34, I think. We promised to correspond, but after a while, I believe early in '35, he stopped answering my letters and I lost track of him." Yes, he used to go out with girls, but evidently nothing serious. The reporter's assiduous research into that aspect of Kondratiev's American activities yielded but meager results: a few old ladies who vaguely remembered some movie and drugstore dates.

"Ah, the non-sins of our youth. That is what we really regret," sighed Kondratiev comically, pointing out the passage to Gorbunov. "But, of course, I had no money to invite a girl for dinner, in those distant days an essential element in American courtship. As for drinking and making love in a car, another quaint custom of theirs, this went against my code as a Komsomol member. There were plenty of professional ladies, and quite cheap—the Depression, you know—but a couple of our lads who tried them ended up with what you might expect. Yes, I kept my word to the Party and my mother, though it is not easy when one is in his twenties."

The *New York Times* correspondent in Moscow reported that Kondratiev's elevation was taken as a sign of the growing importance of the military in the inner councils of the Kremlin. The new secretary was a general's son, himself in his youth a professional officer, and reputed to be a close friend of the minister of defense, Marshal Vorontsov. His recent and unyielding position at the Geneva arms-control talks, where he was chaperoned on behalf of the army by General Savitsky, a notorious hard-liner, was read by many as indicating that profiting by Leontiev's growing debility the hawks on the Politburo were gaining the upper hand.

A piece on the op-ed page of the *Times* took a different tack. Its author's name came as no surprise to Kondratiev, but Gorbunov, who could sense even a slight alteration in his boss's mood, thought he detected a stiffening in his expression as he read the column. Valentin Kerner, identified as a professor of Soviet politics and a noted Kremlinologist, gave his impressions of the significance of the appointment. Obviously, wrote the professor, there was a power struggle going on within the Politburo in anticipation of Leontiev's disappearance from the scene. "Those Westerners who have had an occasion to meet Kondratiev and know something of his career (not all the important facts about which are recorded in his official biographies) have good reason to believe that behind the facade of an orthodox Communist and severe critic of American policies there is actually a man deeply desirous of liberalizing his society, and of seeking an accommodation with the United States. His is then quite a different personality and outlook from those of his two main rivals for the top position, Smirnov and Kubiak, both typical apparatchiki (products of the Party machinery), neither with any close acquaintance or understanding of the West." But, stressed the author, it would be futile to expect the Kremlin's choice to fall on the proponent of a new détente, or even if it does, for Kondratiev to be able to reestablish East-West dialogue, as long as the White House persists in its opprobrious rhetoric about Russia, and the Administration keeps rejecting out of hand the Soviets' often quite reasonable initiatives on nuclear arms control and reduction. Irresponsible talk about protracted and/or limited nuclear war, the Pentagon's senseless quest to achieve military superiority over the USSR, leaves the Russians, with their memories of what they had suffered from Western aggression in the past, no alternative but to respond in kind. It is therefore up to the Congress and public opinion to impress the Administration with the need for a new approach toward the USSR, thereby enabling the more enlightened and peace-seeking elements within the Soviet establishment to gain the upper hand, thus opening a new and happier era in East-West relations.

"It is good to know you have such great admirers in the United States."

"What? Ah, yes, Mitya," Kondratiev finally smiled. "We haven't heard anything directly from the good professor since that letter in Geneva, have we?"

"No," said Gorbunov, concealing his surprise. How, amid all his preoccupations, could the boss be concerned about a silly letter written by an insignificant professor? "But we have had several congratulatory messages from various American diplomats and congressmen whom you had met, including one from Amon."

"Well, send them the usual replies, but make the one for Amon quite personal and cordial. He may be the next secretary of state . . . And have all that junk filed away." Kondratiev pointed to the file of clippings from the foreign press. "They do write the most unimaginable nonsense about us."

Gorbunov felt that he had to say something to cover up his astonishment over the vehemence with which his usually even-tempered chief pronounced the last sentence.

Kondratiev was instantly aware of his slip and laughed. "It may be irritating, but it is much better than that they should know what is really happening here . . . But there is something more important, Mitya: you are being put up for a candidate member of the Central Committee. You'll probably be the youngest one there except for that cosmonaut, what's his name."

Gorbunov was at first at a loss for words. When they came, and after the customary formula that he hoped to justify the Party's confidence in him, he thanked his benefactor in a choked voice and assured him that as much as he appreciated the honor, he trusted it would not lead to any change in their present association.

"Of course, in a while you will take over the personnel section of this department, but we will still be working closely together." He cut short the young man's protestations that he would rather continue as Kondratiev's personal secretary. "We shall see, but now back to business. Send Fomin in to me in about ten minutes, and then, if there is nothing urgent, take time out and celebrate. But I expect you sober and at your desk at eight o'clock sharp tomorrow."

Kondratiev watched with amusement as the young man half rushed, half staggered to the door, but then his smile was replaced by a frown. Gorbunov, as was the case with other secretaries of Politburo members, was regularly interviewed by Grigorian, special assistant to the chairman of the KGB, and Trifonov, head of Leontiev's personal security—the purported reason for such interviews being to make sure that the Party leaders took proper care of their safety and health. Gorbunov would report to his chief about the conversation, but did he repeat *everything* that he had been asked and said? Unlikely, much as the youngster appeared genuinely devoted to him. That damned American: "Not all the important facts about [Kondratiev's career] are recorded in his official biographies." What could he mean, and from where did he get it? Well, he could not know what happened on December 1, 1934. He, Kondratiev, was now the only one alive who did. As for the other thing, which one of his Politburo colleagues did not have a similar thing in his past? All the wretched professor had probably heard was some third-hand gossip. So why was he perturbed, first because of a silly letter, then by a silly column? Probably because the goal, the idea of which had first flashed through his mind as he walked the muddy streets of Moscow thirty-nine years ago, was now clearly within his reach, and he could not bear the thought of something that had happened so long before interfering with it. There were more important things to attend to, such as keeping an eye on Kubiak and his machinations. And now to the business at hand. Where the hell was Fomin?

When the individual in question entered, Kondratiev did not bother to return his greeting. "Didn't Gorbunov tell you to come here some time ago?"

"I waited until you summoned me. I did not want to disturb you, Comrade Kondratiev."

"He must have said ten minutes. Never mind, let's get to business."

He was behaving in the typical manner of a Russian bureaucrat, bullying a subordinate, but felt no inhibitions on that count. Fomin, now in his middle sixties and standing there with an ingratiating smile on his face, had as a young lawyer worked in the office of the procurator general of the USSR as an assistant to Vyshinsky. When this scoundrel went to the Ministry of Foreign Affairs, he had taken Fomin along with him. Stalin's death had put an end to what might have been a brilliant career, but Fomin, even after the disgrace of his patron, stuck somehow in the ministry. As deputy foreign minister, Kondratiev (who could not stand his unctuous manner), succeeded finally in having him fired, but the erstwhile inquisitor and author of forged depositions surfaced again in the apparatus of the Secretariat of the Central Committee, and for the last twenty years had served as its chief investigator and reporter on diplomatic appointments.

Fomin's hands shook as he placed on the desk the list of proposed nominees, and a stack of folders with information about them. It was among Kondratiev's new duties as secretary in charge of the General Department of the Central Committee to approve on behalf of the Politburo any diplomatic appointments above the rank of first secretary of a legation.

"Why isn't the list in alphabetical order?" he asked sharply.

"Comrade Leontiev had instructed me to do it by the names of the countries to which our new personnel are to be attached."

"Have all these appointments been personally approved by the foreign minister?"

"There is one proposed by the personnel department of the ministry, which Comrade Filimonov feels should be left up to you to decide. I personally think the man is unsuitable."

Fomin came from around the desk and leaned over the document, accidentally brushing against Kondratiev, who pulled his chair away.

"There, Vladimir Moiseyevich Vinogradov—ambassador to Sweden. You see what the problem is, Comrade Kondratiev," he added with a little chuckle. "I did not think that those people were still in the foreign service."

Kondratiev, without answering him, picked up Vinogradov's folder and began to read from it aloud: " 'Born 1925, son of Moses and Hannah. Father, head of the Food Trust; repressed in 1937 and fully rehabilitated in 1956. Enlisted in the Soviet Army in 1943; finished war as lieutenant; twice wounded; decorated with . . .' Incidentally, where did *you* serve during the war, Comrade Fomin?"

"I worked in the ministry. I tried to volunteer, but—"

Kondratiev cut him off and continued reading excerpts from the dossier. " 'Completed law course at Moscow University, 1949; first secretary, Helsinki, 1960–1964; commercial attaché, Tel Aviv, 1964–1967; minister, Thailand, 1975–1980; with the legal department of the Foreign Ministry until now. Became Party member in 1945. Expelled from the Party in 1952, but charges leading to the expulsion found entirely baseless, and in 1954 he was reinstated.' What is there in this record that you object to, Comrade Fomin?"

"Nothing, absolutely nothing, Comrade Secretary of the Central Committee."

Kondratiev went on scanning the list, occasionally consulting a folder. Finally, he took off his glasses and looked inquiringly at Fomin. His face was pale, but there was just a hint of defiance in his expression. (He feels unjustly victimized for having done his duty in suppressing enemies of the people. And what does he have to fear?—he'll be pensioned off. Perhaps it was not altogether to the good that a man in Kondratiev's position could no longer order a Fomin to be sent to one of those places where the reptile had helped send so many innocent people.)

"Do you have any observations about anyone else on the list?"

"I shall abide by your decisions, Comrade Secretary of the Central Committee."

"I have a question. I see that Nikolai Mikhailovich Kondratiev is to be appointed an attaché for commercial affairs at the embassy in Lisbon. I thought that appointments of commercial attachés were settled between the Ministries of Foreign Affairs and Foreign Trade without referral to this department. Why this exception?"

"Your son, I mean, Comrade Kondratiev, is actually to have the rank of a minister because of the special duties attached to his office. But insofar as the Portuguese government is concerned, he will be listed as an attaché."

"I think I can understand. This appointment is not to be acted upon. All others are approved. You may go."

He sat for a while, waiting for his initial irritation to pass. Finally, he picked up the telephone. "Connect me with Comrade Zavistny."

Lieutenant General Zavistny was head of the third directorate of the KGB, charged with industrial and technological espionage.

"I am calling you about N. M. Kondratiev, and his proposed appointment. On whose initiative was it done?"

The general went into an elaborate explanation. Lisbon was the key point in Western Europe for this type of intelligence operation. Paris or London was too obvious. Soviet diplomats were watched quite closely. The recommendation for the appointment came from the Ministry of Foreign Trade. "Of course, I should have checked with you personally, Comrade Kondratiev."

"I don't think you understand, Comrade Lieutenant General, something that is surprising for one in your position. I am not speaking as his father—he is thirty-five years old—but as a secretary of the Central Committee charged with passing on foreign appointments. I consider N. M. Kondratiev completely unsuitable for the job in question, in fact for anything to do with intelligence work. You will notify both ministries accordingly." He hung up without giving Zavistny a chance to say anything.

But personal and family irritations must not be allowed to preoccupy his mind, Kondratiev firmly decided, as he turned to the stack of documents on his desk. The first few days in office had already convinced him that things were in a much worse state than he had suspected: Leontiev's infirmity and the general secretary's other duties had not allowed him to exercise that close supervision over all aspects of foreign policy that traditionally had been the general secretary's primary prerogative and obligation. The Politburo laid down the general line, but one needed a strong and authoritative person to pay strict attention to implementation, to make sure that the various organs charged with executing the intricate game—diplomacy, the armed forces, the propaganda and intelligence branches—worked as a team, understood and obeyed the signals. Alas, such synchronization had been largely missing for the last few years.

Take the case of Poland. Ever since 1976 the ambassador in Warsaw had been sending warnings about an impending crisis, claiming that the country's leaders were incapable of coping with the situation. Similar complaints were reaching the Central Committee's apparatus from the Soviet Union's special "friends" among the Polish Communists. But the Moscow officials in question, knowing that the Polish leader Gierek was an old pal of Leontiev's, kept filing such reports away, and Filimonov, the foreign minister, finally had the pesky ambassador transferred. Then, when the Polish workers erupted in August 1980, Filimonov panicked and wanted the Soviet troops to march in right away. Marshal Vorontsov, minister of war, categorically objected.

"The Poles will fight. Of course we would crush them, but it would take three to five hundred thousand troops to garrison the country, and God knows for how long. Where would I go to get them? This would cripple the Warsaw Pact striking force. No, we must exhaust all other ways of bringing them to their senses before we resort to that."

"Think of the economic burden it would involve for us," chimed in Viktorov.

"Why weren't we warned?" bewailed Leontiev. "That comes from trusting a blabbermouth like Gierek," he added bitterly. "He kept assuring me to the last that things in Poland were going swimmingly well and that he had the situation well in hand. He must be kicked out as the Party leader and severely punished for his criminal negligence."

"So much for old friendships," thought Kondratiev as he recalled the scene. Things in Poland had settled down for the moment. Those hopelessly unrealistic people had been ready to fight the invading Soviet armies, but were caught completely by surprise when their own seemingly decrepit government carried out a coup, and put the troublemakers under lock and key. It was a bit embarrassing that this had to be done mainly by the military and that the Polish Communists turned out to be so ineffectual.

"I knew we could trust their generals," declared Vorontsov rather smugly to his fellow Politburo members. "Many of them had been our comrades-at-arms; they all have studied in our staff schools. They would not let a bunch of journalists and priests take over the country and turn it against us. Of course, we had to do a little prodding."

Well, the Polish mess was still far from being over, and it was now largely up to Kondratiev to watch over the situation and devise policies to deal with that turbulent people. Kondratiev's attitude toward the Poles, like that of most Russians of his generation and upbringing, was deeply ambivalent. Those of his acquaintance he found almost invariably attractive: good companions, spirited and full of wit, in the war brave to the point of foolhardiness. But collectively such virtues added up, alas, to national vices: lightheartedness when it came to serious political and economic problems, the foolish pride that made them reluctant to recognize that only the Soviet Union could guarantee the existence and security of the Polish state.

What in fact did they have to complain of? Until that madness in 1980, the average Pole enjoyed a much higher standard of living than his Soviet counterpart. The USSR had generously restored to them the lands that the profligate Polish ruling classes had allowed to fall under German rule. He recalled Pavel's objection, "But Father, they want to be free," and his rejoinder, "When have they really been free? What they call freedom has always been anarchy. I grant you, it was hard for them under Stalin, but then it was immeasurably much more so for ourselves." And indeed, what had this idiotic Solidarity done during the time that it was allowed to demoralize the working class and plunge society into chaos?—caused a catastrophic fall in the living standard, food shortages, virtual paralysis of industry.

He got engrossed in the Polish business because it was the most flagrant example of the disarray in management of foreign relations during the last few years. But there were other almost equally vivid examples. Afghanistan: when the question came up in the spring of '78 whether they should support the Afghan revolutionaries and help them overthrow the previous regime quite friendly to the Russians, Vershinin, the Foreign Ministry specialist on Central Asia, argued that it would be a mistake. The leaders of the so-called revolutionary party were either thugs or persons abroad who had completely lost touch with their own people. "Once in power, they would start fighting among themselves, and try to change Afghani traditions overnight. Why buy trouble? We might have to send in troops."

"It wouldn't be such a bad thing," said Vorontsov, usually sober and realistic. "Our soldiers are getting stale from inaction. And it would take just three or four divisions and a few weeks to pacify the country. Their regular army officers have been trained here, mostly, and would be on our side. As for the tribesmen, they are armed with World War I rifles."

Vershinin spread his arms helplessly. "It might not be that easy. They are religious fanatics, too uncivilized to know when they are licked."

"We cannot refuse help to a Leninist party that seeks to bring socialism to its country. If we do, they might turn to the Chinese," said Lunin.

The mention of the Chinese was enough to make up Leontiev's mind: "Send a signal to Kabul and tell them we shall fully support them. Or do we need a Politburo vote?"

A few of them exchanged looks, but once Leontiev and Lunin agreed, it was useless to argue further. That was four years ago, and for three years now some ten Soviet divisions had been mired in the wretched country.

Kondratiev picked up a folder from the stack on his desk: the Sakharov case. At one time, Kondratiev and Remizov argued that it would be best to let the professor go abroad where he would spend his time quarreling with other émigrés, rather than continue to be a pest at home.

"We cannot let the Americans get the idea that each time they say 'boo' we give in," protested Filimonov.

"But it is not the Americans. It is the whole Western scientific community, which is usually friendly to us but cannot forgive us for holding on to that windbag," pleaded Remizov.

"That is precisely the reason not to let him go. He would be even more harmful slandering our country among all those foreign scientists. Here we can always shut him up." Filimonov's prime motivation in life seemed to be to annoy the Westerners. For all his diplomatic experience, he remained essentially a village boor, suspicious and ill at ease with foreigners.

Again it was Lunin who decided the issue. "Sakharov is not a scribbler like Solzhenitsyn, who only has to open his mouth for everybody to realize that this third-rate Dostoyevsky is a hopeless reactionary. Sakharov speaks in the language that is unfortunately attractive to the decadent intellectuals here and abroad. Yes, he would be more harmful spreading his poison in the West."

It was Lunin himself, thought Kondratiev, who though basically intelligent, was a throwback to the past. Lunin had once told him that he loved Stalin. "Was anyone in your family repressed in the thirties?" "Yes, my own half brother, but I loved Stalin even so."

Kondratiev tried the gambit of last resort: "Lenin would have said 'To hell with Sakharov. Let him go. He who slanders communism bites on granite.' " But apart from Remizov, nobody supported him. It was not only the question of Sakharov. Kuliabko, usually on his side on most issues, reproached him after the meeting.

"Why are you soft about this man, Misha? Those academicians give themselves airs as if they were not like the rest of us mortals. We load them with honors and privileges, and yet they look down on us."

Yes, most of his colleagues disliked anything and anybody they could not completely control and understand, hence their instinctive antipathy toward scientists.

All those things could not now be undone. For the moment one had to be on guard against making fresh mistakes, and get rid of some of the deadwood in the Secretariat and ministry. Filimonov could not be fired. It would give a wrong signal to the Americans, and besides, Leontiev would never agree. When and if . . .

He looked at the grandfather clock that once had graced the manorial home of the Kondratievs. Almost time to go to the airport to meet the Polish delegation. There would be the usual smiles and embraces and speeches extolling the "unshakable unity of the socialist camp." That, in public. Then would come the less pleasant part, a private session where Leontiev, if he was up to it, would shout and threaten: Why can't the Poles put their house in order? They would plead that without more economic help, Warsaw may not be able to continue to control the situation. Viktorov would tell them that he is not a magician who can conjure up billions in hard currency, and that their people should learn to work harder or otherwise tighten up their belts further. It would be up to him, Kondratiev, to soothe the ruffled feelings, persuade the Poles to crack down harder on their troublemakers, mollify Viktorov to promise some help, keep Filimonov from saying something idiotic like, "A hint from us and the Germans would be at your throat again." Tomorrow's papers would report that "the meeting took place in a cordial and comradely atmosphere."

CHAPTER 6

MOSCOW, AUGUST 1982

In August, members of the Politburo, along with the rest of high officialdom, traditionally dispersed on vacations and travels. Leontiev repaired to his Black Sea villa where he would be surrounded and flattered by the Party chiefs of the fraternal states. Most of them secretly hated having to attend the old man and having to listen to the endless reminiscences of his youth and services in the war. Kubiak was traveling through North Caucasus and Western Siberia, ostensibly to check on agricultural prospects; in fact, Kondratiev was convinced he was up to no good with the local Party chiefs. He himself simply had too much business on hand to take a real vacation, but after a day in the office would usually be driven to his suburban dacha rather than the Moscow apartment. Irina would join him after one of her cultural missions, this time to Czechoslovakia and East Germany.

He enjoyed his evening repose away from the tumult and heat of the big city, his walks in the woods, the opportunity to catch up on the recent historical and biographical writing in Russian and Western languages, and an occasional tennis game with Gorbunov or one of his other assistants, though they invariably beat him. At one time they tried surreptitiously to enable him to win a set or two, but he would not be deceived or tolerate such concessions to his age and office.

"Mitya," he once told Gorbunov after the latter obviously threw a game, "if we are to go on playing, you must understand that I am not Goering, who, as I read in a biography of that Nazi swine, used to shout to his partner, 'Why do you hit the ball over there? Don't you see where I am?' " From then on, Kondratiev could feel real satisfaction if he did manage to win a few games. He seldom, however, managed to win more than one or two from Kuliabko, who though in his sixties still had the appearance and agility of the man who had once been the Red Army's middleweight boxing champion.

"A strange game for a Ukrainian peasant lad," Kuliabko was reflecting, sipping a drink after his most recent trouncing of Kondratiev. "Actually, I picked it up as a grown man when stationed in Germany after the war. But here we are playing while Kubiak is scheming. You know what his pals have been whispering: that Smirnov could not carry on long as general secretary because of his health, that you are an inveterate Russian chauvinist who would be hard on our non-Slavic brethren."

Kondratiev shrugged his shoulders. "Give him enough rope and he'll hang himself."

Kuliabko was silent for a moment and then said with sudden intensity, "Misha, you must want the job, fight for it! We cannot go on the way we have. We are drifting. With Smirnov, we will go on drifting. With Kubiak, it would be like Khrushchev's last years, everything falling apart. Who else is there—Remizov? Good man and Communist, but indecisive and a loafer. We need you."

"Depend on it, Mykola, I want it. How could I have done some of the things I have, except to keep in the running?"

"That's what worries me, Misha. You do want it, but there is something that makes you at times appear an observer rather than a fighter. When I used to get into the ring I knew I had to want to kill my opponent, or I would lose. And so it is in this business."

"You did not kill Vishnevsky," smiled Kondratiev.

"I thought he was too ridiculous for words. But that is why I am not fit to be the leader. Politics is not a joking matter, not with us." He looked his friend straight in the eyes: "Is it that business when you were young? But who in our generation has not gone through something equally awful or worse? At seventeen I was proud to be a member of one of those Komsomol gangs that went through the villages looking for 'hoarders,' those poor souls who could not meet the government's quotas for grain and milk deliveries and concealed some food rather than let their children and themselves starve. I believed I was doing my patriotic duty by unmasking the 'bloodsuckers' and 'class enemies' and turning them over to the authorities. My own kith and kin! And some of the things I did when I was a political officer in the army: a soldier once asked me, 'Has Comrade Stalin ever been to the front or visited a field hospital?' Instead of an answer he got a penal battalion. You know how many survived in those. Stalin was my god. But why brood over the past rather than remember that we have also built something? I go to my old village where before the Revolution most of the people were illiterate. Now there is electricity, some of the farmers have cars, their children are doctors, engineers . . . If I did not believe that, for all the terrible things that happened, we have been on the right track, I would have put a bullet through my head a long time ago."

"You emotional southerners," Kondratiev affected a light tone, but inwardly cursed his friend's perspicacity. He got up, walked around the veranda, and then stopped in front of Kuliabko. "Let's be honest, Mykola. I do brood occasionally about the past. But it only makes me all the more determined to be in a position to build the kind of society about which Lenin dreamed."

"That's what I wanted to hear. Here is to your, *our*, success and perdition to you know whom."

"You seem to ignore, Comrade Kuliabko, the unity of our leadership and how we work harmoniously, shoulder to shoulder in the common cause."

"No more jokes. Remember, I shall not be seeing you for two weeks. Leontiev wants me to come and help entertain our fraternal guests. Not my idea of a vacation. But one does not refuse an invitation from the Chief."

They walked to his limousine, embraced, and Kondratiev stood looking in the distance for quite a while after the car disappeared down the road. But he was not going to be alone in the evening, for after he came back to the house his bodyguard informed him that his son Nikolai called, and after ascertaining that his father would not be entertaining any official guests announced that he would be joining him for supper. At first his impulse was to call his son and ask him not to come, pleading that he had to prepare for an important meeting in the morning. It had been announced, in fact, that he was going to receive the Chinese trade delegation.

But then it occurred to him that Kolya might have gotten into a new mess, or be on the verge of committing some fresh idiocy—he had not seen him since that business with intelligence work. If neither, he still needed some serious talking to.

Kondratiev was still pondering several opening gambits, ranging from "I do expect that you are now seriously thinking" to "How could you be such an ass at your age," when Nikolai appeared, as usual breathless and smiling, and began by congratulating his father on his new job, inquiring about what it involved, and then, uncharacteristically, engaging him in a serious conversation about the international situation. Taught by previous experience, the older man refused at first to be reassured, but gradually as the conversation flowed easily with no sign of some catastrophic announcement in the offing he began to yield to the eternal fatherly hope that his son was finally getting some sense into his head. But the suspense was proving too great and once behind the table he interrupted the discussion of the latest news from America by blurting out, "And how is the master spy?"

"Oh, that," said Nikolai lightly. "I did not know that you heard about it, but of course, now that I think of it, you must have. In any case, it did not pan out, and I am glad it did not. I told my minister that I was completely ignorant about technology, could not tell a computer from a dictaphone. He kept assuring me that it was not important, and all that it required was a knowledge of languages and experience in dealing with foreigners. I gave in, but then the Ministry of Foreign Affairs decided that I would be more useful in a straightforward diplomatic post. So now they are thinking of putting me up for a UNESCO job in Paris. I am tired of foreign trade. It is nothing but figures, currencies, and the like, and I don't have a head for those things."

"But how could you even think of going into intelligence work? You know that relatives of people in my position are not supposed to touch it."

"I thought that if my minister proposed it, it could not lead to any complications. In any case, I was going to ask you, Father, before definitely accepting the Lisbon post."

As Nikolai babbled on, it occurred to Kondratiev, not for the first time, that there might have been more than carelessness involved in putting his son in an exposed position. Didn't Leontiev early in his reign get rid of Karsavin, a potential rival, largely on the grounds that the latter's daughter while a student abroad eloped with a young French diplomat? And wasn't Shauro, minister of foreign trade, an old associate of Smirnov's? It might be a coincidence, the same as a KGB informer's befriending Pavel, but then again, it might not.

He became aware that Kolya had stopped talking and was looking at him solemnly, as if he was about to make an announcement, and his heart sank.

"I am going to be married."

"And who is to be my daughter-in-law?" Kondratiev tried to conceal his anxiety, but his voice did not sound natural.

"Sonia is a candidate in historical science. She is twenty-six years old, daughter of Professor ———."

The name was that of an eminently respectable biologist and Party member. (At any rate, not an American, Ethiopian, or Pole.) He asked, this time trying to mask his relief, "I thought there was someone else?"

"No, that was not serious. This is. And unlike Olga [his first wife], she wants children and so do I. It would be important for your career, too."

"My career?"

"Yes, the general secretary ought to have grandchildren. You must have seen those biographies of Leontiev?"

Kondratiev was seized by uncontrollable laughter. It was true. The most recent biography, translated into forty-eight foreign languages, featured several touching illustrations: Leontiev and his corpulent Galina looking fondly at their twin grandsons; the general secretary visiting the kindergarten where the little brats were enrolled; he in the shallow end of his Crimean villa's pool, allegedly teaching his granddaughter how to swim.

"Why this unprecedented attention to our leaders' private lives?" he had felt constrained to ask of Parkhonov, the official responsible for regulating publicity about Politburo members' activities.

"But Comrade Kondratiev," replied the latter, an intelligent, always smiling man in his thirties who had spent a year in the United States studying advertising at the Harvard Business School, "this is extremely important for our image, both at home and abroad, especially for the Americans. Who, after contemplating these pictures of the Chief with the little dears, would think for a moment that here is a man who might plunge the world into a nuclear holocaust?"

It had evidently taken some effort to persuade Leontiev to pose for the pictures. He objected especially to being photographed with his wife, but it was explained to him that she had to be in at least one scene, otherwise it might lead to all sorts of unfortunate rumors.

"Yes," continued Nikolai, "Smirnov's daughter, with whom I used to be quite friendly, keeps telling me that her father is after her to get pregnant. Evidently, her husband can't or won't. I offered my services, but Valya said that that would be political incest. In any case, you are bound to beat him to it, Father. Sonia is in her second month. We plan to get married in two weeks."

The older man tried to look shocked, but not convincingly. It was not very different from the circumstances under which he had married Nikolai's mother. They drank a toast to Sonia and to the future generation of Kondratievs. Nikolai asked to spend the night at the dacha—another encouraging sign, for if not with a woman he would usually keep late hours drinking with friends, and he abhorred the quiet of the countryside. Strangely enough, though he had inherited the looks of his father, but was taller and more handsome than Mikhail Alexandrovich had been in his youth, Kolya's temperament was very much like his mother's, careless and self-indulgent. Maybe it would all change now, if his bride-to-be was indeed the kind of strong-minded, intellectually oriented woman that he described.

The description seemed to fit, when Nikolai presented his betrothed two days later. Sonia was at first in considerable awe of her future father-in-law, but then as she relaxed, she talked interestingly about her work, studies, and childhood. Thank God, she was uninterested in politics. Pavel, who was present for the occasion and tried to draw her out on the subject, succeeded only in making her say that she had read Solzhenitsyn and, while liking his short stories, did not care much for his novels, an eminently sensible opinion, thought Mikhail Alexandrovich. It was still something of a mystery to him what this woman of twenty-six could see in Nikolai to make her want to marry him. Evidently not his father's position. He tried her by asking whether she would like eventually to join one of the academy's research institutes, but

Sonia said with every appearance of sincerity that her ambition did not go that far. She hoped to teach, not necessarily at the university level.

"Kolya may be turning over a new leaf," he said to Pavel after the pair left. "As Tolstoy said, when you are single you have women on your hands. Married, you have a woman on your back, but your hands are free. Think of it, Pavel."

"It is not women who intrude on my freedom." And, seeing his father frown: "Poor Tolstoy should have known better. He had his Sonia both on his back and his hands for the latter part of his life."

"Geniuses have the prerogative of such majestically incongruous statements. Tolstoy also said, 'Nobody who has not been in jail knows what the state is.' Yet he was very sure he knew what the state was."

Pavel was quite tempted to say that had he lived under the Soviet system, the great writer would surely have had the experience he had missed under the tsars, but then thought the better of it.

But the word *jail* triggered another association in the elder Kondratiev's mind. "You never asked me what I found out about your friend Kulagin."

"He is not my friend, and I found out for myself. He is an informer."

"Did he try to involve you in anything illegal?"

"No, he only wondered if I could get him some émigrés' books that are hard to procure and which he assumed you must have in your library."

"And what led him to think I keep anti-Soviet literature in my home?"

"Oh, Father," laughed Pavel, "you are known as one of the few intellectually minded men among all those—"

"Go on."

"—dinosaurs."

"Thank you for not using a stronger term. Anything else?"

"He did not ask me to try to pry out of you any state secrets. In fact, he did not honor me by any special attention. He has tried to befriend all of us who have studied abroad. It became too obvious, and now everybody is shunning him. Papa, why do we need Kulagins? Is the mighty Soviet state going to collapse because a few people read poems or books by an exile, or tell jokes about the government?"

Mikhail Alexandrovich recalled a woman member of a British parliamentary delegation who, in the middle of an audience with Stalin, suddenly shrieked, "When will you stop killing people?" and the dictator's unruffled rejoinder, "When it is no longer necessary." He got up from his chair, walked around the room, drew the chair closer to the sofa on which Pavel half sat, half sprawled, and sat down.

"I shall answer you in two ways. First, in my capacity as one of the men responsible for governing this country. We have Kulagins because we also have irresponsible fools who, under the guise of literature or intellectual discourse, try to besmirch our system and demoralize our young people. There is plenty to criticize in our society, and I don't object to it as long as it is done honestly and aboveboard. But those who do it in an underhanded way help our enemies—Don't sneer! Give the Americans, or for that matter the Chinese, the idea that we are indecisive and divided, and they will not only poke their noses into our affairs even more than they do now, but will threaten the borders of our country and those of our socialist allies, the borders for which we have paid with millions of lives. And then, my friend, we'll be in real danger of war."

"I see absolutely no connection, but I'll wait for your second answer."

"This one comes from private citizen Kondratiev who loves this country, just as I am sure you do. This citizen would right away abolish censorship, kick out all the Kulagins, and dissolve the KGB, if he were not sure that the next day the whole country would be plunged into utter chaos. We still need a firm hand to guide our people. Whenever in our history such firm guidance was missing, the result was not liberty but chaos. But compare the way things are now with what was going on under Stalin. It is like day and night."

"But you worked for Stalin."

"I worked for my country, which at the time meant working under Stalin. As Akhmatova says in one of those poems that are banned, but that you undoubtedly have read and admired, 'I was with my nation in its hour of tragedy.' So was I."

Again Pavel was sorely tempted to object to the analogy: the poetess meant that she was then living and suffering in Russia; his father was one of those who ruled the country. But then, he, too, had suffered before he became one of *them*, had been falsely accused and imprisoned, had lost his own father under the Terror. He respected his old man for what he knew about his early years and war record. But then how could he have gone on for forty years serving this beastly system?

He was still pondering the question while driving back to Moscow. His mother sometimes intimated to him that there must have been something mysterious and painful in her husband's past. "He never told me but I could sense it during the first years of our marriage when we were very close." But then, his mother was hopeless, an unreconstructed Stalinist, and the "secret" she referred to was most likely what everybody in the family already knew—Father's imprisonment in the early thirties. Pavel recalled with distaste what his mother told him on his last visit to her, six months before: "No, I'll never believe that *he* sanctioned executions of innocent people. Let me give you an example of how chivalrous Stalin could be. It was in '48 or '49, your father and I were among the guests at his villa in the south. At the dinner everybody was praising the Georgian wine that was being served. I was young and naive and piped up that I liked French wines and it was a pity one could not get them except at receptions in the embassies. There was silence and then Stalin said that it ill behooved a Russian woman and a Communist to crave capitalist luxuries. I was abashed, and your father would not speak to me for two days. But then I received a case of French champagne with a note, 'Xenia Yegorovna, forgive an ill-tempered remark by an old man set in his ways and tastes. J. Stalin.' How could a man like that have done all those horrible things? If people were persecuted unjustly, I am sure it was done without his knowledge. Fortunately by now, almost everybody realizes that that boor Khrushchev was vastly exaggerating."

One could argue with Father. With her he would not even try; Mother would not admit that anything that had happened in the last thirty years had been for the better.

"There was none of that drinking, immorality—the young people really believed in communism. I don't know what you believe in, Pavel, but at least you love your work; for someone like our Kolya, though, it is simply ruinous to have no sense of purpose and to drift from one job to another. He was such a sweet and bright child, but they [referring to the people who had ruled the Soviet Union since 1953] forgot that young people need discipline, and something to believe in. I had been brought up in an orphanage, but because we had Soviet power, I could become a doctor, something my peasant parents could not have dreamed of under the old order."

Pavel sighed. He ought to visit his mother more often. Nikolai, always her favorite, was almost as neglectful of his filial duties as he himself. She no longer practiced her profession and her circle of acquaintances was mostly confined to women like herself—widows and abandoned wives of past and present dignitaries. Once a week she would take tea with an old admirer, a retired general whose life she allegedly saved after he had been severely wounded in the war. Her one disarming characteristic was that for all her prejudices she professed no bitterness toward the man who had abandoned her for a younger woman.

"You learn about human nature during war. And he was not only the bravest man I ever saw but just and considerate with his subordinates. If our paths parted it was, I think, because of that burden he carried, that he would never reveal to me. And all those responsibilities he has now, and at his age! Even if you don't care about yourself, Pavel, you must never do anything to make his life more difficult."

Recalling these words momentarily diverted Pavel's attention from the road; he swerved his car, just avoiding crashing into a truck. Yes, something he had done recently, though by every reasonable standard entirely innocuous, was in the eyes of Soviet law a crime.

▬

Much as he thought of his evenings as a quasi vacation, Kondratiev felt it incumbent on him to host one bachelor dinner for those Central Committee secretaries who like him were spending August in Moscow. There were but three of them—Smirnov, Lisogor, and Pyotr Korolyov, a wiry little man and former high school physics teacher who headed the department of science and technology. After the swim and while having drinks, Lisogor began to harp on his favorite theme: there were still too many Jews in responsible positions, especially in the learned professions. Korolyov, who usually spoke but little about matters outside his specialty, became quite agitated.

"What would you have us do, Pavel Viktorovich, get rid of some of our best scientists and educators and cripple our higher learning, really the entire education system?"

"Why can't we train enough of our own people? Why go on depending on those who must have divided loyalties, working here but their minds being in New York or Tel Aviv?"

"That's simply not true of the great majority who are loyal Soviet citizens."

"How many of those 'loyal Soviet citizens' would stay, Pyotr Afanasyevich, if we announced that anybody who wanted to leave could?"

"I was very much against bargaining with the Americans about who, how many, and under what conditions they could leave," intervened Kondratiev. "This then becomes a vicious circle, because when some did we started suspecting all of them. And the great majority who ordinarily would not dream of leaving now must feel that the Party does not trust them."

"I thought at the time it was a clever ploy of Leontiev's. Let thousands of people, mostly old men and women whom we don't need, go to their Palestine [Smirnov would never call it Israel], and the Americans would do almost anything to please us: credits, arms agreements on our terms, and so on. But the way it has turned out, I must agree that you were right, Mikhail." Smirnov was in an unusually friendly mood. Was it just for the sake of sociability?

"Above all, it is below the dignity of a great nation to bargain about its own internal affairs with a foreign power. But," continued Kondratiev, "much as I dislike the Zionists and what they are doing in Israel and America, I cannot extend those feelings to the majority of our Jewish fellow citizens. I saw too many Jewish lads fight and die at my side during the war. Believe me, they were just as brave as the best among our own people."

"So did I," said Korolyov. "You were too young to serve in the war, Pavel Viktorovich."

But Lisogor would not give in easily. "Is it true that Stalin wanted to resettle the whole lot of them in Siberia?"

There was a sudden silence and Lisogor realized from the expressions of his two senior colleagues that he had committed a serious gaffe.

"It's a vicious slander," said Smirnov, finally. "Why repeat such inventions by our enemies, even among ourselves?"

Their conversation turned to other less emotionally charged topics. Shortly after the dinner, Lisogor and Korolyov, as was usual even on social occasions (and quite uncivilized, thought Kondratiev—was there no respite from the hierarchical order and politics, even on a hot August night?) hastened under a variety of excuses to take their leave—the two full Politburo members might want to be alone.

"They evidently think we are going to hold a summit meeting," he joked after having escorted his guests to their limousines and coming back to find Smirnov looking and laughing at the *Paris Match*, which was one of the Western periodicals usually found on his drawing room table.

"And why not? We have a lot to talk about. I envy you your knowledge of foreign languages. I learned German in high school, but it is all gone. Always told myself I would pick it up again—perhaps some English, too—but when could I find the time?"

It was true: Smirnov was probably the hardest working Politburo member. When not in the Secretariat until the late hours, he was visiting local Party organizations all over the USSR, going through their files and delivering two or three speeches every day. This, it had been felt for a long time, earned him the right to be heir apparent to Leontiev, but undoubtedly had contributed to the stroke that had jeopardized his chances for the succession.

"Give me a cigarette, Misha. Damn the doctors. I have to smoke when something gets on my nerves, and this business with Kubiak certainly has. We don't see eye to eye on many things, but I think you'll agree that the way he carries on is simply intolerable."

Kondratiev repeated what he had told Kuliabko: Give Valentin Valentinovich enough rope to hang himself.

"That is what his colleagues probably said about the late and lamented Josif Vissarionovich when he started *his* little games. They gave him enough rope . . . and he hanged most of them."

Kondratiev laughed. "What a comparison! Kubiak is not Stalin. Those were different days. How many of the four hundred Central Committee members will fall for that nonsense of 'rejuvenating the leadership'? Most of them are only too happy to go on with their jobs and leave policy-making to us. He is more preposterous than dangerous."

"I would not use the word 'preposterous' about a whispering campaign directed against both of us: that you were once thrown out of the Party and that I am unfit for leadership because of the state of my health."

"There is to be a session in October to discuss the agricultural mess, and that will be the time to trim Comrade Kubiak's wings. But until then, what can we do? Leontiev would never agree to have him dropped because of what he has been insinuating about us. The Chief, as you know, is far from being displeased that his potential successors entertain less than brotherly feelings towards each other. It is regrettable, but not too surprising for one in his condition."

Smirnov was watching him in a way that suggested there was something on his mind that he was not sure he should reveal. Finally, it came out. "Misha, must we be rivals? I have been thinking about our predicament. For all his past and great services, Viktorov has now become an obstacle to the necessary reforms in the economy and overall administration. He is still physically fit and would make a good Chairman of the Presidium of the Supreme Soviet when he retires as premier." He hesitated, and then added, "At least with his memory, he is not likely to become confused about people the way Leontiev occasionally does. Remember how, when receiving the Indian ambassador, he assured him that the Soviet people entertain the warmest feelings toward the Pakistani nation he represented?"

It had indeed been most embarrassing. Special inducements had to be offered to the ambassador to make him keep quiet about the incident, and the secretary of the Presidium was sacked.

"But what makes you think Leontiev would be willing to give up the presidency? For all such goofs, it is certainly less taxing than his real job."

"Don't be coy, Misha. You know what I have in mind. Once he gets back from his vacation and realizes what lies ahead of him—those speeches and meetings, and the Party Congress in

January—the Chief, as he has done on most occasions in the past two years, is very likely to offer his resignation. Suppose this time we accept it rather than begging him, as before, to stay on?"

Kondratiev shrugged his shoulders.

"No, wait. If you and I agree, we can carry the others with us. You would make a perfect Chairman of the Council of Ministers, and of course with you, it would be a much more important position than it has been—not only the economy that you could start moving again, but also the overall supervision of foreign affairs, about which Viktorov neither cares nor understands much. I am primarily a Party man. Should the general secretaryship go to me—that is, if Lunin feels that at seventy-six he is too old—I would devote all my attention and powers to strengthening and revitalizing our great Party. Right now, it is in danger of sliding into a lifeless association of jobholders. We must not allow that to happen."

How typical, thought Kondratiev, that it was the most hardened bureaucrats and enemies of reform who would perorate about infusing new spirit into the Party and the need to fight bureaucratism.

Smirnov was for a moment lost in thought. Undoubtedly, in his mind he saw himself on the podium addressing the Central Committee as the general secretary. Then he recovered and looked questioningly at his host.

"I share your concern, Dmitri," the latter finally said, "but I see practical difficulties. We are both Russians. We know that it is hard for our people to understand how anyone could resign the supreme position of his own free will. It is even difficult for them to believe that their rulers die of natural causes. Remember the rumors after Stalin's death?"

Smirnov started and gave him an anxious look, but Kondratiev went on.

"And so we must cover up for Leontiev, until he is really completely unable to function, or dies. If he still can deliver an occasional speech but steps down, we would be opening a Pandora's box. . . ." Seeing incomprehension on Smirnov's face—he probably thought Pandora's box was something in the Central Committee's archives—he said, "There would be general anxiety, and it would present a wonderful opportunity for Kubiak and others to stir up trouble. We came close to that when we sacked Khrushchev, necessary though it was. Fortunately, the Americans chose that moment to start bashing their heads against the wall in Vietnam, and our Chinese comrades obliged us with their idiotic Cultural Revolution, distracting attention from our domestic troubles and enabling Leontiev to get on top of the situation. Otherwise, we would have been in a pretty pickle both at home and abroad. We cannot risk it again—we have already had some food riots, and you know what the international situation is like."

For a while they sat just looking at each other, like two fighters between rounds trying to gauge their own and each other's powers of endurance.

"I am almost seventy. He is sixty-four," went through Kondratiev's head. "An age when most men think of retirement, rather than preparing for the struggle of their lives. But if I quit, I'll die, and he probably feels the same."

It was Smirnov who broke the silence: "In any case, he cannot go on much longer. My doctors tell me that all those little strokes will lead inevitably to a major one. What do you think of my other suggestion?" His tone did not indicate much hope.

"I am very much flattered by your proposal, Dmitri. I shall go on serving the country in any position with which the Party entrusts me. But as to your idea, as I understand it, of partnership between us—you on the Party side and I on the government one—well, we tried dual leadership after Stalin's death and after the abrupt departure of Nikita Sergeievich, and it did not work."

"Viktorov was not the man for the job. He is a walking computer, not a leader."

"I don't think it could work under any circumstances. This is against our national characteristic: the Russians—I am not speaking of other nationalities—need and want a single leader. They become distraught if there is any ambiguity about power. Look at ourselves. The more ailing Leontiev has become, the more we heaped additional honors on him. He is not that vain and would have preferred not to take on the additional, if mostly ceremonial, burden of being Head of State. But we insisted, and correctly so: his image must remain that of one fully in control, dominating his associates. Our people must not suspect that their supreme leader is a sick man capable of working only two or three days per week, and that with difficulty."

"Do you think the people are really fooled?"

"They want to keep being reassured, let the foreigners say what they want in their malicious broadcasts. The average Russian craves to believe there is a firm hand guiding the ship of state, otherwise he might go berserk."

"If I thought that the Party and you would be happy with Mikhail Alexandrovich Kondratiev as general secretary, I would consider it my duty to support you. But let me be frank, Misha, you lack experience with the rank and file of the Party. You've always been either in the central apparatus or on foreign missions. I began as a factory union organizer and worked my way through district and regional Party jobs to where I am now. You've known ministers and foreign politicians. I can tell you in detail how the borough secretary in Kaluga and a district one in Tashkent live, work, and think. And that is why I thought we might reach an understanding and avoid a struggle for the leadership."

Kondratiev felt his patience running out. It was infuriating to have Smirnov, just like his son Pavel, imply that he did not know and set himself up above the common man. For one, the *real people* were the gray mass of Party functionaries; for the other, a bunch of disgruntled intellectuals. He must end this conversation before he said something he shouldn't. "There need not be any factions within our leadership. When the time comes, and mind you, he may yet outlast both of us, the Politburo will take a vote, and that will be that."

"You cannot believe it is ever so simple. Well, I tried. At least we agree that Kubiak must be watched."

"And you must watch your health, Dmitri. If you keep on chain-smoking, the Party may lose an eminent leader . . . Shouldn't we talk about next week's agenda?"

The end of August brought the usual flurry of rumors and speculation about possible Russian moves in the fall. A noted British authority on Soviet military affairs detected ominous portents in Marshal Vorontsov's cutting short his vacation to fly back to Moscow. (In fact, the minister of defense, a perennial sufferer of dental troubles, was in urgent need of being outfitted with artificial teeth.) Was the USSR, after all, going to intervene directly in Poland, where the Communist regime was still far from being master of the situation and had incurred Moscow's displeasure by its dilly-dallying around with the opposition and its continuing appeasement of the Catholic Church? A secret CIA report, which was promptly featured on the front page of America's newspapers, discounted the possibility of an invasion of Poland, but predicted a massive Soviet effort to crush the insurgency in Afghanistan, employing as many as three to four hundred thousand troops, with the possibility of an armed intrusion into Pakistan under pretext of cutting off the rebels' routes of infiltration and supply.

Many foreign observers, while not necessarily endorsing either of the above hypotheses, still expressed foreboding that after harvest time the Kremlin might put on a show of force. Russia's rulers, it was held, were determined to block deployment of NATO's intermediate nuclear missiles, which could reach the territory of the USSR in a matter of a few minutes. What better way of demonstrating to Western Europeans the fateful consequences of such a move than a dramatic display of military might? The harsh tone of the Soviet press about events in the Middle East, where Israel was fighting the PLO in southern Lebanon, helped feed such fears. The Soviet Union, noted some Western commentators, could not indefinitely tolerate blows to its prestige, such as NATO's defiance of its warnings and the trouncing of its Arab friends. Hence the urgent need for Washington to display flexibility and willingness to meet the Russians halfway on strategic and tactical nuclear arms questions, to mute its criticism of events in Poland, and in general restrain its anti-Soviet rhetoric. But time was of the essence. Unless the West moved quickly to mollify the Russians, their injured pride and the fears generated by their long experience of foreign invasions were almost certain to lead them to a rash step; and the subsequent crisis, though initially localized, might escalate with fateful consequences for the whole world.

Such dangers were being quite irresponsibly discounted, many Europeans and Americans felt, by the American administration's spokesmen. At a press conference in Washington, Doherty, now acting chief of the American delegation to the suspended arms control negotiations, argued at length that the Kremlin was simply continuing its old game of trying to intimidate the East and divide the Atlantic alliance. In fact, the USSR was most unlikely, "for the present," he stressed, to undertake a military venture. Its economy was in bad shape, and the Russians neither needed nor wanted to add the occupation of Poland to their burdens. In Afghanistan, they were content to carry on a war of attrition, for years if necessary. In the Middle East, they still had Syria to step in if the PLO were crushed.

"Why do we need the MX, the Trident, and all those European missiles, if the Soviets do not plan to move anywhere?" asked a newspaperman known for his critical views about the administration.

"I said for the present moment," answered Doherty, whom the papers described as having a note of exasperation in his voice.

"Then when?—tomorrow, next year, in 1990?" pursued the man.

"Whenever they feel they can get away with it."

"Why was Marshal Vorontsov summoned back to Moscow?"

"How should I know? Maybe he was not summoned, but got something wrong with his prostate. At his age—"

"How can one joke when we may be on the eve of a most dangerous confrontation?" exclaimed a shocked French correspondent.

"Ivan Yakovlevich's prostate was removed some years ago," volunteered Kondratiev to Gorbunov as they sat perusing the digest of the foreign press. "But unlike the Americans, we know how to keep our secrets. Such a talented nation, and yet what a silly system."

"In any case, our propaganda appears to be quite effective."

"Yes, as long as we don't fall for it ourselves, my boy. I've seen it happen. The late Comrade Khrushchev would publicly boast how we could destroy the U.S. in a nuclear exchange with minimal damage to ourselves, and he almost came to believe it."

In addition to alarm over the international situation, both the foreign press and the Soviets' own confidential sources bore witness to the lively speculation about the problem of succession in the Kremlin. A prominent West German politician, who in view of his being courted by the Soviets was given the unusual, for a non-Communist, honor of being personally invited to Leontiev's Crimean retreat, was quoted to the effect that he found his host in excellent health and an ebullient mood. However, a Soviet agent in Bonn reported that the same man, when with his intimate friends, had said that he was shocked by the Communist chieftain's condition—easily fatigued and short of breath, frequent lapses of memory. As to his successor, in America, at least, the experts' opinion had shifted: instead of Kondratiev or Smirnov's being touted as the most likely choice, Kubiak was now considered to be ahead in the race. The evidence offered was Kubiak's selection to head a high-powered Soviet delegation that had embarked on a tour of several African states. The youngest of the contenders, it was pointed out, was thus given exposure to foreign affairs, undoubtedly a special blow to Kondratiev, who, in view of his position, must have expected to be entrusted with this important mission.

Gorbunov looked inquiringly at his boss.

"No, Mitya, do not ask why it is Kubiak who should be traveling to Africa. It would be an indiscreet question, even coming from a candidate member of the Central Committee." There was just a hint of jocularity in Kondratiev's tone, and his assistant felt greatly relieved.

It had been in fact an amusing scene. Kubiak could hardly contain his anger when talking to the other secretaries prior to embarking on his errand.

"Perhaps you can explain what is going on? I was in the middle of my tour of inspection, several important meetings scheduled ahead in North Caucasus and Georgia, when I received this message from the Chief. He is unable to head this mission to the savages, so I must go in his stead. But Konstantin Leonidovich was never supposed to travel there in the first place. The delegation was to be headed by the minister of foreign trade. Who are they to rate a member of the Politburo?"

"We must be very careful of our African friends' sensitivities. Keep it in mind, Valentin," proclaimed Smirnov solemnly.

It was not wise at this point to provoke Kubiak too much, decided Kondratiev; they must keep up appearances. "We who were minding the shop had to make a quick decision. We couldn't give the Africans even a fraction of the credits and arms for which they have been begging us. It all goes down the drain. And several of those states had just been visited by a Chinese delegation headed by a member of their Politburo. We contacted Comrade Leontiev, who expressed his readiness to go himself—which of course was unrealistic. He then was strongly of the opinion that you, as our agricultural expert, were the logical choice and that it would help soothe their feelings."

The Central Committee's expert on African affairs was then summoned and delivered a thumbnail sketch of the politics and leaders of the fifteen countries to be visited. "It is not the best time of the year to be there, but we'll have doctors from our Institute for Tropical Diseases with us. Their politicians may be trying, Comrade Kubiak, but you'll enjoy the sights and the animals."

"I've been to zoos," was the disconsolate reply of the chief figure-to-be in what an American journal described as "the most ambitious venture yet by the Soviets to undermine Western influence in the Third World."

Smirnov was afterward quite keen on bringing their traveling colleague's transgressions before the first regular Politburo meeting in September and trying to have him fired there and then, but Kondratiev told him flatly that he would not cooperate. The reasons he gave were those of high policy: the West would be presented with a confirmation of what until now had been unsubstantiated rumors that there were splits in the leadership and the struggle for succession had begun. The Soviet Union's bargaining power in the international arena would be weakened. The Africans would feel bitter at what they would see as another indication that Moscow was not taking them seriously, and that they had not entertained and negotiated with a prestigious leader but a discredited politician.

Privately, he also had his own reasons. If Kubiak was making any inroads at all among local Party secretaries and the like, it would be among those who otherwise lined up behind Smirnov, rather than himself. Where it really counted, in the Politburo, he did not want to appear as an accomplice to a Smirnov intrigue. Leontiev might be enraged by the realization that he had been used and turn against both of them. Lunin, for one, would very likely see the whole thing as a breach of Politburo collegiality on their, rather than Kubiak's, part. How could this man, with his constant sermons about Communist morality, have worked as a secretary of the Central Committee under Stalin and still venerate his memory?

All those thoughts went through his mind as he sat listening to his wife's account of her travels. Noting that he was distracted, she stopped.

"I am sorry, dear," he said. "What were you saying?"

"I haven't said anything for a minute or so."

"Please forgive me. In your absence I get into the habit of

bringing my official worries home. But you know that within a very short time, I become again the most attentive husband."

"I know what you were thinking. Everywhere I went, Sofia, Prague, Budapest, I was fussed over much more than ever before. You and I know why it was, and I must say it frightens me."

"It is still just a possibility."

They shifted to more mundane subjects. There was to be a party for Nikolai and his bride.

"And Mikhail, whom would you like to be invited to your own birthday? Should we just have the family and a few friends?"

He contained his irritation: was she pretending, or had she really forgotten that for people in his position it could never be just a family affair? They were going to celebrate it quietly the day before, but on the actual date there was to be a reception in the Kremlin. Leontiev was cutting short his vacation to present him personally with the Order of Lenin.

"How many will that make?"

"Five. It will tie me with Lunin. Only Viktorov, with six, and Leontiev himself, with seven, have more . . . Now don't say, 'You men are like children.' I remember your excitement when you were named Honored Artist of the Russian Soviet Republic."

The ceremony took place in the very same hall from which, thirty-nine years before, Mikhail Alexandrovich was summoned to the meeting that marked the beginning of his official career. Party and government notables, Kondratiev's past and present associates, ambassadors from the fraternal Socialist countries, listened solemnly to the congratulatory address on the occasion of his seventieth birthday, presented on behalf of the Central Committee, the Presidium of the Supreme Soviet, and the Council of Ministers. Experts on such things among those present listened attentively for any nuance in the wording of the greetings that might carry a political portent. But the text did not depart from the usual formula for these occasions: "Faithful son of the Soviet people . . . an outstanding leader of the party of Great Lenin . . . many fruitful years of service to the nation . . . indefatigable fighter for peace and the welfare of the Socialist Fatherland." Leontiev—it was one of his good days—delivered the message in a firm voice, and followed it by a brief speech of his own before pinning the order on the honored guest's already heavily medalled chest. The speech was delivered without notes, and merriment and hearty applause greeted the words, "For a man like you, dear Mikhail Alexandrovich, seventy is just the beginning of middle age," a phrase that was to lead to much silent reflection among the Soviet oligarchs, and elaborate commentaries in the foreign press. Did Leontiev hint that he himself, at seventy-six, felt fit to carry on for several more years, or did he seek to indicate that the man being honored was his preferred choice for succession?

Kondratiev's response was appropriately modest: "No higher honor than serving the Soviet people . . . whatever modest contribution . . . under the guidance of the Central Committee . . . special thanks to thee, Konstantin Leonidovich." The only departure from the set pattern was to include a few sentences on international affairs: "Having not long ago on behalf of the government of the USSR conducted negotiations with representatives of the U.S., I had occasion to reaffirm our people's sincere devotion to peace, but also their staunch resolve to rebuff any attempt to intimidate us. . . . We seek to have not only correct, but friendly relations with the great American people, as with all nations. . . . Certain persons in Washington should get it through their thick skulls that we shall never submit to blackmail, whether on the question of nuclear arms or any other international issue. . . . We have always desired to maintain the best possible relations with the People's Republic of China, and whenever Beijing decides to sit down to constructive talks, it will not find us wanting."

The international part of the speech had naturally been composed at an impromptu meeting of the Politburo. Vorontsov had wanted to insert, "We have capabilities to smash any would-be aggressor," and Filimonov had proposed, "We extend a hand of friendship to our Chinese comrades," but both were out-voted. In its final form, the statement bore witness to the Soviets' readiness to lower the level of tension with the West and their continued reserve vis-à-vis Communist China. As such, it was greeted with relief in the United States, some analysts hailing the speech as a bid for renewal of negotiations on arms control, several Kremlinologists seeing it as a confirmation of their thesis that Kondratiev represented the moderate wing of the leadership.

At the reception that followed, Smirnov toasted him on behalf of the Central Committee, Viktorov for the government. He had to take exception, the octogenarian prime minister declared, with

Comrade Leontiev's identifying seventy as the beginning of middle age: their colleague and friend still retained all the characteristics of youth. It had been his, Viktorov's, privilege to have had Mikhail Alexandrovich work with him during the war in the Commissariat of Munitions. In his first year as assistant commissar he had been largely responsible for tank production, which had risen from 400 to 625 per month. Andronnikov reminisced pleasantly about Kondratiev as a fellow officer on the Stalingrad front. The head of the State Publishing House displayed the two-volume collection of the honored guest's speeches and writings, fresh off the press and entitled *In the Service of the Country and Proletarian Internationalism*. The president of the Union of Writers praised the book for the felicity of its style, and the lapidary vigor of the language. It was an inestimable contribution to Soviet literature.

"How could he have read it, if it has just been published?" whispered Kuliabko to Remizov.

Such incongruities were not allowed to interfere with the festive atmosphere of the party. Several notables were already visibly affected by the repeated toasts. Finally Lunin, after an imploring look from Leontiev's aide, took the general secretary firmly by the arm.

"Even for a middle-aged man, you have had enough, Kostya."

The two of them, having embraced Kondratiev once more, took their leave. Kondratiev stayed for another half hour, then after hugs for Politburo colleagues and handshakes with the others, followed their example. He felt pleasantly fatigued. It had gone well, had not turned into a brawl as such functions frequently did in Khrushchev's time, on at least one occasion the general secretary himself having to be carried out. Somehow the thought of those days stirred up other troublesome memories. By the time he reached home, the pleasant mood was gone.

"I did not want to bother you on your birthday, and yesterday we had to recuperate. It was a great tribute to you, Mikhail Alexandrovich. People were not just going through the motions."

"I am grateful for your contribution, Lieutenant Andronnikov. You said you wanted to see me in connection with the matter we discussed two months ago. Anything new and important?"

"Yes, something new, or rather bizarre. As to whether it is important—frankly, I don't think so. But I had to bring it to your attention and let you judge for yourself, Mikhail Alexandrovich."

Andronnikov sighed and pulled out some notes from his attaché case. Kondratiev lit a cigarette.

"I regret that our original information on that American professor was not as complete as it should have been. Remember, he was here four years ago studying the archival materials about the Imperial Ministry of Justice, for the period from 1900 to 1910. There seemed to be no reason for our people to pore over a lot of crumbling old documents. But after our conversation, I ordered the archive checked. Or rather, I had it brought to our offices—and personally supervised a special team of investigators going through several cartloads of that junk. After rummaging in it for several weeks, we found something that did not belong there at all. It was a box, marked only with a number. All the others also had dates on them. Inside, you won't believe it, was a copy of—"

"The Solovyov Report?" asked Kondratiev, calmly.

The head of the KGB had in his professional capacity seen and heard too many strange things to be astounded by even the most incredible occurrence. But this time his face expressed utter stupefaction.

"You must be clairvoyant," he said, finally.

"Not quite. I got to thinking about it the other night—just after the party—and it occurred to me that one possible explanation for that phrase in the American's letter was that somehow he had got wind of the report. It was most unlikely that any surviving member of the commission would have volunteered the information, certainly not to a foreigner. So I figured he must have seen the document itself."

"But how is it possible?"

"It is up to you, my dear Sasha, to find out. My clairvoyance goes only so far, and you have 170,000 operatives working under you."

Andronnikov's amazement was understandable. The Commission to Investigate the Circumstances Surrounding the Death of Comrade S. M. Kirov had been set up in 1961 by a secret resolution of the Politburo, and chaired by its candidate member, Pavel Solovyov. It had delivered its findings in late September 1964. Within two weeks Khrushchev was dismissed, and the Politburo decided to suppress a number of documents from the Stalin era that the fallen leader had intended to make public. All the copies, save one, of the Solovyov Report were ordered destroyed. The single remaining copy was placed in the personal archive of the general secretary, access to which was limited to full members of the Politburo and only by his specific authorization; in each case, the document in question was to be examined in the presence of the head of the KGB.

"We don't know how the report got there or when. But we do know, well, insofar as we could ascertain, that the box in question was seen by only one person. The box, according to the register, was charged out for use in the library reading room on five consecutive days in November 1978, by Valentin Kerner."

"There must have been others, our own as well as foreign scholars, working on the ministry archive?"

"Yes, there are eighteen names listed as having signed out various portions of it, but they asked for the materials by years, and the damned box, as I said, has no dates on it, only a serial number. Kerner evidently went through all the documents marked with dates, then asked if there was anything else. So they gave him the box."

"The archivist?"

"The woman in charge has been there since 1975, when her predecessor died. She swears she has never seen the contents of the box, and I believe her. Like most of her kind, she is out of this world—couldn't tell you who Solovyov was, or Kirov, for that matter."

Kondratiev got up, strode around the room, and then sat down again. "Is the report there in its entirety?"

"Here." The KGB chief opened his attaché case and pulled out three bulky volumes. "File One. File Two. This contains—"

"The depositions of people not directly charged with the crime, but who had some knowledge of the circumstances that led to it, including one by M. A. Kondratiev."

"Yes, and File Three contains the conclusions and recommendations of the commission. You want to examine it?"

"No, you take it and have it burned, Sasha. You said it was not important."

"No, here is why. We can be sure that if the professor decided to come out with some story, he would have nothing to prove it."

"Photocopies, verbatim quotations?"

For the first time, Andronnikov smiled. "All got lost in transit.

Our man in charge of departing foreigners' baggage looked into the trunkful of notes dispatched by the good professor, decided, quite correctly, that an American has no business prying into the records of our ministries, whether Soviet or imperial, and put them through a shredder. The airport and customs authorities received a series of irate letters from Kerner, and as late as 1981 they were assuring him they were still searching for his trunk."

"He would not have sent it through the American embassy?"

"No, we have a pretty good idea what goes into the diplomatic pouch, and in general," he smiled again, "what goes on within the embassy . . . Look, Mikhail Alexandrovich, we have now learned a great deal about the man. We have an operative in Indianapolis, a recent émigré whom he has befriended. He likes to hint that he discovered some grave secrets while in our country, but will not say what they are. His sort is not likely to come out with anything until you-know-what happens. And then, how could it hurt you?"

Kondratiev, realizing he was stroking his chin, moved his hand and began playing with a pencil.

Andronnikov continued. "To us in the leadership it is an old story, and compared with what some of our older colleagues did in those years, it is . . . well, trivial. Vorontsov sat in a camp and was released only at the beginning of the war. The things Lunin did in Latvia . . . We both could go on. As to what the foreigners might say, who cares? And how many of them would believe a wild, unsubstantiated tale by a quack academic? They spread so much nonsense about us in the capitalist world, that most people even there have learned to consider such 'revelations' as rubbish. Take myself, when I was appointed head of the Committee on State Security. One of those American 'experts' on us wrote that he knew for a fact that in 1937 I had been a member of the execution squad in the NKVD headquarters in Moscow. At the time, I was a Komsomol official in Omsk. My pals were being arrested right and left, and I died a thousand deaths each time there was a knock on my door at night. Frankly, Mikhail Alexandrovich, I could never understand your agitation over this business."

"You must admit that it is somewhat disturbing that a copy of the Solovyov Report should be discovered in the Lenin Library? How did it get there, and why?"

"When it was ordered destroyed, Karsavin was in overall control of the security organs. He may have had some cute ideas as to how it could be useful to him in the future. Well, Karsavin has been dead these past ten years. We may never know."

"I should think it would pique your professional pride not to have found out."

"We'll go on trying." Andronnikov stood up, replaced the documents in his attaché case. He placed one hand on the doorknob, hesitated, and turned. "There are, of course, special ways of handling the problem, if this fellow Kerner becomes a pest. Let me know."

Kondratiev did not answer immediately. He recalled a scene some years ago—Andronnikov making a similar hint at a Politburo meeting about a Ukrainian nationalist leader in West Germany who indeed was proving a "pest." Leontiev had banged his fist on the table and shouted, "I don't want to hear about it. You are head of the State Security Committee. You do whatever is necessary to protect the security of the state. I don't want to know anything of how you go about it."

He smiled. "That would not be smart. I can just see the headlines in American newspapers: MAN WITH KEY TO SOVIET LEADER'S PAST FOUND FLOATING IN———. I forget whether there is a river in Indianapolis."

The KGB chief was not amused. "As a rule, we don't like to do these things, but if absolutely necessary, we are more subtle than that." And then, more cheerfully, "I am glad you can now joke about the whole thing, Mikhail Alexandrovich. Good. You ought to keep your mind on really important matters. I shall see you at the Wednesday meeting."

When the door closed on his visitor, Kondratiev sent out word that he was not to be disturbed until further notice. He had to think. Indeed, insofar as the inner circle was concerned, there was nothing disgraceful in what he had gone through in December 1934. Vorontsov had been beaten into signing a much more incriminating confession, sentenced to fifteen years, and saved only by the outbreak of the war—when he was released, restored to his previous rank, and thereafter rapidly and deservedly promoted. In fact, his popularity within the officer corps was largely due to the fact that, though the story had been naturally omitted from his official biography, many within military circles had been privy to it. Smirnov was briefly detained for "falsifying his class origins" on the Party questionnaire. They were given as those of a poor peasant; somehow it was discovered that his family before collectivization had owned three cows. He also was released for army service at the outbreak of the war. Every Russian over forty could understand why people in Kondratiev's situation had happened to sign false confessions during those years. Much less forgivable was what Lunin, or for that matter Leontiev, whom Andronnikov tactfully had not mentioned in this connection, had done: signing not confessions, but orders that had directly or indirectly led to the doom of so many.

How often before had he gone through such ruminations and decided that it was ridiculous to worry? Why, then, the continuing anxiety? There were now several cigarette butts in the ashtray—he must not again become a chain-smoker. Why not switch to a pipe, much more sensuously satisfying and less of a health hazard? How come no one within the inner Party circle was a pipe smoker? Oh, yes. Too reminiscent of *his* public image.

Was Stalin the only other person who knew the real secret of December 1, 1934, something that was not in the Solovyov Report, but that a diligent reader of the report just might be led to suspect? How about old Molotov, now, at ninety-two, a doddering ruin of a man, but incredibly enough, until a year or so ago, seen occasionally in the Lenin Library, reading and taking notes? The aged scoundrel's appearance there had led to an acrimonious exchange within the Politburo. Molotov, declared Remizov, should have had the decency to die a long time ago. It was most indelicate of him to appear in public places, and he should be put away.

"He is not doing any harm. I see Molotov occasionally. He is writing his memoirs," said Lunin.

Several of those present burst out laughing, with Kuliabko, true to form, asking, "But hasn't someone in the Institute for Party History already written them?"

Lunin reddened with anger. "I don't see why Comrades Remizov and Kuliabko should be so sarcastic about a helpless old man. He has paid in full for his transgressions. Let him spend his few remaining days in peace and with some dignity."

Leontiev, who hated being reminded of the old times, cut the debate short by turning to Remizov. "You are the boss in Moscow, Arkadi; do what you see fit. For heaven's sake, let us not revert to the bad habits of the early sixties: going on and on about what happened in the past. Our business is the present and the future."

And so is mine, Kondratiev reminded himself firmly. Both Kuliabko and Andronnikov had been visibly troubled by his brooding over what they considered an insignificant episode in his youth. Their personal loyalty to him notwithstanding, neither would wish for the leader of the Party and nation to be a man given to bouts of remorse and melancholy. Not to mention his other potential supporters. He himself had laughed at this fashionable fad in the West—rich people seeking relief from their anxieties by paying quacks to rummage around in their childhood memories.

Leontiev had once read a confidential report from Rome revealing how a prominent Communist leader there was undergoing analysis with a famous professor and was consequently in serious financial straits. Finally, he had been constrained to ask his colleagues to authorize payments to the analyst out of the Party's funds.

"I think this explains a great deal about our Italian comrades' behavior," observed Kondratiev. "He should come here. Our KGB does it for free."

He opened his gold, diamond-encrusted cigarette case, a birthday present from the Council of Ministers, and tossed all but two cigarettes into the wastebasket, then pressed the button. "The reports on Lebanon and Syria and the latest dispatches from Washington. Call Comrade Filimonov's secretary. I shall be ready to receive him in one hour."

CHAPTER 7

THE ASCENT, MARCH 1943–MARCH 1953

Being an assistant minister in wartime, Kondratiev soon discovered, was in many ways more nerve-racking than front-line duty. At the front one went through periods of boredom, punctuated by moments of fear and exhilaration; one's duties were clearly defined and simple. Being responsible for supplying the army with one of the most important weapons of modern warfare meant constant anxiety, at times bordering on panic. Physical danger he had learned to live with, but the fear of failing in his obligations to the country, of others finding him inadequate to his task, stayed with Mikhail Alexandrovich for nearly two years following the moment of his elation at his appointment.

Soon thereafter it dawned on him that he was a novice to administration. It was one thing to help run a single plant or command a regiment, and quite another to direct enterprises employing hundreds of thousands of workers. One could not call a plant manager and tell him to step up the output of armored cars the way one ordered a company commander to advance, or else. One director would plead that his factory did not receive an adequate quantity of steel from the Ministry of Heavy Industry, another that the Ministry of Transport failed to provide the necessary number of trucks and railway cars to fetch the supplies. In one case the local Party boss decided that all the technical personnel of one of the largest factories who were under fifty should be conscripted for military duties.

"How am I going to run the place with just a handful of staff?" lamented the unfortunate manager.

"You yourself know, Comrade Kondratiev, what happened to most of the older generation of specialists in the prewar years. There are not enough of them to go around."

In quite a number of places, workers were not given the food rations to which they were entitled, leading to a high incidence of illness and consequent absenteeism.

The mournful legacy of the years of terror weighed heavily on the performance of Soviet industry even now. Most industrial officials were incapable of improvising their way out of the difficulties, or in fact, of departing in the slightest from the prescribed routine without explicit orders from above. They still remembered how a snag in the production schedule, or an unauthorized variation of the organizational chart or of working hours, had often led to the charges of "wrecking" and "sabotage." Local Party bosses still considered it their prerogative to rule on the staff appointments in the enterprises within their bailiwicks. In this third year of the war, few workers needed lessons in patriotism or on the importance of doing their utmost to defeat the Germans. Yet the old habits persisted: dead-tired from backbreaking labor, men and women would be herded to mass meetings, there to listen to propagandistic perorations on themes and events long familiar to them from the daily press. Such forced exposure to endless oratory, Kondratiev soon became convinced, was definitely counterproductive insofar as the morale and performance of its victims were concerned.

After a few weeks' experience he decided to present his conclusions to the minister. Viktorov had originally greeted him coldly, as someone not of his choice and with dubious qualifications for the job. But now he listened attentively, often nodding with approval.

"I wanted to see if you could find out for yourself what the main problems were, and I am glad that, for the most part, you have."

As to his recommendations: the intraministerial committees, instead of improving coordination, tended to make it more difficult, or just wasted time. But things were going to change.

"I have been appointed to the State Defense Council to be in overall charge of the economy, while still continuing in the ministry. Now that we are winning, our leader wants to devote all his genius to the military and diplomatic side of the war."

Kondratiev looked at him in amazement. There was no detectable irony in his voice, but how could he be saying such things to someone he had known for just a few weeks? "Consequently," continued Viktorov, "there will be no need to negotiate with other ministries."

"You will specify in detail what is needed for your branch. They will deliver it."

He fully approved the suggestion that Mikhail Alexandrovich be given full authority in matters of management. The Party people would be told firmly to stop interfering. If they did, *they* would be sent to the front.

"*They* certainly are not indispensable to the war effort, and it is strange how many of them are at an age at which they should be shouldering a gun or driving a tank, rather than sitting in an office and pestering others."

Kondratiev would remember these words when surveying his Politburo colleagues' biographies. About half of his cronies, though in their twenties and early thirties during the war, had spent their time as minor Party or government bureaucrats.

As for the managers and engineers, they would have to make do with what was available. They would continue to comb the camps for members of those prewar cadres who had survived and were still fit to work.

Viktorov sighed. "It is only recently that I managed to persuade Beria to release from his clutches some of our best aircraft, tank, and artillery experts. He insisted that they could work perfectly well when locked up—no distractions. I asked Lavrenti Pavlovich if he would like to try it himself, and when Comrade Stalin laughed, our worthy minister of internal affairs conceded the point."

He agreed only partially with Kondratiev's plea not to be confined to his desk.

"If a serious bottleneck develops in some place, by all means fly there. I don't approve, however, of ministers rushing frantically to and fro. It is an old and bad Russian habit of mistaking commotion for activity, of keeping your subordinates in constant dread of a superior suddenly descending on their place of work and expecting them to grovel. Our industrial cadres need help to develop a sense of self-reliance—after all they have been through."

For the first time in their association, he smiled at his assistant. "Enough chatter. Let us get back to work."

Returning to his office, Kondratiev could not get over his sense of wonder. He had heard people whisper with awe about Viktorov's peculiarities and outspokenness, but this was really mind-boggling. How could a man like that have survived, let alone gotten to where he was? Lately he himself had been thinking in terms of serving the country, and tried to avoid any reflections about the system under which his countrymen lived. Now he felt his sense of identification with the Party returning. Here was exactly the kind of man Lenin had had in mind as the Communist official of the future. There would be no Nikiforovs or Berias in that future. They were just accidental byproducts of the cruel struggle to bring socialism to a backward country. And Stalin? No longer an idol, but still the supreme commander of his embattled nation.

For all his increasing self-assurance and familiarity with the work, the job continued to strain his nervous and physical powers. The most harrowing moments would come during appearances before the State Defense Council. A summons from the Kremlin usually came in the late evening, with little warning, leaving just an hour or two for a frantic search for the requisite charts and statistics. The sight that confronted him on entering the Politburo room gradually grew familiar, but always made his heart beat faster: Stalin walking around with an unlit pipe in his hand; on one side of the table three or four other members of the committee; on the other, two or more high-ranking military men, with maps and other papers spread before them. He would be greeted dryly and invited to sit down.

Stalin would immediately get to the point: the army group commanded by—here he would nod in the direction of the general or marshal in question—had been unable to advance as planned, or its offensive was being contained by the Germans. The explanation, sometimes he would say "excuse" with a hard look at the commander, was lack of sufficient armor. The chief of staff, or whoever was deputizing for him, would then tell his part of the story. The latest tank model that was supposed to be superior to the German panzer actually proved to have serious defects. Or, there were not enough tanks in the High Command's reserve, the Munitions Ministry had promised to deliver eight hundred new ones before the start of the offensive, but, in fact, they came up with only five hundred. Perhaps Comrade Kondratiev would explain what was going on?

Comrade Kondratiev would then be questioned in a way that would occasionally remind him of his examination at the hands of the NKVD inquisitors. Almost invariably, he had the data to support his case: the new model had come out without some of the originally planned features because the chief inspector of the armored forces insisted on its being ready in a hurry for the battlefield, and to hell with these newfangled devices. It was the logjams in supply and transport that were responsible for the failure to deliver the assigned quota of armored units. Comrade Viktorov had clearly stipulated what was needed from the given ministries; they had not come through on their obligations. Stalin would ask some questions indicating, at times, considerable knowledge of technical details. Then would come the verdict: most often, Kondratiev and the officers would be asked to withdraw to an adjoining room, to try to work out a solution and come back in an hour. At first during such conferences, the military leaders, their names now renowned throughout the world, tried to bully the man they still saw as a plain major. But as he stood his ground in the face of threats and curses they eventually would grow quite businesslike, and they would reappear before the committee with an agreed-upon solution for the problem.

At times Stalin upbraided the soldiers for trying to shift the blame for their own failures onto the production people. They now had a definite edge on the Germans in both men and matériel. Why couldn't they move faster? Were they afraid of their reputations and hence wanting an absolutely crushing superiority before they proposed an attack? The generals would as a rule respond meekly, but on one such occasion, Marshal Zhukov, his face growing red, begged to remind Comrade Stalin how despite *professional*—he stressed the word—advice to the contrary, the High Command had ordered an offensive in the spring of 1942, and it led to a rout, the Germans then advancing all the way to Stalingrad. There was a moment of silence in the room, during which no one dared to look at the dictator, and then he said softly, "You are right, Georgi Konstantinovich. We all committed serious errors during the first two years."

Yet, no one could be sure of the outcome of such sessions. At one, Stalin berated a four-star general who then made a very convincing case for the way he had handled his army group and apparently carried the day. Shortly afterward, the general was stripped of his command and spent the rest of the war as a lecturer at a military academy. On another occasion, Kondratiev presented what seemed to him, and evidently to the military people, an irrefutable argument citing figures and dates. Stalin had looked at him as if he were a total stranger and turned to the other members of the council.

"Do you think, Comrades, we might have to replace Comrade Kondratiev with someone who could produce fewer statistics but more tanks?"

Never since the horrid moments in the thirties was Mikhail Alexandrovich so close to a breakdown as during the next two days. He then saw Viktorov, who had been on a tour, and asked him whether he should go back to the army. There was no question of his being dismissed, Viktorov informed him.

"The Boss told me about the incident and also that he thinks quite highly of your work. He just likes to keep people on their toes."

More precisely, to make them feel like a man with a rope around his neck and a trapdoor under his feet, thought the victim, as he skulked back to his office.

Under the circumstances, anything resembling domestic life was, of course, virtually impossible. He began to work early in the morning and, even if only half-awake, at the end of the day he still did not dare leave the office. The telephone might ring at two or three o'clock at night.

"Comrade Stalin will speak to you" or "Marshal Vasilevsky needs the following information. . . ." Usually it was preferable to catch a few hours' sleep at the ministry. At home there was the added unpleasantness of Xenia sulking and crying over his not infrequent failure to perform his conjugal duties.

His wife, after recuperating from a miscarriage, resumed working at her profession. Barring an emergency in the hospital, she kept regular hours and bitterly resented being alone at home for most of the time. They had a three-room apartment, with a kitchen and bathroom of their own, heated in the winter—amenities that could not even be dreamed of by the mass of Muscovites. Yet after the initial rapture, Xenia's mood became one of irritability: the life of a minister's wife was quite unlike what she had imagined it would be. Mikhail Alexandrovich was at first naively surprised that a woman who had uncomplainingly faced the dangers and privations at the front and the horrifying sights of a field hospital could now be so demanding and disaffected. All the other dignitaries' wives in the apartment building had intimated that their husbands were supplementing their food rations by drawing on their institutions' special stocks. Why did he have to be so uniquely virtuous? She found it hard to understand—and at first she suspected that her husband was not telling the truth—why the few official parties to which he went were exclusively male affairs. Eventually, he grew philosophical about her behavior: the miscarriage, boredom, his own constant tension—it all certainly explained and excused those fits of bad temper. Once peace came, they would be able to resume real intimacy, have children. Life was *bound* to be better after the war. The way the people had fought and sacrificed, how could anyone wish to revert to the ways of the thirties?

To be sure, those traitors who collaborated with the Germans in the occupied territory had to be punished. Officially, every Soviet soldier who let himself be taken prisoner while conscious was also held to have committed a crime. But with the appalling losses in lives compounding the gigantic task of restoring the shattered economy, it would be sheer folly to start rounding up again and keeping in the camps millions of able-bodied men and women. Whatever else anyone might think of *him*, he was not a fool.

And yet . . . He received a shock after having reported to Viktorov a sudden and inexplicable difficulty in obtaining railway cars for transporting new workers, mostly veterans who had recovered from wounds but were no longer fit for military duty, to the factories that suffered from labor shortages. His boss picked up a recent copy of *Pravda*.

"You must have read this."

The Presidium of the Supreme Soviet, ran the announcement, had decreed that in view of the high incidence of collaboration with the invader by their populations, the Crimean Tatar and Chechen Ingush Autonomous Republics were being demoted to the status of districts.

"What does it have to do with the shortage?"

"All those people are being deported to Central Asia. It takes quite a number of cars."

"All of them?"

"Every man, woman, and child, including some who had actually been in the underground fighting the Germans."

"And what is happening to the lands they've inhabited?"

"They are being resettled, mostly with Russians. More cars."

Years later, he heard another part of the story. At the meeting of the State Defense Council that was considering the measure, Viktorov had handed Stalin a paper with calculations of how many divisions and how much in the way of military supplies and stocks of food could be transported in the railway cars that would be required for the operation. Stalin tore up the paper, saying, "Tend to your own business."

"Of course, it *was* my business," related Viktorov, "but what could I do? And Beria, as dumb in such matters as he was wicked in everything, had added reassuringly, 'These will mostly be cattle cars.' "

In October 1944, Kondratiev was dispatched to the United States, a member of a delegation to discuss Soviet requirements under Lend-Lease. Though the pace of his work there was almost as hectic as in Moscow, he found the two weeks' stay in America soothing for his nerves. It was a strange experience. How could he feel more relaxed in a foreign capitalist country than at home? But the sense of relief was soon joined by a feeling of irritation with the Americans. They were indeed most accommodating and hospitable to their Russian guests, but still so insensitive! He grew resentful of their talk about "wartime hardships." What hardships? Compared with the America of the Depression years he remembered, the country was thriving. Rationing, about which some grumbled, was at most a trivial inconvenience. He had stopped in London on the way and knew that the average Englishman would find the Americans' complaints incomprehensible. And as for his countrymen . . .

His hosts—both the officials and the journalists and intellectuals he met at the party given in honor of the Soviet delegation—were very flattering in their references to the bravery of the Red Army, the heroism of the Russian people, and so on. Yet he found their occasional boasts about U.S. victories in the Pacific and, recently, in Europe, infuriating. Nobody seemed to realize that the Soviets had had more soldiers killed in a single battle, such as that of Stalingrad, than the Americans had in the whole course of the war until then, and that his country had been bled and ravaged for three years before the Yankees and the British finally deigned to open the Second Front.

The questions one was asked! The head of the delegation, the deputy minister of heavy industry, paled and was struck dumb when asked by a newspaperwoman: "After the war, is Generalissimo Stalin going to authorize free elections?" The ambassador had to come to the rescue, which he did by citing the relevant provisions of the Soviet constitution, and stressing the fact that 98.5 percent of those eligible had voted in the last elections to the Supreme Soviet, whereas the estimates about those likely to cast their ballots in the forthcoming American presidential elections ranged between 55 and 60 percent.

"Will there be more than one official candidate in each district?"

"There are no official candidates. People can nominate and elect whomever they choose," answered the ambassador severely.

"I should think, ladies and gentlemen, that after what the Soviet people have shown in this war, nobody could accuse them of being easily intimidated or incapable of governing themselves!"

There was an approving murmur in the room, several reporters casting reproachful glances at the tactless questioner. But then another pest said that the Americans were eager to learn more about the family life of the leader of the gallant ally—did Generalissimo Stalin have a wife, and if so, was she, like Mrs. Roosevelt and Mrs. Churchill, engaged in war work? This strained even the ambassador's diplomatic resources. His people, he announced in a choked voice, had a highly developed sense of privacy, and such subjects must not be discussed. The situation was saved by an alert press attaché of the embassy: after the war, they would invite a number of American gossip columnists to instruct the Soviet press in that indispensable part of the journalist's trade. There was a burst of laughter, and after that the discussion took an amiable turn.

Even later on when he would laugh over the episode, Kondratiev still retained some of the deep resentment he had felt at the time. Maybe, probably, it was ignorance, rather than malice, that had prompted the questions. But how could the Americans be so unfeeling about what his nation had gone through, and not merely since the beginning of the war? Would they be having their silly elections and revel in "human interest" stories if they had suffered a small portion of what the Russians had?

Yet, in another way, one could not help admiring the Americans. Their production figures, whether it came to tanks, shipping, or aircraft, strained one's credulity. He would have dismissed them readily as another example of their boasting or capitalist propaganda, except that their country, while carrying on war on two major fronts and several minor ones separated by vast distances, was at the same time shipping huge supplies of army food and other commodities to its allies, the USSR included. He had known since his days at the front that the trucks and other vehicles sent by America had greatly contributed to the Red Army's successes, first in stemming the German tide at Stalingrad, then in its ability to advance rapidly. The two million or so tons of food received from the transatlantic giant had been even more important: they represented the essential margin between the Soviet civilians' being just barely adequately fed and their dying of undernourishment. His professional pride had been somewhat relieved by the discovery that in certain categories the American tanks were inferior to the corresponding Soviet models. But the quantity, the sheer quantity of everything! And the Americans' ability to improvise! Their automobile factories had evidently shifted to production of tanks and armored vehicles practically overnight. Equally amazing was the self-assurance of the plant managers. They ran their enterprises without any detailed instructions or supervision by the War Production Board, very often standing up to the bureaucrats in Washington and showing them better ways of raising output and labor productivity. To most of Kondratiev's colleagues in the delegation, it was equally incomprehensible how an industry in wartime could be run under the profit system, and how the workers could be paid such high wages for doing what was their duty to the country.

"They are headed for a lot of trouble once the war is over," argued the economic counselor of the embassy. "There will be this vast production capacity with no market for its goods, mass unemployment. There will have to be much higher taxes to pay what the capitalists had grabbed in their profits. Even their own economists are afraid that a year or two after the fighting stops, there will be a new depression that will make the old one seem like child's play."

"They may try the usual capitalist way of dealing with an economic crisis and start new wars. It is quite frightening to think what would happen if they picked on us."

Kondratiev shook his head: "Quite improbable. Wall Street and the generals would probably like to, but their people have no stomach for further wars. Look, the Americans sat twiddling their thumbs while the Germans and Japanese were arming to the teeth."

"It is not up to us to worry about what the Americans might or might not do," announced the head of the delegation, decisively. "I am sure Comrade Stalin sees clearly all the postwar problems and is already devising ways to deflect any danger from the Fatherland."

The American trip had beneficial effects on Mikhail Alexandrovich's domestic and official situations. Xenia's mood was visibly brightened by the dresses, stockings, and other gifts he had purchased for her in New York. He wrote up his impressions of the visit for the minister, and then in turn presented them to the State Defense Council. Another summons to the Kremlin, but this time the atmosphere was quite different from that of the previous harrowing session. Stalin began by praising him as a young man who kept his eyes and ears open, and reported honestly on what he had seen and heard.

"So many of our people, when reporting on the West, feel constrained to repeat the textbook twaddle: 'The working masses are growing increasingly restive under the oppression of their capitalist bosses. The American economy is headed for a crash.' Those are pipe dreams. America is the world's most powerful nation and will remain so for a long time."

"If it comes to any trouble with the Americans and the British, our army could sweep them out of Europe in a matter of weeks," Marshal Voroshilov sounded off.

Stalin turned on him: "You are sixty-three years old, Klimenti, but you talk like a schoolboy. We would march to the Channel and then what? Industrial power is what wins modern wars. Hitler was at the Channel, and where are his armies now?"

"But Josif, the Americans will still have a long way to go after the Nazis have been crushed. They insist on invading and occupying Japan. Then they will really bleed. It will take years," expostulated the marshal.

Beria gave Stalin an inquiring look. Stalin barely perceptibly shook his head and said quickly, "The Japanese might be finished off much sooner."

Molotov hesitated but finally asked, "Josif, d-do the Americans have some trick up their sleeve?"

"Perhaps . . . Comrade Viktorov, please read the citation."

Viktorov, who rarely smiled, grinned broadly and read: "The State Defense Committee decrees: Comrade Kondratiev, M.A., for his services on the industrial front and exemplary performance of his duties as Assistant Minister of Munitions, to be awarded the Order of Lenin and a prize of fifty thousand rubles."

On December 31, Kondratiev was called by Poskryobishev and ordered to report to Stalin's dacha at 11:00 P.M. The plans for a New Year's Eve celebration with his wife and the Perventsevs, then on a visit to Moscow, had to be canceled. It was the first time he had been summoned to the dictator's rural residence, and for all the recent signs of favor, he felt some trepidation. On his arrival at the villa, he found there a number of officers and government officials. They were standing in the large living room; each time the door opened, several of them would start visibly. A few conversed in hushed tones.

"What is this all about?" he whispered to an acquaintance from the General Staff.

"God only knows. This is the first time I was told to report here, and without any maps or other stuff. You don't suppose something has gone wrong?"

"I don't see what. The Germans are—"

But at this point all conversation suddenly stopped. Stalin had entered with the Politburo members trailing him. He looked severely around the room, and then his face broke into a mischievous smile.

"Happy New Year, Comrades."

There was an outburst of merry noise. Servants, a number of them in NKVD uniforms, began to put plates with *zakuski* and all kinds of potables on the tables.

Yes, it would be a different Russia after the victory, Kondratiev told himself at seven the next morning, as he climbed into bed pleasantly fatigued and rather inebriated.

"It is just a matter of a few months or perhaps weeks," Viktorov told Kondratiev on a snowy February afternoon. "The Germans are on their last legs."

The latter agreed. "But we have been told to start shipping supplies to the Far East . . . Japan will be a hard nut to crack. Especially if we have to fight them on their soil."

"Maybe we won't have to . . . Tell me, Mikhail Alexandrovich, do you know much about physics?"

"Only what I learned in high school."

"Hm . . . Well, I asked you to come in to tell you about the changes that are going to take place here. I am leaving the ministry at the end of the month. The Boss asked me to head the State Planning Commission and to concentrate entirely on postwar economic problems."

Kondratiev was too startled to react and ask the obvious question. Viktorov, to his mind, was unique, and it would be hard to get used to working under someone else.

"You don't seem to be interested in who the new minister is going to be."

"I assume Comrade Zarubin," said Kondratiev, referring to the current deputy minister.

"No, he is going to have another job, a very important one. As to my successor here, Comrade Stalin and I discussed the problem at length and came up with a man we both agreed on: M. A. Kondratiev."

"Alexander Ivanovich, I hope—"

"Of course you will," Viktorov cut him off, as laconic in his prime as he was to become garrulous in his old age. "Whom would you recommend as your deputy?"

Kondratiev thought for a while, then suggested Perventsev. His boss shook his head.

"Out of the question. Not a Party member. Two years ago, perhaps it would not have mattered. Now it does again. He is very able, but how can an intelligent man like him be a believer? Think of someone else and also of a replacement for yourself. I must have the names tonight before I go to the Kremlin."

Original elation was soon replaced by the sobering thought of the vastly expanded scope of his future responsibilities: to be precise, elevenfold. There were eleven assistant ministers, the others all older than himself; some, important Party figures in their own right. How would they take to having a thirty-two-year-old boss? Never mind, he would cope. Kondratiev was glad he would not have to work with Zarubin, essentially a decent and able man, but given to terrible fits of temper, possibly a result of the two years he had spent in a camp before the war. He was also quite condescending in his manner, not letting anyone forget his being not just an administrator, but also a member of the Academy of Sciences. What was that important but unspecified job Zarubin was to have? He remembered when in America being asked by someone whether there were any physicists in high positions in his ministry. As to all similar queries, he gave an evasive answer. Well, Zarubin had been a theoretical physicist before switching to the field of telecommunications. Why did Viktorov ask if he knew much about physics? Were they developing a death ray or some microwaves that could cripple an entire country's communications system? That would explain hints that Japan might not stay in the war much longer.

Shortly before the public announcement of his elevation, Kondratiev was invited to the offices of the Central Committee. There he was met by Lunin, with whom, up to now, he had had just a nodding acquaintance. Tall, with an ascetic's face and, though still in his thirties, completely white hair, Lunin was a deputy to Malenkov, head of the Personnel Department of the Secretariat. It was a rather incongruous pairing, in view of Malenkov's being short and chubby. Lunin had a disconcerting manner of speaking: rapidly, with his head cocked to the side and lowered as if he were reading, once in a while raising his eyes and giving his interlocutor a piercing look. (He was to overcome this idiosyncracy in his later years, his manner becoming one befitting a senior statesman.)

"Welcome, Comrade Kondratiev. Please have some tea. I am afraid there is no sugar. I've run through my own ration, and do not like to draw on the Secretariat's allotment."

Kondratiev made appropriate noises and, though he anticipated what was coming, looked inquiringly at his host.

"Yes, only a matter of great importance would make me tear

you away from your work. Several of our leading comrades proposed you for the Central Committee, and the requisite number of its members have expressed their wholehearted approval."

"It is a great honor," said Kondratiev, solemnly, fully aware that the whole thing was a charade. The Central Committee had not met since the beginning of the war, and in all likelihood, quite in violation of the Party rules, it had been one man who both nominated and "elected" him.

"It is a sign of the great trust and esteem in which the Party holds you, Mikhail Alexandrovich."

Lunin rang an assistant. An athletic-looking man in his twenties (why was he out of uniform? wondered Kondratiev) placed a thick folder on the desk.

"By your leave, Mikhail Alexandrovich, if we could go through the data for your official biographical sketch . . . Father, Alexander Nikolayevich, Colonel General in the Red Army."

"He was actually a major in the Imperial Army when I was born."

"Of course, but for the sake of brevity . . . Mother, Maria Andreyevna, daughter of a teacher."

"My maternal grandfather was a lawyer. He once did give a series of lectures in the law faculty of the university."

Lunin put his pen away. There was just a shade of annoyance in his voice. " 'Lawyer,' forgive me, Mikhail Alexandrovich, has bourgeois connotations."

He himself did not understand what made him quibble, but still said, "Vladimir Ilyich Lenin was a lawyer by profession."

"So he was. Shall we put 'lawyer who defended victims of tsarist oppression'?"

This was perfectly true, and Kondratiev nodded his assent. There was a period of silence while Lunin kept shuffling the papers. Then he stopped and said, rather too nonchalantly, "We need not mention the period 1934 to 1941. Quite understandable; many comrades had similar troubles; still, rather awkward. Shall we say 'Party member since 1931' and leave it at that?"

"I shall abide by your judgment, Pyotr Nikolayevich."

The rest went smoothly: war service, decorations, appointments. Lunin stood up.

"A remarkable record, worthy of a member of the central organ of the Party of Lenin and Stalin. I shall not take any more of your valuable time, Mikhail Alexandrovich, but permit me to embrace you."

▪

The end of the war found Kondratiev firmly ensconced as a Party and government potentate. In September 1945, he became minister of heavy industry, at that moment the key position in the overall effort to bring Soviet production of steel, machinery, and other sinews of industrial might to a level compatible with the Soviet Union's status as a superpower. At a meeting held about the same time, Stalin addressed a select group of Party, government, and military leaders. His message, far from reflecting joy over the victory, was most somber in its tone: the next few years were going to be harder in some ways than what they had just gone through.

"As Communists, we must face the facts squarely: if the Americans told us, 'Pull out of Germany and Eastern Europe, or else,' we would have to. Our economy is in a shambles. We lost twenty-five million lives. Yes," he said, seeing stupefaction on many faces, "those are the correct figures. Isn't that so, Comrade Viktorov?"

"Most unfortunately, yes."

"And no one outside of this room must even suspect the real extent of our losses."

And so they would have to strain every nerve to rebuild the economy and start catching up with the capitalists before the latter realized how strong they were and how weak and vulnerable was the Soviet Union.

"We should have the Bomb in three or four years," said Zarubin, who, as head of the innocent sounding Ministry of Medium Machinery Building, was supervising the scientific and technological side of the nuclear program, with Beria in charge of what might be called its human side, as well as the gathering of relevant information through the intelligence network abroad. The Boss (by now Kondratiev, like the other bigwigs, had fallen into the habit of thinking and referring to him by that term) shook his head.

"Not fast enough. But even that is not the most important thing. The Americans would like to scare us with the Bomb, but they don't know how." He smiled. "Their humanitarian scruples would not allow them to drop the bomb on an ally. But that is why we must avoid the slightest appearance of weakness when dealing with Washington. We must impress the U.S. that we're ready to fight, rather than yield even on a minor issue. We'll have a breathing spell of five to ten years. If by the end of it, we don't have not only the Bomb, but also our heavy industry going full blast and gaining on the capitalists, we'll be in a worse situation than in June 1941."

It was at the same meeting that Stalin raised the question of whether he was not too old to guide the country and the Party in the gigantic tasks ahead. There was a chorus of protests. He was the picture of health and vigor. Who else knew so well and could rebuff so effectively all the capitalists' tricks?

"Do not leave the people fatherless."

"Well, let it be then, but some of you may come to regret forcing me to stay on and carry the burden."

There was a moment of silence at this remark, then an outburst of seemingly unstrained laughter.

As they were awaiting their limousines, with no one else within earshot, Kondratiev observed to Viktorov that while mentioning the possibility of his resigning, the Boss had looked around the room, taking in their expressions.

Viktorov shook his head wearily. "A bad omen. And he had seemed to be getting over his suspiciousness during the last year or so."

The subsequent growing strain within the inner circle failed to dampen Mikhail Alexandrovich's spirit. When in later years he would review this period of his life, he would be amazed how confident and even lighthearted he felt during the early postwar years. He had been denied a normal youth, but now in his middle and late thirties he was experiencing a buoyant mood that is the usual prerogative of one's twenties. The dark shadows of the past had receded; only very infrequently his mind would revert to December 1, 1934, and what followed. What he would not realize until the very end was that, in those days, the system conquered him to the point that not only his earlier fears but any doubts and scruples he might have experienced were almost completely repressed through the enjoyment of power and the pleasure he took in his work. The rising stars on the Soviet political firmament, such as Malenkov and Zhdanov, courted him, both because of his being in favor with the Boss and also, no doubt, because of their anticipation of the day when the Leader would be gathered to his reward, and Kondratiev could turn out to be a valuable ally in the struggle that would ensue. He, while avoiding a too-close identification with any one faction, managed to be on good terms with all the great, except for Beria, with whom he tried to have as little contact as possible for one in his position.

As to the aging deity who towered over the whole edifice, Kondratiev now stood much less in awe of him. At times Mikhail Alexandrovich surprised himself by feeling something akin to gratitude to Stalin. The Boss had forgiven him for possession of the damnable secret; he evidently appreciated his talents and devotion to the country. Yes, one could get along with the dictator if one could read his moods: as long as his terrible suspiciousness was not aroused, he could be the most reasonable of men. In public, one had to praise him to the skies. In private intercourse, effusive flattery would often arouse his unfeigned wrath. Kondratiev's original and naive faith in the Leader never came back, but at times it was difficult not to fall under the man's spell, or not to believe again that much of what had gone on before the war was done without his knowledge.

"But why are the peasants in such a plight?" asked Stalin reflectively, when, in the spring of 1946, the minister of agriculture reported near-famine conditions in many areas. "They have been through hard times, but so has our urban population. And the city worker is performing heroically in rebuilding the economy. He has barely enough to eat, housing conditions are frightful, but our industry is recovering at a faster pace than we dared to expect. So what is it with the peasants?"

No one said anything, so Stalin continued.

"I think I know why. Many of our peasants still hope that if they don't produce enough food, they will force us to abolish the collectives and restore private property in land, and then they could charge exorbitant prices that would delay our industrial recovery for decades. So they must be taught a lesson like the one they had in the thirties. It sounds hard, but in the long run, it is the only solution: if a few of them starve, the others will start producing enough to provide abundant food for themselves and the whole country. We shall not lower our quotas for compulsory requisitions of meat, grain, and other foodstuffs."

At the time, it sounded quite convincing. It was only after

Stalin's death that Kondratiev learned the true causes of the Soviet peasants' ordeal.

Absorption in his work provided a convenient shield from other disturbing developments in postwar Russia, as he would later recognize. Early in 1949, he was asked to receive a deputy minister of state security. His visitor came right to the point: there was a rather large proportion of Jews in leading positions of the Ministry of Heavy Industry and the enterprises it controlled. Would Comrade Kondratiev object if the security organs winnowed out those who they had good grounds to believe were Zionists, or had other undesirable ties, such as relatives in the West?

"I certainly would. If you have any compromising data on some persons, give them to me and I'll do the winnowing myself."

The security official was abashed. Surely Comrade Minister had noted that many people in the academic and journalistic worlds had recently been censured and removed from their positions for slandering Soviet culture and for other acts of disloyalty towards the state, and a majority of them had been Jews.

"What do I have to do with academicians or writers? My job is to run this ministry."

He spoke in the same vein at a meeting of the Party cell of the ministry that met a week later to consider some vague charges against two bureau chiefs who happened to be Jewish.

"I speak here as a Party member and not your superior. If it is proven that Feinman and Gurevich have slandered the Russian nation, then I shall of course vote for their expulsion. But if the charges turn out to be false, it will be my duty as minister to take appropriate steps against those who by slandering our coworkers impair the efficiency of this organization and thereby do harm to our Socialist Fatherland."

The chairman of the Party organization hastily moved the meeting to be adjourned, since they obviously needed more in the way of evidence, which until now had been in the nature of hearsay. Even so, Feinman soon quit his job, having suffered a nervous breakdown, and another Jewish official's promotion to assistant minister was vetoed by the Industrial Department of the Secretariat of the Central Committee.

"You are absolutely right in sticking up for your people," volunteered Stalin out of the blue, after they had finished discussing a new industrial complex to be built in the Urals. "Just because a few Jewish scribblers have been spanked for lifting up their noses at the achievements of our Russian artists and writers, there is no reason to suspect the loyalty of the vast majority of our Jewish fellow citizens. Anti-Semitism has no place under communism." He made his usual tour of the room, waving his unlit pipe, stopped, and looked out the window. "Still, it is somewhat disconcerting that so many of them have a cousin, aunt, or whatever in New York."

"I myself, Comrade Stalin, may have relatives in the United States." When Stalin turned and looked at him sharply, he related the story of his great-granduncle.

Stalin laughed uproariously and said that Beria would have to make appropriate investigations. Mikhail Alexandrovich started to leave, but the dictator motioned him to stay seated.

"How is Maria Andreyevna?"

By now, nothing coming from this man should have surprised him. Still, it took Kondratiev some moments to compose himself before answering that the doctors considered his mother's condition hopeless and gave her at the most a few weeks.

"She has not been really well since my father's death," he added, on a sudden impulse.

"You mean, since Alexander Nikolayevich's unjust and outrageous arrest. We missed him sorely during the war . . . Yes, that scoundrel Yezhov brought ruin to many innocent and irreplaceable people. We ought to have caught on to him much sooner." Stalin sighed and resumed, very softly. "Remember me to your mother. It must be a great comfort to her that *both* of her sons are serving the country so well and in such important posts."

How the devil had he had time and occasion to follow his brother's career? Cured of his alcoholism, Volodya now held a comfortable, though not very prominent, position in the Ministry of Civil Aviation.

The conversation preyed on Kondratiev's mind when, after awakening in the middle of the night, he tiptoed out of the bedroom to have a cigarette in his study. One voice within him kept saying, "What a consummate actor, what a performance!" but another one pleaded, "Maybe it is self-deception. Can any man be utterly devoid of conscience and occasional feelings of remorse?"

That led to the recollection of another scene about which he had not thought for a long while. Unable to sleep, he spent the rest of the night studying data about the forthcoming Five Year Plan.

No, if it was not the kind of Russia he imagined it would be after the victory, still, what was going on could not be compared with the horrors of the thirties. He knew by virtue of his job that some four million people were confined in the forced-labor camps, but it was many fewer than between 1937 and 1940. The death penalty had been abolished in 1947. He became annoyed at Perventsev, who when he alluded to that fact in one of their conversations smiled ironically and said, "Misha, you certainly cannot believe that people are no longer being executed?"

"I haven't heard of a single case, and if there have been any, I certainly should know."

"Are you sure that even in your position you know everything that is going on?"

No, he admitted to himself later, he didn't, and, to be honest, would not want to. But then, how could things be *much* better with the international situation being what it was? Though Stalin had been proved right and the Americans did not know how to use their power, it was undeniable that they were scheming against the Soviet Union. For the moment, they were too engrossed in their materialistic pleasures and concerns to contemplate an actual onslaught on his country. But it was clear that they would rearm West Germany and Japan and use them as their cat's-paws to try to establish U.S. hegemony in the world. It was only a question of time, and that was why the U.S. was pouring billions into the Marshall Plan and other programs of economic aid. Whoever heard of the capitalists giving away money just to help foreign countries, especially their recent enemies and potential competitors on the world market?

The Americans were unhappy over what the Soviets were doing in Eastern Europe. After what his nation had been through, how could anyone question its right to have friendly and dependable regimes in neighboring countries? And will not all those states in the long run be better off under socialism and Soviet protection than they were between the wars, ruled by their militaristic and feudal-like cliques, exploited by Western capitalists, and in constant dread of German aggression? Privately, Kondratiev would admit that Moscow had made serious mistakes in dealing with Tito—

again an example of Stalin's inordinate suspiciousness and vanity. (Then how could one tolerate Tito's megalomania and his ridiculous claims that he and his beggarly Partisans could have seized and held on to power even without Soviet help and support?) But now it was clear that Yugoslavia was edging ever closer to the capitalist camp, and that Washington would like to use it to subvert other Communist states in Eastern Europe.

And so a marked improvement at home had to await the time when the Soviet Union realized its economic potential and became so strong that the capitalists would not dare to challenge it. As to what this marked improvement would be, Mikhail Alexandrovich's ideas were rather hazy. Before he had had experience in governing, he would have said, "Return to Leninist principles." But as he now went over what he knew about the Lenin era, he developed increasing doubts about the desirability of returning to the practices of those days. Great man though he was, Lenin tolerated too much in the way of free discussion and turbulence within the Party: you had factions *openly* fighting each other about power and policies. A rank-and-file Party activist would not think twice about impudently challenging a member of the Central Committee, or even criticizing one of the top leaders. Now that he had seen the system from the inside, he realized that you could not run the modern USSR that way. One might as well institute a multiparty system with those phony Western-type "freedoms" and let the country go to ruin.

What, then, of the future? Well, by the time the Soviet Union would become powerful enough to afford internal change, *he* would be gone. That in itself would bring a great relief. Most of the people in positions similar to his looked to that day expectantly, but also with considerable fear. After they both attended one of the innumerable public meetings held to celebrate Stalin's seventieth birthday in December 1949, he asked a fellow minister to stop for a drink in his apartment. Xenia having excused herself to attend to little Kolya, his visitor sat silent for a while, probably hesitating whether to reveal what was on his mind, and then blurted out, "How could we carry on without him? Eh, Mikhail Alexandrovich?"

"It would be exceedingly hard, but the Party will manage," replied Kondratiev diplomatically.

"I . . . I don't know. When you think what has happened in

our history each time a strong ruler left the scene . . . the masses running wild . . . And you cannot even compare the strongest of the tsars to—" His guest stopped and then, in a different tone and with a smile, "Of course, those were feudal times. And anyway, it is not going to happen for a long, long time. Josif Vissarionovich is in excellent health."

"Of course," agreed Kondratiev.

The conversation switched to Mao, currently in Moscow at the head of a delegation from the People's Republic; and how those Chinese gave themselves airs . . .

He did not share such apprehensions about what might happen after "the Genius-Leader of progressive mankind" was gathered to his reward. The Russians did not have to be manipulated through fear and mystification. Stalin would be succeeded by a new generation of leaders, people like himself. The Molotovs and Voroshilovs were by now good for nothing. The people needed to be ruled firmly, but justly. Beria and his ilk would be not only cast aside but made to pay for their crimes. The secret police would cease to be a state within a state, and would be made strictly accountable to the Party. The camps would be emptied of most of their inmates, including former soldiers who through no fault of their own had been taken prisoners by the Germans and after returning to their homeland, instead of being welcomed with joy and gratitude, were arrested for "desertion"; also those guilty of "violating labor discipline," that is, in some cases being half an hour late for work; and others imprisoned for equally perverse reasons. Yes, there will be a new spirit throughout the land. This great nation had done wonders. What would it be able to achieve when no longer driven by the lash! For the moment, one had to be patient and carry on with one's work, no matter what.

Kondratiev could date with some precision the occasion when his complacent mood changed to that of renewed anxiety.

It was late September 1950. They were returning from a party at his friend Pavel's dacha. Xenia had been silent, which for her was a bad sign, as she usually chattered excitedly during and after a social occasion. All of a sudden it came out: "Why do we have to see so much of the Perventsevs?"

"You know they are old friends who were very kind to me during a rather difficult period of my life," he said, trying to control his impatience: he had answered less direct variants of the same question on several previous occasions.

"But they are not our kind of people. Someone in your position ought not to be seen with them so often."

"What do you mean? He is deputy rector of the Engineering Institute and a corresponding member of the Academy."

"And he will never make rector or full member," she burst out. "There are no pictures of Lenin or Stalin in his place—instead a couple of icons on the wall. And the people one meets there! I bet, except for the two of us, there was not a single Party member among that crowd tonight. If they are real friends, they should avoid compromising you by inviting us or coming to our place . . . at times like these!"

He asked Trofim to stop the car and he got out, saying that he needed fresh air and would walk home. His irritation increased at the realization that he did not know how to get there. He almost never walked in Moscow's streets, and as for the subway, he'd been on it only two or three times, showing it off to some foreign delegations, and wasn't sure what station his home was near or how one got a ticket. Were there different classes as in the Paris Métro, or devil knows what? Finally, with the help of a militiaman, he got his bearings and, inwardly cursing, set on the trek.

First of all, he was furious with himself. Unlike practically all the bigwigs of the time, he let his wife share his social life, partly because he hated the all-male parties that were the rule in the Kremlin circle, partly because he imagined that it compensated her for his occasional infidelity and increasing lack of warmth in their relations. From now on, let her stick to her home duties—it would be advisable to have another child—and her job, much as she grumbled at the work in the hospital where, as she put it, she was treated *almost* as if she were "an ordinary person."

Then it dawned on him that his irritation had deeper causes. Perhaps it was *not* wise to see so much of Perventsev. The thirties would never return, he had kept telling himself. Well, the death penalty had been reinstituted. A secret memorandum that had reached his desk some weeks ago announced that the former minister of finance, Kozlov, two former secretaries of the Leningrad Party, and several others had been sentenced to the "supreme penalty" by the Military Collegium of the Supreme Court of the USSR for "plotting to subvert the Communist Party of the Soviet Union." Again, Leningrad and the Military Collegium! Kozlov had been a quiet, unassuming individual, a protégé of Viktorov's who appeared completely absorbed in his professional duties, and the writer of rather platitudinous treatises on economics. God only knows what was behind the whole affair. The others had served under Zhdanov in Leningrad, and perhaps now that their rival was dead, Malenkov and Beria had combined forces to eliminate his closest followers, before they could regroup around another would-be heir to the Boss. Was he then losing his grip?

Certainly Stalin's behavior had become rather weird. He had announced some months before that since he proposed to devote himself increasingly to theoretical work, Malenkov and Molotov would take turns in presiding over the Council of Ministers. Then from time to time he would appear at the sessions unannounced and ask that they go on with the business as usual: he had just been sitting in and observing. And so he had, often becoming irritated when asked for an opinion, but once in a while interrupting the speaker with "That is sheer nonsense" or "You will never learn"—something quite different from his normal and indirect manner. On several occasions urgent business had to be postponed when Stalin suddenly announced in the middle of a discussion that a new movie was about to be shown in the Kremlin theater, and would they care to attend it with him? There had been that awful session when Molotov and Viktorov argued whether the peasants should be subjected to additional taxes, with the latter repeating, "But Vyacheslav Mikhailovich, you cannot draw blood from a stone," and Molotov maintaining that each peasant had plenty of rubles secreted under his mattress. Then Stalin had cut in.

"What Comrade Molotov," he now seldom called him by his first name, "is saying reminds me of what we used to hear in this room from Trotsky."

There had been a long pause, but for once Molotov, taking off his pince-nez, stared hard at Stalin, and equally amazingly, it was the latter who had lowered his eyes first.

"Trotsky was not always wrong; in some ways he was a very talented individual. By all means, let the peasants pay."

Not long afterwards, Polina, Molotov's wife, had been arrested and sent to a forced labor camp.

Whatever else he had felt about the man, Kondratiev had always given Stalin high marks for his management of foreign policy. He had certainly run circles around Roosevelt and Churchill. But now he recalled when the dictator had deigned not only to appear but also to take the chair at a meeting of the council. There was the urgent matter, he announced, of equipping the North Korean army in a hurry with the most up-to-date weapons.

"Our comrades there are fed up with the constant provocation from the South. They asked us for advice, and we told them to go ahead and crush the Fascist regime of Syngman Rhee and reunite the Korean nation."

"Will the Americans stand idly by and allow their protégés to be liquidated?" asked Bulganin, whom Stalin for some unfathomable reason had been highly favoring, even though Bulganin was a notorious drunkard and womanizer.

But this time he had turned on him. "What have you been drinking lately, Comrade Bulganin? The Americans let Mao and his armed rabble swallow up all of China. Not a chance they would screw up their courage to do anything that matters about South Korea. Of course they will be in a tizzy, send more troops to Japan, and make a lot of noise. What can they do now that we have the Bomb? And the resulting confusion will give us a chance to settle our accounts with Mr. Tito and his bunch of renegades."

Here Stalin had rubbed his hands as if already relishing the vision of the perfidious Yugoslavs getting their just deserts.

At the time it had sounded very convincing and it appeared that the old man had not lost his cunning insofar as foreign affairs were concerned. But then came this pitiful spectacle: The Americans had the North Koreans on the run; it was only a question of time before they would conquer the whole peninsula. Once the Americans did intervene, Kondratiev had asked Viktorov if the Politburo was considering the dangerous situation and was amazed to hear that the Politburo had not met since May. Viktorov and the minister of war, Marshal Vasilevsky, were acting on their own, since efforts to discuss various contingencies with the Boss had proved unavailing.

It had seemed therefore reassuring that Stalin had called this meeting of the Council of Ministers and announced that he himself would preside. He had appeared brisk and businesslike at the beginning. It was obvious they were facing a very serious situation:

the armed forces had to be strengthened and put in combat readiness.

"Yes," said Vasilevsky. "Once the Yankees conquer all of Korea, they might get some funny notions about Eastern Europe."

"I don't think so for a moment," Stalin said. "As I anticipated, they rushed headlong into the Korean trap. Let the Chinese worry whether they will conquer the North. What is it to us? What if the U.S. drops a few A-bombs on Peking and Canton? It will teach Mao and his crew to be more respectful toward the Soviet Union. What I meant was that we must be ready to move when Tito attacks Bulgaria. Comrade Vasilevsky, please present the contingency plan that we have worked out."

Vasilevsky, in a shaky voice, had begged leave to summon the chief of staff and head of operations, who had all the requisite data.

"Well, it can wait. There is another thing that is perhaps more important. All of you comrades must have received copies of the draft of my treatise on linguistics."

One could have heard a pin drop as they sat, not believing their ears.

"I see you are all surprised, and it may seem odd that we should turn to philosophy and science at a time when the forces of imperialism are threatening us. But that is precisely why it is so urgent that we should work out a sound dialectical basis for our policies. V. I. Lenin's work, epoch-making as it was, has lost much of its relevance with the advent of nuclear energy and the emergence of the U.S. as the capitalist superpower. I propose to bring Marxism-Leninism up to date. We must begin with language as essential to the understanding of social phenomena. Then I shall turn to the realm of economics, which Marx, quite correctly, though in my view in an oversimplified fashion, considered as underlying all human activities. Then, if the time allotted to me permits, I would conclude with a treatise on the relationship between scientific socialism, nuclear energy, and science in general. What do you think, Comrades?"

"A truly grandiose enterprise, one that very likely will be the crowning scientific and philosophical achievement of modern times," Beria had said.

Stalin had given him a scathing look. "How could *you* tell, Lavrenti?" He surveyed the solemn row of faces. "Comrade Kondratiev is the youngest here, young enough to remember his Marx and Engels. I know that most of you don't bother to study the classics. Tell me, Comrade Kondratiev, does my latest work adhere to the canons of dialectical materialism?"

All eyes had turned on Kondratiev. Viktorov's face showed real concern; there was a barely perceptible smile behind Beria's thick glasses; the others just watched. Fortunately, he had taken care to read through the drivel, thought Mikhail Alexandrovich. He began with seeming hesitation.

"I wrestled with the question and at first could not be sure."

He stopped and looked at Stalin, who appeared to be the only one not paying attention to him, his head lowered, writing or doodling on a pad with his pencil.

"At first it appeared to me to go against everything I had learned about the Marxist approach to linguistics." Stalin raised his head. "I read and reread the treatise. And then it dawned on me: in asserting that language was not part of the superstructure, but part of basic social relations, Comrade Stalin was creating a completely new dimension of dialectic. I do think that this discovery must have a profound impact on every branch of science. I earnestly hope that the Academy of Sciences holds a special session to clarify some parts of the argument that to me, a layman, an engineer and not a philosopher, are still not entirely clear."

Stalin had nodded gravely. "The basic principles of science should be made understandable even to laymen. I shall stress this point as I rework the treatise for publication. We have allowed our linguists to become an ingrown clique, writing in an esoteric jargon, forgetting that, under socialism, science should be the common property of the entire people."

Malenkov had chimed in, "I don't think it is just pedantry. Scratch an alleged advocate of scholarly objectivity, and you will often find the class enemy. We all remember how it took Comrade Stalin's personal intervention to unmask those pseudoscientists among our biologists who kowtowed to the bourgeois notion that heredity is everything, and environment nothing."

"Yes, Georgi Maximilianovich, you might look into the background of those gentlemen, the 'pure scientists.' And now, unless somebody has another matter to bring up, shall we go and see a movie?"

When, after an hour's march, Kondratiev finally approached his apartment building, those previously isolated painful sensations assumed the proportions of a comprehensive nightmare: Xenia might get it into her head to denounce the Perventsevs to the secret police. Her sister and brother-in-law had been victims in the thirties' purge, yet she was a fanatical Party zealot and worshiper of Stalin's. The country might very well be in for a new wave of terror or war. Bad enough to face such cataclysms under a ruthless and deceitful ruler, but in the past he at least hadn't been . . . Kondratiev did not know how to describe his present condition: occasionally demented, senile, certainly not the Stalin of the interview just before his mother's death. What a change within a few months! For the first time he thought dispassionately about something that, until this evening, he would have dismissed as both heinous and fantastic, but that he now realized had flashed through his mind that April afternoon in 1943, when he first understood what this man was really like and what he had done to his country and the Kondratiev family. No, it was impossible, and he must not even think about it. Mad though the tyrant might be, he still had this uncanny gift of reading what was on your mind. He felt again the burden of the secret the two of them shared. Mikhail Alexandrovich Kondratiev, minister and member of the Central Committee, would have to be even more on guard and disciplined in thought and behavior than he had been as a lonely youngster during the exile in Tula.

His wife was in bed, but awake, when he entered her bedroom. She had been crying, and now the tears started again.

"I was thinking of your career, your safety . . . Humiliating me in the presence of Trofim."

There was only one way of appeasing her, and he proceeded to give her satisfaction. Concern about what Xenia might do to the Perventsevs impelled him to engage in lovemaking on several subsequent nights, and indeed Xenia, awed by this quite unusual outburst of amorousness, subsided into a mindless cheerfulness. In due time the product of their exertions made his appearance; she readily agreed to name him Pavel.

"A lovely name. How thoughtful of you to remember it was my favorite uncle's. That reminds me: Why haven't we seen the Perventsevs for so long?"

And, in general, things took a turn for the better in the next few months. The Chinese did move against the Yankees, who rather stupidly let themselves be taken by surprise and were forced to retreat as rapidly as they had been advancing. Then the war became a stalemate—from Moscow's point of view, an ideal situation. This at least partial fulfillment of his prophecy temporarily rejuvenated Stalin.

"Mao kept sending me messages saying that they would not come in unless we sent at least token units to fight along with them. Some of us," here he cast a contemptuous look at Molotov, "were indeed of the opinion that we must send Soviet soldiers to save our Korean comrades. But I let Mao understand that it was entirely their own business; if the Chinese felt comfortable with the American army on their borders we would not object. Later on, if they themselves were invaded, we might send them some planes and other equipment, but no soldiers. We lost enough Soviet lives during the last war while he and his people pretended to fight the Japanese and, in fact, were waiting for Japan to be defeated by us and America so they could make their move. Now our Chinese comrades may have to fight for years on end."

"What should the Soviet Union do," someone asked, "if the Americans help Chiang invade the mainland from Taiwan? After all, the Soviet Union has a military alliance with the People's Republic."

"We shall protest most vigorously, arouse the world's public opinion about this most outrageous yet act on the part of the imperialists. We never promised to assist Mao in a *civil* war."

He seemed to have recovered his zest and some of his old shrewdness when it came to foreign affairs. The great theoretical work was, for the time, laid aside.

Another good sign was that those linguists whom he had denounced in his famous treatise were not sent to the camps, and in some cases were even allowed to keep their jobs. As Kondratiev later heard the story, Stalin had brushed aside a list of names prepared by Malenkov, saying, "Let them be. Why bother with a bunch of old fools? We must not create the impression abroad that we are persecuting men of learning for holding unorthodox views, the way they do it in the capitalist countries."

All of which led Kondratiev to wonder whether the despot's spell of strange behavior might not have been largely due to the depression he had experienced in the fall of 1949, at the realization that the Chinese Communists were in the process of conquering all of the mainland. Throughout the preceding few months he evidently had clung to the hope that the Nationalists would make a stand and retain some territory in the south, and in the northwest. Then a jarring blow to his pride was caused by Mao's insolent behavior when he had come to Moscow in December 1949 and for three months stoutly resisted the Russians' demands that they be allowed to retain the bases and special rights in China that they had wrested from Chiang's government at the end of the war.

He remembered the look on Stalin's face when, at a reception in honor of the Chinese delegation (held, characteristically, in a hotel, not the Kremlin), the Bulgarian ambassador had been foolish enough to exclaim that among all the birthday gifts presented to him, the most precious one must be that the ideas of Lenin and Stalin had conquered the world's largest nation. Stalin kept staring at the man, with the latter growing visibly alarmed, and finally said, "All socialist nations are equal, regardless of their size." Within days the unfortunate diplomat was recalled, and when back in Bulgaria he was soon imprisoned on charges of having ties with the Tito gang. Sanity in a despot, Mikhail Alexandrovich concluded, was a relative term. Anything that appeared to undermine his powers was bound to affect his reason.

The improvement was only temporary. Toward the end of 1951 Stalin relapsed into isolation and a misanthropic mood. On the rare occasions he now saw him, Kondratiev noticed that the dictator's manner was startlingly different from the one he had gotten used to, even more so than during that late 1949–1950 interlude. The old restlessness was entirely gone, at least on the surface. Whereas before he could never sit still, getting up and wandering around the room, or fiddling with his pipe, he now usually just sat, cupping his chin in a hand or doodling, apparently lost in thought. From time to time, he would cast an anxious look around. When silence would fall over the group after an argument and they would turn to him for a decision, he would act as if aroused from a dream, often asking for the argument to be repeated, and then would deliver the verdict in a soft and barely audible voice. With age, his Georgian accent had become more noticeable. At times he would get up and leave the council with, "Let Comrade Malenkov attend to this"—on a few occasions, without even answering their unspoken question. Kondratiev's requests for an audience were, as a rule, answered by Poskryobishev, his previous jovial manner gone, with, "Unfortunately, Comrade Stalin is busy. If this touches on Party matters, he wants you to consult with Georgi Maximilianovich; on economic ones, you will get your instructions from Comrade Viktorov."

Malenkov was seldom of much help—strangely indecisive and ill at ease for a man who had lived through and connived at so many intrigues. His frequent refrain was, "I cannot decide it on my own. I shall consult the Boss and telephone you what ought to be done." Or, "We must ask Comrade Beria for his opinion."

"But how can the government be run this way?" complained Mikhail Alexandrovich to Viktorov, early in 1952. "Or is he more talkative at Politburo meetings?"

"Somewhat. He keeps telling us that he may not be around much longer, and that we must get used to making decisions without him. At last week's meeting, the first in three months, he spoke for quite a while. He still had a few years left in him, he announced, and as of old he watched our faces as he was talking. When this time nobody said anything, the Boss raised his voice and declared that he'd much rather devote the time he had to writing, but does not want to leave the country in a condition where it would become prey to warring factions and internal enemies. 'Even now, the imperialists are laying down plans to attack the Soviet Union, once Stalin dies. Well, I still have a few surprises left for them,' and then, with an indescribable expression, 'and for some of you.' "

Molotov, Viktorov continued, then broke into tears and begged Stalin to believe that all of them wanted him to live and lead for many, many years. But he must not isolate himself the way he had recently. "The people are growing anxious at not seeing their beloved Leader. There has not been a Party Congress in thirteen years."

"You'll have your congress, all right," said Stalin, dismissing them.

"All in all, a pleasant meeting. Don't be deceived by the way he behaves at the Council of Ministers. Be extra careful, Mikhail Alexandrovich. Anything may happen."

Things did begin to happen. People sentenced during the thirties who somehow had survived their ten- and fifteen-year terms in the camps were being rearrested and sent back to the Gulag. A conspiracy was uncovered in a region of Georgia, and a number of Beria's henchmen were executed. Several Jewish writers and artists were unmasked as having maintained, through the intermediary of the World Zionist Organization, links with American intelligence. They were shot.

The Jewish question was very much on Kondratiev's mind during the next few weeks. Lunin, recently made a secretary of the Central Committee, raised it during one of the regular meetings they held in connection with the Secretariat's confirmations of managerial appointments in industry.

"You know, Mikhail Alexandrovich, your ministry, next to that of health, has the highest proportion of persons in responsible positions who are of Jewish nationality."

"Have you established a quota for Jews in such posts?"

"No. Well, not in any formal sense. But couldn't their numbers be reduced? Surely some of them are not irreplaceable?" Kondratiev explained that a few were indeed quite replaceable.

"But the trouble is that if I fire them and it is obvious why, the morale of those who are among our best experts would be affected. One can tell that they are already under considerable strain. I don't have to tell you, Pyotr Nikolayevich, how important our work is. Where would I find a man to replace the country's leading authority on computers? And how could he keep his mind entirely on his work if he saw people being sacked just because—"

"I can see your point," sighed Lunin. "Let us hope the others will, too. Well, a piece of advice. If you cannot bring yourself to 'thin out' your Jews, at least don't hire any more, and I must tell you categorically that the Secretariat will not approve promotions for persons of that nationality."

Were there any guidelines concerning half or quarter Jews, or men who, like several Politburo members, had Jewish wives? wondered Kondratiev, but he kept his thoughts to himself. He remembered Viktorov's warning; he would have to heed Lunin's advice.

In Poland, where Mikhail Alexandrovich went in July as head of an economic mission, he was struck by the nervousness of his opposite number who happened to be Jewish, and at first he attributed it to the severe talking-to he had given the Poles for their falling behind schedule in deliveries of coal to the Soviet Union.

But at the reception in his honor, the general secretary of the Polish Party took him aside.

"You are probably surprised, Comrade Minister, that we still have so many Yids in our economic agencies. But believe me, we are getting rid of them. We cannot do it in a hurry because our people remember the Nazis and might draw erroneous conclusions."

Kondratiev shrugged his shoulders. "I am here on an economic mission, not to check up on your personnel policies."

"But I hope that you will report to Comrade Stalin that in this, as in everything else, we are following the example of the great Soviet Union."

The man would have been astounded to learn that he had not reported to Stalin in person for several months, and in a fit of irritation Kondratiev blurted out, "To paraphrase an old saying, some of my best friends in Moscow don't give a damn how many Jews you have and in what positions."

The man's eyes widened and then he began to laugh, much too uproariously. "A wonderful joke, Comrade Minister. How I admire the Russian sense of humor! But it also must come from having lived under socialism for thirty-five years."

Here it took Kondratiev a considerable effort not to burst out laughing himself.

He did so, however, on getting back to the hotel, but then reflected he had not been very prudent. What if the wretched Pole repeated the remark, and it got back to Moscow? No, quite unlikely: those leaders of the "fraternal parties" were currently in a state approaching panic. With so many of them being unmasked as "Titoists" and agents of "the Wall Street–Zionist conspiracy," gossiping about a high Soviet official was the last thing they would do. Was there anything to those charges? Probably not much more than to similar accusations that had led to the execution of a group of Jewish writers in the Soviet Union. And yet . . . the Soviet ambassador to Warsaw told him he suspected that the Polish comrades envied Tito in their heart of hearts, and if they thought for a minute they could get away with it, they would try to follow the Yugoslavs' example. But they knew that their own people would kick them out the minute they lost Moscow's support.

"How come, Mikhail Alexandrovich, the Yugoslav people

haven't done it to their leaders, and how long are we going to tolerate this renegade who is now openly plotting with the capitalists?"

"Comrade Stalin said that it was just a question of time before the majority of Yugoslav Communists and working people came to their senses and got rid of this Wall Street agent and his gang," replied Kondratiev dryly. He was sure that the ambassador was reporting everything he said to Moscow. Privately, he had come by now to consider the whole Yugoslav business as a piece of lunacy on Stalin's part. And it was bound to give ideas to the Chinese.

On his return, he was questioned closely by Malenkov and Beria about his impressions of the Polish leaders.

"They have been dragging their feet about unmasking their own Titoists and putting them on trial," complained Malenkov.

"Who among the people you met, Mikhail Alexandrovich, appeared to you to be, well, less than fully reliable?"

"We talked almost entirely about technical matters."

"But you've had experience at spotting traitors and enemies of the people, Comrade Kondratiev," observed Beria casually, as he cleaned off his pince-nez.

It was as if someone had hit him in the midriff, and whatever it might cost him, he would return the blow: "All of us must be constantly on our guard against disloyal and double-faced persons in our midst. But my own experience in this field is nothing compared to yours, Lavrenti Pavlovich. I admired the way you unmasked those alleged loyal servants of the Soviet power in Georgia."

A shadow of a smile crossed Malenkov's face. Beria said nothing, but poured himself a glass of mineral water and gulped it down. After leaving the two, Kondratiev felt that he must see Stalin as soon as possible.

The audience was granted and went off better than might have been expected. The dictator listened thoughtfully and asked sensible questions about the condition of Polish industry, to what extent Warsaw had been rebuilt, and whether the Poles were being honest in claiming that it was technical difficulties that were causing delays in the deliveries. Then, at the end:

"I am not quite the old, tired man who is losing his grip; what do you think, Comrade Kondratiev?"

"If I ever thought so, it was a delusion, Comrade Stalin. No one shouldering the enormous burden you do could avoid moments of fatigue."

"You always give the right answers, young man. Comrade Beria does not like you very much, and it could be hard for you after I am gone." Then he smiled, the first time in a long while that Kondratiev had seen him do so. "On the other hand, it is quite possible Lavrenti Pavlovich may be gone before I am."

Was one to be cheered by the tyrant's occasional reasonableness, or on the contrary, depressed at the thought that he would not leave the scene very soon? It was like wandering in a maze, except worse, for one knew that there was no exit and the whole structure might collapse. If a minister and member of the Central Committee felt like that, what must an average Soviet citizen feel? Recently Kondratiev suspended his exploration of the common man's mind because his two sources of information on the subject, Trofim and the servant girl, Marfa, had both confessed that they had been summoned to the secret police office—he was appalled to learn that there was one quite close to the house in which he and other dignitaries lived—and questioned about his habits and opinions. He was sure that both of them would let themselves be torn to pieces rather than say anything compromising about him. But of course, *they* did not tear you to pieces. They had scientific and almost infallible ways of extracting what they wanted. So it was better not to continue his probe of public opinion.

An occasional insight into the problems encountered by the mass of his countrymen came in his meetings with his brother. During the latest one, Vladimir had announced that he and his Raissa were going to be married. Mikhail Alexandrovich expressed his warm approval of the woman, whom he had seen and liked on the one or two occasions they had met. Then he added reflectively that, in view of Vladimir's official position, this was perhaps not the most propitious time to marry a Jewess. Couldn't they wait?

"Wait?" screamed Volodya, who recently had taken to drinking again. "Do you realize how it feels to have to make love in the one room she lives in with her mother, or in my place where I share the bathroom with a couple with two small children? If you hadn't occasionally lent us your dacha, we simply could not have gone on. If we get married, we should get an apartment with a bathroom and kitchen of our own, and begin to feel like human beings."

He took another drink and then said more quietly: "That's how I live—a fairly high official, a partly disabled and decorated veteran. Can you imagine what it is like for most people here in Moscow? As to elsewhere . . ." He waved with his artificial hand. "Where is that bright future we were promised during the war? It has been seven years. And this business with Jews! I don't remember anything like this even when the Nazis and we were friends."

"I will not have you talk like this. And for your own sake, hold your tongue when talking to others."

The marriage did take place. Mikhail Alexandrovich was not at the ceremony or at the party following it, and Volodya broke off relations with his older brother. They would become reconciled in the early sixties, but the two still did not see eye to eye on politics. Both Vladimir and his wife had by now become staunch defenders of the old times: they used to have order, discipline, and the young people had a sense of purpose.

"I am positive that several people in my ministry take bribes. Under Stalin they would have been shot."

Raissa was shocked that a woman teacher in her little son's school at times read to the pupils what she described as "anti-Soviet poetry." But it was completely apolitical and published by the State Publishing House, a friend protested. "Literature should not be apolitical. If it is, it has a disturbing effect on young minds. Nobody would have dared to write, let alone print, such trash before they came out with those slanders about Stalin."

But during 1952, one as a rule did not discuss politics. To do so would have meant talking about *him*, and that was something no one, from a man in the street to a Party potentate, was eager to risk. In August, it was announced that a Party Congress, the first since 1939, was going to take place in October.

"Do you realize, Mikhail Alexandrovich," asked Viktorov at the end of one of their regular weekly meetings, "that we have all been holding our Party offices illegally? The statute stipulates a Congress at least once every four years, otherwise all appointments to the governing organs, the Central Committee, and the rest lapse."

Kondratiev was nominated to be a delegate from a Leningrad district. Why was he being "elected" from Leningrad? he inquired of Khrushchev, who was in charge of preparations for the congress.

"I am a deputy to the Supreme Soviet from a Moscow district, and it would have been logical for me to represent the Party members from the same area."

"I would have thought so," answered Nikita Sergeievich, "but the Boss himself reviewed the assignments of the Central Committee members, and, seeing your name, said that you were an old Leningrader and should be delegated from the city in which you were born and spent your first years as a Party member. It is amazing how he can remember such details about so many people. About one of our famous generals, he said that he had 'sat' for some time before the war in a camp in Kolyma and consequently should represent a district in the Far East."

Stalin had evidently recovered his sense of humor, thought Mikhail Alexandrovich, bitterly. But how could the general secretary in his present state of health deliver a report of seven to eight hours, as ritual required he do at the opening of a Congress? It might just prove too much, he thought unsentimentally, for a man who had had a heart attack in 1946, and evidently—one could not be sure—another one at the beginning of 1950.

But if the same uncharitable thought occurred to other "comrades-in-arms" of the Leader, they were in for a surprise. At a meeting of the Central Committee that preceded the Congress, Stalin announced that, as they all knew, he had been extremely busy with writing his opus on economics. Would the comrades agree that the General Report be delivered by Comrade Malenkov? Would they also approve that Comrade Khrushchev prepare proposals concerning changes in nomenclature of the Party and its organs. The present names dated from V. I. Lenin's times and were no longer appropriate for the Party of Lenin *and* Stalin. Take the name *Political Bureau*, which suggests a secretive body directing a group of conspirators. Wouldn't *Presidium* be a more suitable and dignified term to describe the leading organ of a great organization that functions completely openly and democratically?

It was Kondratiev's first Party Congress, and he found the proceedings almost unendurable in their dullness. The speakers droned on, the only moments of animation coming at the mention of Stalin's name, usually in the beginning and at the end of every speech, when the whole gathering would burst into tumultuous applause, at times all leaping to their feet and shouting "Hurrah." The object of the adulation did not bother to sit through any of the sessions, usually walking out after fifteen or twenty minutes.

When present, he sat with the dignitaries grouped in ascending rows surrounding the speaker's platform and facing the mass of delegates on the floor, his place on the extreme right of the first row, two empty seats separating him from the other Politburo members, who were bunched together.

The only dramatic moment came at the last session. Stalin strode wearily to the tribune, but once there, was transformed. The years appeared to have receded, and what the Congress saw and heard was not an aged tyrant repeating the usual platitudes, but a fervent revolutionary, hailing the delegates of the foreign parties and prophesying the eventual worldwide triumph of communism. It lasted only ten minutes, but it was a remarkable performance. And then he was again a little old man in marshal's uniform, impatiently motioning the wildly shouting crowd to resume their seats, gingerly stepping down from the podium and walking slowly back to his place.

It was quite a different scene when, the day after the Congress ended, the freshly elected Central Committee met to select what would now be called the Presidium. Members of the old Politburo were grouped behind a table facing the others. There was a stir in the room when Malenkov, who presided, announced that the new highest body would have twenty-five full members and twelve alternates, rather than as before eleven and four, respectively. The list began with Stalin, but then proceeded alphabetically—"Kondratiev, M. A."

Mikhail Alexandrovich started. He was one of the twenty-five! Did he really hear correctly? By the time he recovered, Malenkov was asking the routine question: Did anyone have any objections or would they place in nomination another name? The usual shouts replied, "No, let us vote," when suddenly Stalin raised his hand and silence fell on the room. The dictator stood up, his usually pale face flushed, his speech this time verging on the incoherent. He did not object to any of the names proposed for the Party's highest organ, but felt constrained to observe that there had been of late some irregularities in the work of Comrades Molotov, Mikoyan, and Voroshilov. They were among the Party's oldest and most deserving members, but past services did not give anyone the right to—he groped for the words—make trouble. He moved that the list be accepted as proposed. There was an uncomfortable pause. They looked at each other and at Malenkov, who seemed to be as much taken by surprise as everyone else. Finally he said, "All in favor . . . approved unanimously."

Stalin stood up again: He appreciated the honor of being nominated as one of the secretaries of the Central Committee. But he must state categorically that he would not accept reappointment as *general* secretary. "In fact I have not used this title since 1934 when it was agreed that Comrade S. M. Kirov would eventually assume those duties, freeing me for government work. But as you know, a vile assassin's hand robbed the Party of our dear Mironovich." Stalin looked around the throng. Was he imagining that those greenish eyes rested for a moment on him? Kondratiev loosened his tie and shifted in his seat. "And so I continued to carry this burden. But by now I have served you as general secretary for thirty years. Long enough." And with this he walked out of the room. They looked for an explanation or some hint from the presiding officer. But Malenkov just proceeded to read a list of ten names headed by J. V. Stalin, and again they were elected unanimously to be secretaries of the Central Committee.

The new Presidium—everyone still referred to it as Politburo—met only once, on January 13. Earlier that day a communiqué in *Pravda* announced the discovery by the organs of state security of a "terrorist group of doctors who had made it their aim to cut short the lives of active public figures of the Soviet Union through wrecking methods of medical treatment." Nine names of the treasonous doctors were listed; all of them had worked at the Kremlin clinic and had attended the highest dignitaries. Six of the nine were Jewish.

Though it was the announcement that was on everybody's mind, the agenda provided for only one item of business, an evaluation of the international situation in view of the results of the recent presidential elections in the United States. Malenkov began by expatiating on what everybody already knew: the new Republican administration headed by Eisenhower spelled trouble. Its dominant figure was likely to be Secretary of State John Foster Dulles, who in the course of the electoral campaign and since then had made several aggressively anti-Soviet statements. Marshal Vasilevsky then presented his views: the overall picture called for vigilance, but not alarm. Nothing as yet indicated that the Americans would follow their rhetoric with aggressive actions.

"Not against us, at any rate. They might strike at China—

help Chiang invade the mainland, perhaps even drop an A-bomb or two on Manchuria. But as Comrade Stalin said, that would not be so unfavorable from our point of view. Still, we are putting our Far Eastern forces on alert, and strengthening the army in Germany."

"Why isn't Comrade Stalin here to give us directives in a matter of such importance?" asked Khrushchev.

Most of the newcomers to the highest body were startled by both the question and the tone in which it was delivered. But the veterans, Kondratiev noticed, did not appear to be surprised. Was Khrushchev, hitherto among the most servile to and worshipful of the Boss, speaking on their behalf?

Malenkov did not answer. The discussion continued, and it was finally decided to approve the minister of defense's dispositions and to send a message to Peking proclaiming that the Soviet people stood shoulder to shoulder with their Chinese brethren in scorning the imperialists' boasts and threats, but refraining from specifying what the Soviet Union would do, should the People's Republic be attacked. With the business of the meeting concluded, Khrushchev stood up again and asked Comrade Ignatiev about the morning announcement in *Pravda*. Was it fitting that members of the Party's leading organ should learn about so grave an affair from the newspapers? The minister of state security cast imploring looks at Malenkov and Beria, but when they remained silent, he informed the group that he himself could not add much to the announcement: the investigation was being handled by one of his deputies. All he could tell them was that some of the guilty—he corrected himself, *accused*—had already confessed to having been in the employ of the American and British intelligence services.

"Some?" exclaimed Beria. "He does not seem to be very proficient at his job, that deputy of yours."

In 1956, Kondratiev was to learn about the sequel to that meeting. The senior members of the Politburo, except for Malenkov and Beria, went to see Stalin. Speaking on their behalf, Khrushchev assured him of their absolute loyalty, but at the same time warned that they were unalterably opposed to a new purge. With the Americans in a militant mood, the country could not afford another 1937.

"As to the doctors, you yourself, Josif Vissarionovich, as well as practically all of us here have been treated by them, and we have always found them to be honest and skillful physicians. Marshal Vasilevsky, who had been named as one whom they had allegedly harmed, told me he had not been in the Kremlin clinic a single time since the war, never even consulted any of them. In all likelihood, it is a vile provocation."

Stalin told them he had definitive proof, a deposition by a fellow physician, confessions . . . Finally he sighed and said, "Perhaps we have been overhasty. Let the judicial organs ascertain the facts."

Shortly afterward, Ignatiev confided to Khrushchev that he had been ordered to secure confessions "one way or another" from the doctors by the beginning of March.

Late in February, Kondratiev was summoned by the Boss. He was amazed to find an unfamiliar figure presiding over the reception room—there had been rumors in the last few days that Poskryobishev had been arrested. He was even more amazed that Stalin, though not looking at all well, had renewed his habit of pacing around the office while carrying on a conversation. Mikhail Alexandrovich was questioned closely as to when the Soviet Union would be likely to manufacture steel in quantities approaching those of the United States; and why they were lagging in the production of the intercontinental bomber . . . Then, standing with his back to his visitor and looking out of the window, Stalin shifted the subject.

"Your wife has been working in the Kremlin clinic. Has she ever noticed anything irregular going on there?"

No, said Kondratiev, she had expressed great surprise at the news. (He did not feel it necessary to repeat what Xenia had then added: "Well, if they've been arrested, it must mean they are guilty.")

Stalin came back to the table and sat across from Kondratiev. "It is difficult to spot a skillful practitioner of treason. My own doctor—I have known him for years—always appeared to be most solicitous. Now, he has confessed that the treatment he prescribed for Comrade Zhdanov was bound to bring a massive heart attack. If not a gun, then pills . . . Yet some of our colleagues keep insisting those scoundrels are innocent. Yes, at first many could not believe that Trotsky and Zinoviev were behind the murder of Comrade Kirov. Do you think *they* genuinely regretted their part in the foul deed?"

Though he could feel a prickly sensation going up and down his back, Mikhail Alexandrovich managed to say gravely: "Nothing, nothing could atone for a crime of that enormity."

"You think so . . ." Stalin was looking past him now, as if seeing another person in the room. "When I was a youngster studying in the Tiflis Theological Seminary, the priests used to tell us that by being sincerely contrite one could atone for all the evil one had done. What do you think, Misha?"

It was the first time he had ever addressed him so familiarly. He replied, somewhat incoherently, that he himself had never had religious instruction; the Revolution came when he was five, and, anyway, his mother was a freethinker and his father had believed the Orthodox church to be responsible for many of the misfortunes that had befallen the old Russia. But yes, he thought that that was the standard Christian doctrine.

Stalin got up and, also unprecedentedly, walked him to the door. "Remember, we must step up the production of steel. Goodbye, Comrade Kondratiev."

On the evening of March 3—during the past few days, forsaking both prudence and long-standing habit, he came home early to see and play with the children—the telephone call did come: he was wanted at the Central Committee within half an hour. That was not the way it was usually staged, but still . . . He looked at his desk—there in a locked drawer was a gun. One must not jump to conclusions. He picked up the phone and called the Planning Commission: Comrade Viktorov had just left for the Central Committee, and so had two of his deputies. Relief was mixed with a perverse feeling of frustration. How long would this drag out?

The hall was filled, not only with the committee members but also members of the Moscow City Council, borough Party secretaries, uniformed security and militia officials. But before he could give any thought to what all this meant, the senior members of the Politburo filed in and, instead of taking their seats, remained standing on the podium. Only then did he notice that there was no table. There was only a lectern with a microphone. Voroshilov stepped up to it and began to read in a completely normal voice—he might have been dedicating a power station.

"Dear Comrades, a great tragedy has befallen the Soviet people and the entire progressive mankind."

The rest he heard but dimly.

"A paralytic stroke . . . no possible hope . . . within seventy-two hours at the most . . . a public announcement to be made tomorrow. Imperative need to avoid panic and disorder. Comrade Beria to order the dispositions . . ."

Only when Voroshilov concluded and Beria started to bark orders did Mikhail Alexandrovich realize that he was trembling. A feeling of rage surged up within him—rage at the dying lunatic, at the idiots who were sobbing all around him, at himself. Then the rage subsided. He had an almost irrepressible urge to laugh—say what you would about Stalin, he always had an unerring sense of timing.

CHAPTER 8

MOSCOW AND WASHINGTON, SEPTEMBER 1982

Evgeni Malandin's elegant apartment played a unique role in Moscow's social scene. For some years now, it had been one place where the young Establishment could mix, talk, and drink with young dissenters without undue fear that what transpired there would hurt one's career or surface in an interview with a security official. Few of Malandin's guests were ready to believe that what went on at the parties remained completely unknown to the KGB. That there had never been any ostensible consequences for those attending such gatherings was attributed to various reasons: by some, to the host's connections—he had been a son-in-law of Remizov's and was still on friendly terms with Moscow's Party boss. Others, more cynical, saw the self-restraint of the secret police as another example of its lately developed sophistication—they needed a place like Malandin's to learn what was really on the minds of the young intellectuals and bureaucrats.

Pavel Kondratiev leaned toward the second explanation. He remembered Andronnikov's cautioning him at a dinner at his father's house.

"We really don't care, Pasha, what young people say. It is only when they do something naughty that we are reluctantly constrained to spank them."

Still, those evenings at Malandin's filled a vital Russian need: to talk volubly and not in whispers about subjects like Afghanistan, current Polish events, Solzhenitsyn's latest work, the most recent trial of dissidents, and so on. Once in a while, while arguing about such contentious subjects with a rising Party bureaucrat, Pavel could perceive a glimmer of understanding or hesitation on the other side, quite different from his now quite ritualized political disputes with his father.

Malandin himself was head of a research group in one of the Academy of Sciences institutes. Among his published articles and papers, there had been quite a few containing explicit criticisms of Soviet economic planning and management. For all that and an occasional reprimand, he kept his job, and considered himself, and was, a loyal Party member. What impressed and at times infuriated Pavel about his host, whom he otherwise liked for his intelligence and wit, was that Malandin was the most apolitical person he had ever met. All problems, he asserted, could be reduced to their technical dimensions; all the ailments of Soviet life would be remedied by better planning and application of scientific methods of management. The same was true of foreign countries and the international situation in general.

And so, once most of the guests had left, Vadim Troyekurov, who worked in the Central Committee's International Department, chose to come back to a remark casually dropped by his host earlier in the evening: all the recent troubles in Poland were to be traced to glaring defects in the country's economic structure and policies.

"But Zhenia, how could you have said that? Aren't we also and primarily confronted with an attempt by the counterrevolutionaries to bring back the capitalist ways and to detach Poland from the socialist camp?"

Malandin, who had been emptying ashtrays and collecting dirty glasses, stopped and took off his spectacles, usually a preliminary to a lecture. But before he could launch into it, Pavel erupted.

"Good God, Vadim, this is not a propaganda meeting. Why should the Polish workers want to bring back capitalism?"

"And how could they, even if they wanted to?" added Lisitsin. "It would take a miracle. One would have to resurrect the bankers, manufacturers, and landowners moldering in their graves all these years and distribute to them factories and state and individual peasants' land. Really!"

"This is hardly a subject for jokes," Troyekurov defended himself. "You know what I mean. *Objectively*, Solidarity is a counter-revolutionary and anti-Soviet movement."

Pavel audibly groaned. Even his father eschewed the "objectively," which in officialese had come to mean something quite opposite to what common sense would make you believe. Thus, as a boy he had learned—this was before the textbooks were cleansed of the most glaring accretions from the Stalin times—that Ivan the Terrible must objectively be seen as a progressive monarch. And now they were being told that "objectively" and for all his "errors," Stalin had rendered great service to the Soviet people.

But before Pavel could demand that the wretched word be banned from their discourse, Malandin began his lecture. Employing statistics profusely, he demonstrated how the whole hassle in Poland had been caused by incredible mismanagement of the economy by those in power between 1970 and 1980. Not only were huge foreign credits wasted through the government's ineptitude, the credits aggravated the crisis. From 1976 on, it was only a question of when, and not whether, an explosion would come.

"Of course, Solidarity was bound to make the mess worse. How can the workers manage an economy? They are not capable of it, any more than those generals, who with Vadim's bosses' evident approval, are now running Poland. It is a job for the experts," he concluded.

The remaining three guests all spoke up at once.

Troyekurov: "Marxism is also about the class struggle."

Pavel: "It is more than a question of statistics and planning."

Lisitsin: "The workers need to feel free."

Malandin raised his hand. "I can readily dispose of your objections. What class struggle? Poland is a socialist state; the exploiting classes have been eliminated. Like it or not, Pavel, statistics and planning are the key to the understanding of economic conditions, which in turn determine social and political life. As for you, Igor" (turning to Lisitsin), "freedom in concrete terms means efficiency and material abundance. What has your Solidarity accomplished during the year and a half it was allowed to run wild? A catastrophic decline in industrial production, scarcity of the most essential goods, and general impoverishment. Some freedom." He resumed clearing the debris of the evening.

"I am not done yet. Don't take away the brandy," exclaimed

Lisitsin, snatching the bottle from the tray Malandin was about to carry into the kitchen.

"Nor am I," echoed Troyekurov. "Apart from distorting Marxism, you are violating the traditions of our great nation by allowing your guests' glasses to become empty."

He was going to bring out whiskey, the host defended himself. Once he reappeared with drinks, Pavel resumed the attack.

"If all human emotions are to be traced eventually to statistical data, how about the problems of our friend Natasha?"

Natalia Smirnova had staggered out of the party on the arm of a journalist renowned for his amatory exploits. "I don't want to sound vulgar, but this is obviously a case of what might be called statistical deficiency on the part of her husband."

"Let's be serious, Zhenia and Pavel." Lisitsin would not let the evening conclude on a jocular note. "We've had scientific socialism in this country for sixty-five years. Where is your economic efficiency and material abundance?"

Troyekurov took up the challenge. "You forget, Igor, such trifles as a war that cost us twenty million lives and general devastation, and the huge sums we have to spend to protect ourselves against the capitalists."

"I shall leave international relations to you, Vadim," began Malandin, but Lisitsin interrupted him.

"I will not. I grant you that the capitalists have no love for us, but who is it who stirs up the most trouble around the world? It is not the Americans who invaded Afghanistan. How is the security of our country enhanced by the billions we give to such progressive regimes as those in Syria and Ethiopia? Why not cultivate our own garden?"

"Because the Americans don't leave us in peace."

And, realizing that he had not really answered Lisitsin, Troyekurov added, "How can you and Pavel, who consider yourselves liberals, object to the Soviet Union helping those people in Afghanistan who want to bring their country out of the Middle Ages into the modern world, and assisting the Arabs who are fighting to liberate their brothers from the Zionist yoke?"

"As for me," declared Pavel, "I believe with Stalin in concentrating on building socialism in one country—our own."

Troyekurov could be quite patient and condescending when

confronted with criticisms of the regime, but anything smacking of sarcasm on this subject made him lose his equanimity. "Stalin. Always Stalin. That's what you people always say when you run out of rational arguments. He's been dead for almost thirty years. What does Stalin have to do with any of our problems today?"

"Unfortunately, a great deal. Anyway, I was quoting him with approval. Too bad he did not stick to what he said, and insisted on bestowing the blessings of communism on the Poles, the Czechs, and the others."

It began to look like the makings of a first-class row. A similar discussion some months before had ended with Troyekurov exclaiming, "I am willing to listen to reasoned arguments, but not to slander," and Lisitsin rejoining, "Say it: I should be locked up." But now the host, more sober than either of them, was quick to deflect the coming confrontation.

"You are beginning to sound like those nineteenth-century Russian intellectuals with their endless disputes about politics and ideology. They prattled on while the country was sinking ever deeper into misery and backwardness. Neither the late J. V. Stalin, nor our, to my mind generally regrettable, exertions on behalf of the riffraff we keep calling the Third World have any bearing on our most pressing problems. We live in an age of nuclear fusion, genetic engineering, and computers."

This led the discussion to take a new turn, with both sides decrying Malandin's mechanistic approach to life and with Lenin, Orwell, and Solzhenitsyn summoned to buttress the argument.

Eventually, the whiskey ran out. Troyekurov got unsteadily to his feet and announced that he had to have some sleep.

"I must be in my office early. And with a clear head, so I will be able to prepare new blows against the free world."

"And Pavel and I have to spend the rest of the night plotting against Soviet power," proclaimed Lisitsin in the same vein.

"I would not dream of interfering with such important activities. Mine is a pedestrian task: I am writing a paper showing how we can improve the productivity of state farms and improve the system of distribution in the food industry. I have great hopes that it will clear the Ministry of Agriculture and not end up in a wastebasket until it reaches the Central Committee."

Vadim patted him on the back. "Cheer up. We have some forward-looking people. I will not embarrass Pavel and Igor by mentioning their names. Most of the others mean well, but they are set in their ways, and at their age—"

Instead of finishing the sentence, he flashed what was meant to be a conciliatory smile and was gone. The two of them lingered for a while, then bid their host good-bye. They were at the bottom of the stairs when Malandin's shout recalled them.

"I found another bottle," he announced.

Pavel was tempted, but Lisitsin pulled at his sleeve. And so they departed again, after Malandin exacted a promise that they would attend another soiree of his two weeks hence.

"It will be a purely social affair. I am getting tired of ideological discussions."

"Sorry to drag you out," said Igor once they were in the street, "but we should discuss something while we are relatively sober." He paused, but Pavel, though he knew what was coming, remained silent. "I cannot find anyone else with access to a Xerox machine. You could not possibly do another batch, could you?"

Two months before, Pavel had been persuaded to use his institute facilities to reproduce copies of the letter sent to the procurator general of the USSR, whose signers, including a number of prominent intellectuals, had protested the arrest of a couple of dissidents.

"What is it this time?"

"A petition to the Presidium of the Supreme Soviet from several foreign scientists, decrying the persecution of Sakharov."

"I told you I don't like doing this kind of thing. In the first place, people who are likely to be moved by the latest swinishness perpetrated by the government already know about the petition—heard it on foreign radio. The news travels. As for others, they could not care less. So what is the use? In the second, I don't like deception. When I get into trouble, I want it to be for something I do or say openly."

"I know you too well to believe those are the only reasons."

He was being used, thought Pavel, and Lisitsin and his ilk were in some ways as devoid of scruples as the representatives of the system they loathed. They counted on his having a certain immunity because of his father. Or conversely, it would be a little triumph for them to have the son of a Politburo member publicly identified as having violated the law and defamed the regime. All for doing something that was bound to have no effect whatsoever.

"I respect your feelings," continued Lisitsin. "My own old man was quite shaken when I was thrown out of the journalists' union and lost my job for refusing to go as a correspondent to East Germany. I explained to him that I could not go abroad and write the kind of trash that would be expected of me—how happy our Germans are to have the Berlin Wall and thirty Soviet divisions protecting them from the capitalists. But since that time, he has become resigned to having a nonconformist son. We are quite friendly. We simply never talk about politics."

Lisitsin's father, once a minister of higher education, currently a vice president of the Academy of Sciences and a member of the Central Committee, was widely considered as a progressive influence in the cultural field.

"Really Igor, this has nothing to do with *my* father. It is simply that under the present conditions, I do not believe in the usefulness of clandestine activity. People at large know only too well what is going on. It is childish to think that we can change anything by printing leaflets and playing hide-and-seek with the KGB. I am quite willing to risk my job and even freedom for what I say and write openly, but not for that. We cannot compete with our government when it comes to playing conspiratorial games. It is only when someone stands up to the rulers in full daylight that our society can be stirred up. Take Solzhenitsyn; take Sakharov."

"One has been thrown out of the country; the other is in internal exile . . . You may have a point, and I shall not press you. We'll manage to circulate the petition somehow. Doesn't Malandin sound like a broken record, with his 'scientific planning' as a cure-all?"

At home, while undressing, Pavel kept going over the conversation. In a way, he would feel better if Igor believed that his refusal was motivated by fears for his own safety. Why was it embarrassing to care about one's father's feelings, even if he was one of "them"? No, he really believed in what he had said about the uselessness of clandestine activity. Still, when Lisitsin made his request, he recalled his mother's words about that mysterious burden her former husband carried with him, and that he must never do anything to make his life more difficult. And then a thought flashed through his mind that made him sit up. Had Igor been hinting that it was not simple filial devotion that made him refuse the request? But of course . . . his friends were bound to whisper about how ambition can change a person's perspective: "Take Pavel Kondratiev; he's become very careful. Obviously, he would relish being the son of the man at the very top of the pyramid, and will not do anything that might jeopardize his father's chances of getting there." He got out of bed and dialed Lisitsin's number.

▬

All during the ride from Bethesda, Jim Doherty kept telling himself that this time he must be patient, refrain from making sarcastic remarks, and appear to pay close attention to what was said and to what he had heard innumerable times before. The Senate committee hearings were scheduled for next week. His nomination to be the chief arms negotiator had brought mixed comment. The pro-administration press hailed the appointment: "For the first time, the American team will be headed by someone who is thoroughly at home in the Russian language and politics and who does not harbor any illusions about the Kremlin's ultimate goals," editorialized a conservative weekly. By the same token, a liberal journal castigated the administration for designating as its chief spokesman on arms control a man "who in his public pronouncements has repeatedly questioned the desirability of reaching an agreement, except on terms that are clearly unacceptable to the Soviet Union. The Senate Foreign Relations Committee has an obvious obligation to inquire whether Mr. Doherty has altered his views on the subject. If not, he is hardly the person to lead the U.S. delegation in these most important and delicate negotiations."

A German commentator had reported great concern in Bonn about the latest reshuffle of personnel in Washington. Charles Amon's appointment as the U.S. Ambassador to the UN was seen as the result of machinations by the "hawks" in the administration, who had thus succeeded in getting rid, insofar as any real influence on American foreign policy was concerned, of the one man known for his conciliatory views toward the Russians, and who had succeeded in establishing personal rapport with influential Soviet personalities. Now that he had been kicked upstairs and Doherty nominated to replace him, there was scant chance of the Soviets' returning to the negotiating table. A London *Times* correspondent was worried by the nominee's reputation as a wit: "It is his sarcastic barbs about the Soviet Union that reputedly endeared him to the president and helped advance his career. One does not begrudge

Mr. Doherty his sense of humor—a rare quality indeed among America's public figures. But East-West relations, and especially nuclear arms control, are not proper subjects for frivolous quips. For Western Europeans, at least, constant verbal baiting of the Russian bear, and scoffing at the Soviet Union's legitimate security concerns, are seen as poor credentials for the office to which Mr. Doherty has been nominated."

"The son of a bitch is right in one respect," reflected, irritably, the object of the debate as his car entered the District. Americans demanded solemn demeanor in their public figures. A politician might be forgiven and occasionally applauded for cracking a few jokes, but in general, levity on the part of the officials was considered bad form. The typical middle-class American was almost as humorless and suspicious of humor in others as was his Soviet counterpart. In one case, that suspicion went back to the Puritan forefathers and Dr. Freud and was nourished by the wretched social scientists with their inane prattling about "issues"; in the other, the fault lay with those solemn assholes who presided over Soviet society and the KGB (the latter, the closest thing the USSR had to the psychoanalytic tribe in the West, when it came to repressing normal human impulses to gaiety and replacing them with feelings of guilt).

Such reflections had been with Doherty ever since last evening, when he had struggled with the draft of what was to be his opening statement before the committee. One version began with "Mankind is confronted with a fateful choice." He crossed out "Mankind" and replaced it with "Humankind." The next few paragraphs followed in the same somber vein. But then after "Hence the awesome burden of responsibility placed upon the two superpowers," he got stuck. He would write, and then erase: "Men of goodwill on both sides have come to realize . . ." What had they come to realize?—*what?*—that we should not let the bastards screw us once more? He finally tore up the draft and decided to compose the statement at a more propitious moment.

The massive bulk of the Pentagon came into view, bringing another rush of irritation to Doherty's mind. No, it was too easy to blame the predicaments of this country, when it came to dealing with the Soviets, on the innocence of the average American, perversity of the media, or thoughtlessness of the politicians. Why hadn't those charged with formulating the foreign and defense policies of the U.S. been more alert and intelligent? He would now have the well-nigh impossible task of persuading the Soviets to reduce the number of their intercontinental and intermediate land-based missiles.

"Why did we allow the Russians to get ahead of us in ICBMs, both in number and power?" he had once asked the Defense Department's chief expert.

"Ours are more accurate. Besides, we never figured they would go on building and deploying their rockets. It didn't seem to make any sense. It still doesn't. They can destroy this country with a fraction of what they have," the chief of the technological section of the Pentagon had replied.

How could the man be so obtuse! Of course it made excellent sense to other experts. The man in the street in America, Britain, or West Germany did not care how accurate our missiles were against theirs. He believed, and was absolutely right, that once those dreadful toys started flying, all bets would be off anyway. What he did know and what scared him out of his wits was that the Russians had *more*. Perhaps this was not very logical or sophisticated, but such was human psychology. The Kremlin had understood it, but it was only now that the secretaries of defense, chiefs of staff, and those damned experts were waking up to the fact that the numbers *did* matter.

Doherty recalled a dialogue during the previous round of negotiations. "Would the American delegate kindly explain why the Soviet Union should cut down or, still more absurd, completely eliminate its heavy intercontinental missiles?"

"We agreed that we should seek equivalence in nuclear weapons, and the U.S. has nothing approaching in power your SS-18, of which you have deployed over three hundred."

Kondratiev spread his arms, simulating both surprise and helplessness: "And was it we who persuaded the American defense planners not to construct heavy missiles? You obviously feel quite secure with the smaller ones."

"But SS-18s are destabilizing. Theoretically you could wipe out all of our land-based missiles with just a small portion of yours," protested General Powell.

"Excuse me, gentlemen. Theoretically yes, but as General Powell knows, the Soviet Union has solemnly pledged never to be the first to use nuclear weapons. The SS-18, as well as our other nuclear rockets, is designed to discourage any madmen who might dream of launching a preemptive strike against our Fatherland. As for stability, you should have thought about it before producing and using the first A-bomb. *That* was highly destabilizing, as are your current plans for what I understand has been dubbed in your country Star Wars."

What could you answer to that? thought Doherty with exasperation: that we have never used our nuclear monopoly and former superiority to pressure the Russians, while they quite effectively at times resorted to rocket rattling, and now that they have a quantitative advantage are unabashedly trying to blackmail Western Europe? Once when the State Department man just hinted at that theme, Kondratiev pulled out a book by a well-known American writer on international affairs and read the passage in which the author listed thirty-three occasions on which the U.S. allegedly threatened to use nuclear weapons.

"As against those *facts*, it is well known that the Soviet Union has never, I repeat, *never*, used such tactics of intimidation. Come, come, gentlemen, let us not indulge in propaganda rhetoric. We're here on a most serious business."

There was no possible way of reacting to such barefaced lies, short of grabbing and shaking the mendacious bastard. Instead of which, Amon said soothingly, "I shall not comment on the content of Chairman Kondratiev's statement. But I agree with his conclusion: we are here to deal with the current and most important issues and not to engage in recriminations about the past."

Doherty groaned inwardly. He had felt it politic to invite Charles Amon to preside over today's meeting. While awaiting the resumption of negotiations, the American team held periodic discussions with the country's leading Kremlinologists and arms experts in and out of the government. He was rather skeptical about the value of such sessions, but it was one way of whiling away the time—and who knows? it was always possible that one of the outsiders would come up with a brainstorm. And it was good public relations: by seeking outside advice from academic figures, the administration was demonstrating that it did not have a closed mind on arms negotiations or other aspects of its relations with the Soviets.

Amon greeted him cordially. While he had opposed Doherty's appointment as his successor in the intra-administration discussions, with the nomination made public, he loyally defended him against the charges of being a "hawk" determined to sabotage the negotiations.

"It was kind of you to invite me, Jim. It's now your show—I have no doubt you'll be confirmed. But I appreciate an opportunity to deliver a valedictory and listen to what our experts have to say. Isn't it a good sign that Kondratiev appears to be taking over in Moscow? I have always believed that he is one man with whom we could do business."

The rest of the delegation was unchanged: Art Hill, for the State Department; General Powell, representing the Joint Chiefs; Hilmar Turnquist, the chief scientific adviser. Several others from various government agencies had also been invited to sit in on the session. Amon opened the proceedings by reiterating his gratitude for being invited. He was sorry to leave the delegation, but confident that his successor would more than fill the bill.

"Perhaps the job calls for more vigor and especially endurance than a man of my years can command," he said rather wistfully, provoking loud protests from the gathering.

He could not say that the Russians were the easiest people to deal with. Yet, for all the frustrations they've experienced during the past two years, he firmly believed that there would eventually be an equitable U.S.-Soviet agreement.

"In the course of my long law practice, I have at times encountered people even more obdurate than the Kremlin's representatives, and yet, by being patient and persevering, by convincing the other people of our good faith, we were eventually able to get together. There are those who say that we can never trust the Russians. I prefer to hold with what a great American statesman and lawyer, Henry Stimson, once said, that one way of making a person trustworthy is to show trust in him."

He paused and looked expectantly around the table, obviously awaiting some reactions, but the only one came from the University of California Sovietologist George Steinberg who said loudly, "Hear, hear."

Doherty, who had a slight cold, felt an almost irrepressible urge to sneeze, but with effort managed to suppress it. Amon's voice took on a special note of solemnity.

"We all realize that mankind faces a grave choice . . . The United States and the Soviet Union share a fearsome burden . . ."

This time, Doherty's self-control broke down and he erupted into a prolonged sneezing fit, which compelled the speaker to stop. Once he resumed, he did not continue in the previous vein, but quickly concluded, "Anyway, I am here not to preach, but to wish Jim and all the rest of you the best of luck."

Doherty answered in a brief speech: They would all treasure the memory of having worked with a man whose name would be indelibly inscribed in the annals of American diplomacy. If—he corrected himself—when an agreement is finally reached, a lion's share of the credit would belong to Charles Amon who so vigorously and yet with patience and courtesy pleaded America's case to the Soviets and before the entire world. This country was fortunate that rather than seeking a well-earned rest, their erstwhile leader had agreed to accept a most important post where his sagacity and negotiating skills would help the cause of democracy and peace.

It was only when he sat down and wiped perspiration from his face that he realized that his little speech was a close paraphrase of the encomium for a deceased Soviet Party leader he had recently read in *Pravda*. But the old man appeared genuinely touched.

It was now the turn of the experts. George Steinberg launched into a lengthy survey of Russian history. The key to the present behavior of the Soviets—incomprehensible to the average American—was the agelong search for security that had guided the Russian state ever since its beginning. Its people, unlike the Americans, have long historical memories. They have repeatedly been exposed to foreign invasions. The Mongols ruled and devastated Russia for three hundred years.

"Let us not exaggerate—some two hundred," interjected Peter Stankiewicz, a historian specializing in medieval history.

"They may have ruled for only two centuries, but they kept raiding Muscovy and exacting tribute well into the sixteenth century," insisted Steinberg.

"A political scientist, unlike a historian, does not define *rule* in the narrow sense of the word."

"If you talk about the sixteenth century, those were Tatars who were Turkic, rather than Mongol, and anyway, Ivan the Terrible—"

"Gentlemen, we will have a discussion later on," interposed

Amon. "Professor Steinberg, please go on with your fascinating synopsis of Russian history."

"Then in the seventeenth century we have the Polish invasions," continued Steinberg, with a hard look at Stankiewicz, as if holding him responsible for the aggressive doings of his distant ancestors. It took him another half hour to get to Peter the Great.

"I hate to cut in, Professor," Doherty felt constrained to say at this point, "but we have only some forty minutes until the lunch break, and in the afternoon we have scheduled a discussion and talk on the contemporary Soviet political scene."

Steinberg, with a hurt expression, declared that one could not really understand the Soviets' concern about national security without going into the broad historical background of the problem, but he would try to be brief. For the next hour and a half he expounded upon several social science models of Russian development from Peter the Great to Stalin. The one he found most applicable was that of a developing society whose efforts at modernization have been again and again interrupted by foreign aggressions. He illustrated this model by drawing a graph on the blackboard: an ascending line punctured by dips standing for foreign invasions—Napoleon's in 1812, the Japanese in 1904–1905, Germans in 1914, the Western powers' intervention in the Civil War, 1918–1921, and Germans again in 1941.

"One can easily see," he concluded, "how the trauma caused by repeated invasions and defeats at the hands of foreign powers lies at the root of the Russian fears and explains much of what to us, a nation that has never experienced such traumas, appears as unreasonable emphasis on military power."

"How has a country that, according to you, has been continually beaten come to spread over one-sixth of the earth's surface?" asked Arthur Hill.

"We shall have questions in the afternoon, Art," said Amon with a hint of reproach. "I cannot speak for the others here, but personally I found Professor Steinberg's presentation most illuminating."

The postlunch session threatened, for a while, to erupt into a raging battle. The two historians, Stankiewicz and Hilary Ford, attacked Steinberg's exposé, accusing him of oversimplifying, and implying that, being a political scientist, he should stick to current events and his models, and not attempt to pontificate about history. Far from being concerned mainly with self-defense, the Russian state, Ford maintained staunchly, had from its earliest days been bent on expansion.

Vasili Konovalov, an émigré who had become a popular press commentator on Soviet affairs for American TV, criticized both sides for neglecting the deep spiritual impulses of the Russian people. The West could never tame the Soviets by awing them with its own military might or by appeasing them with credits and technological transfers. It was only by appealing to the hearts and minds of the Russian people that one could counter the nefarious designs of their Communist masters. The heated debate, references to obscure historical personages and events that no one but the academicians in the room could identify, finally got to be too much for Amon, who said softly, but firmly, "Speaking as a layman, I am both astounded and grateful for the rich intellectual fare to which our visitors have treated us. Now that we understand Russia's past better, it is perhaps time to plunge into a subject directly relevant to the concerns of this group. All of us who have been involved in or concerned with Soviet-American relations over the past twenty years are greatly indebted to Dr. Carlson both as an adviser and as a writer on this subject. When I was appointed ambassador, I had but the most rudimentary knowledge of the history and politics of the country to which I was being sent to represent the United States. When I confessed my predicament to some old Soviet hands in the State Department, they told me there was one book that would tell me all I needed to know about the USSR and communism, and that was Carlson's *Not an Enigma but a Challenge: The Anatomy of Soviet Politics*. I found the book a veritable treasure trove of information. Several high Soviet officials confided in me that for a bourgeois writer—they have such a quaint way of putting things—Dr. Carlson was amazingly well informed about their society. Evon has been kind enough to take time out from his busy schedule to give us his views of the current Soviet scene."

As behooves an oracle and former adviser to several secretaries of state, Carlson had hitherto remained silent, not deigning to participate in the academicians' fracas. Now he laid aside his pipe, and looked reflectively at the ceiling. He lowered his eyes and finally said, "Communality . . . yes, that is probably the closest

English term . . . I have listened to this very enlightening discussion, and I believe that for all their apparent disagreements, the participants have given us several most interesting insights touching on the roots of Soviet political behavior. But what is so difficult for us in the West to grasp is this peculiar Russian characteristic of seeking agreement, nay, unanimity on social and political issues. They do not view politics, as we do, as a process of give and take, where decisions are eventually made by voting, where you have majorities and minorities. They believe in consensus. They deliberate and argue, but finally someone enunciates an idea that all the others recognize as the only solution to the problem, and that there could be no question of opposing."

He puffed on his pipe for a while. "I remember talking with Khrushchev in '58 or '59—I saw him both those years—and I vividly recall his explanation of why Molotov and some others were expelled from the Politburo. He told me, 'Oh, they wanted to settle issues by voting, and because they had a majority, they thought they had won the game. But we Soviet people don't believe that a chance arithmetical majority should prevail over the truth, and against the Party spirit. And so although the Central Committee had voted for it, they recognized their error and decided to punish them.' Unanimity—that is the essential thing with the Russians . . . in some ways reminiscent of the Orthodox Church's doctrine."

He took a few more puffs. "You may remember that in my book, to which Ambassador Amon so kindly referred, I stated that the closest analogy in America to a Politburo session is probably a Quaker meeting. To be sure, in the case of the former, the members do not sit in silence. Still, the discussion is constrained until someone, usually but not invariably *the* leader, comes out with a formulation that the others immediately recognize as what they all had been groping for."

"How the hell does he know?" Doherty whispered to Hill and closed his eyes, but opened them again as the latter kicked him in the shins.

The speaker shifted to the current scene. The Soviet Union was already coping with the problem of succession. If he had to put his money on someone, it would be Smirnov, since he was of peasant origin and thus best fitted the requirement of being able to elicit that unanimity that was so fundamental to Russian politics. His two rivals were less qualified, one the son of an industrial worker, the other of an army officer.

"Forgive my ignorance, but why should being of peasant origin be such an advantage?" asked General Powell.

Carlson, obviously peeved at being interrupted, answered brusquely that behind the veneer of communism and modernization, Russia was still essentially a peasant country. "I discuss this at length in my *Peasant Roots of Soviet Political Consciousness.*"

The effects of Smirnov's succession on Soviet-American relations could be quite significant, Carlson went on . . .

Doherty was experimenting with something he once heard in a lecture on Zen Buddhism. The lecturer had stated that by contemplating a beautiful experience in one's past, a person could completely tune out his immediate surroundings, sound and all. He was now evoking his more memorable sexual experiences, but found that the theory worked only partially. Voluptuous images blended with incongruous phrases, "a period of transition," "expansion is not inconsistent with but complementary to the search for security." Finally, the sounds prevailed, the pleasurable visions receded, and he once again could hear the speaker clearly. Yet there was something to the Buddhist prescription. Irritation and the urge to scream gave way to a feeling of inner peace. He was amazed to find some things Carlson was now saying quite sensible. Perhaps he should try the technique when and if he sat down again with the Russians.

The meeting broke up for cocktails.

"I saw you suffering and fully sympathize," whispered Hill as they were getting drinks. "What drivel."

"Oh, it wasn't so bad. Actually, the point Carlson made toward the end of his harangue is well taken. It was his disquisition on the Russian soul that almost drove me up the wall. He and Konovalov. Have you noticed how people who are engrossed in studying the Russians tend to take on some of their characteristics? The same balderdash about their deep spirituality and their strong communal feeling. I have never seen more materialistically minded people, not even here in the good old U.S.A. As for that other deeply ingrained national trait: have you ever met a Soviet bureaucrat who was not ready to slit his best friend's throat if by doing so he could be assured of a promotion?"

"You are too hard on them, Jim. I admit the people we deal with there are hardly paragons of virtue. But the average Russian—Here comes our superexpert. Dr. Carlson, I cannot tell you how much I enjoyed your *mise-en-scène*."

"Oh, when it comes to the contemporary scene, there is hardly anything I can teach you two fellows about the Soviets," said the man known as the dean of America's Kremlinologists.

"I cannot speak for Art, but though I try to keep my nose to the grindstone, I am always astounded by your insights. It would never have occurred to me that a Politburo meeting might be analogous to a Quaker meeting."

"Ah, yes, I remember how surprised our business leaders were when I made that comparison while briefing them before they went to Moscow in 1973. They later related to me that they repeated it at the banquet in the Kremlin. At first the Soviet officials took offense: the interpreter made a slip and said 'Shakers' instead of 'Quakers,' and then thought it necessary to add that the Shakers were somewhat similar to that weird old Russian sect that practiced self-castration. But then it was explained to the Soviets that it was the *Quakers*, and how the latter abhorred war and violence of all kinds and engaged in a multitude of good works. Leontiev beamed, saying, 'Yes, we Communists may have a good deal in common with the Quakers.' "

They all laughed, Doherty a bit wildly, and Hill, spotting portents of danger, steered the conversation on to another subject.

At the dinner Doherty found himself seated between Steinberg and Konovalov. The two soon found themselves in a dispute, the professor maintaining that the Soviet Union was moving toward liberalization and pluralism.

"That is why I disagree with Carlson as to the succession. My bet is on Kondratiev, since he believes in reform and friendlier relations with the West."

The Russian begged to disagree; no matter who would replace Leontiev, the current trend was toward greater repression and neo-Stalinism. Doherty listened distractedly, trying to size up Konovalov. In his late thirties, Konovalov spoke English almost without an accent. He had defected six years before while with a Soviet delegation in London. The CIA file on Konovalov described his position in the USSR as that of an interpreter for the Foreign Ministry, quite likely with links to the KGB, but he put himself out as having been an official of the Central Committee's International Department. Almost immediately after his defection, he had become much sought after as a media commentator on Soviet events. His opinions usually followed whatever at the moment was the prevailing fashion in Kremlinology, but were delivered with an air of self-assurance befitting one who had known people within the inner circle in the USSR. Konovalov thus impressed editors and television producers, but was less than popular among the Soviet émigré community, some of whose members hinted darkly that there was more than met the eye to their successful compatriot. It was probably only envy, thought Doherty; propagators of such rumors were finding it hard going in this country. Still . . .

"Speaking of Kondratiev," Steinberg continued, "I am rather surprised not to see Professor Kerner here. When I was giving a lecture at his university last week, he told me he had once had an occasion to chat at length with Kondratiev. Also implied that he got to know a great deal about the background of that man, who at the very least must be considered one of the three leading candidates to succeed Leontiev."

"We asked him; he couldn't come," said Doherty curtly. It was not true. Some time before, he had received a letter from Kerner in which it was also implied that the professor had some information about the Soviet potentate that might be of use to the government, but it was of such a confidential nature that it could not be committed to writing. He recalled his irritation at the letter: did the writer think that something he dug out of old issues of *Pravda* could be so earthshaking, and that he, Kerner, was being watched by Soviet agents? He had his secretary answer the professor: he was indeed grateful for his offer of help, but he and his colleagues were concerned exclusively with the issue of arms control and not with Soviet domestic politics. Should an occasion arise to avail themselves of Dr. Kerner's information, they would communicate with him. Now he half regretted his impetuosity. Certainly, whatever the professor had to say could not have been more trivial than the stuff they had been hearing today.

He turned to Konovalov. "Could there be something really compromising in Kondratiev's past?"

The Russian smiled. "You know better than to ask that question, Mr. Doherty. There has to be a great deal that is compromising about a man who has been a high Soviet official for forty years."

"I mean from *their* point of view."

"If there is, you can be sure that the others in the Politburo know about it. It is not like here, when someone in a responsible position is suddenly discovered to have not paid income taxes for years or to have an unconventional sexual preference."

Only three days later, after his nomination was confirmed by the Senate Foreign Relations Committee with minimal trouble, Jim Doherty began to feel uneasy about the session with the experts. Sure, there were phonies among the academic people, but so were there in every profession. For every Carlson and Steinberg, there were serious scholars in the Soviet field, but because they did not pretend to be oracles and lacked self-advertising skills, they were seldom asked to be government consultants or invited to diplomatic conferences. What if this fellow Kerner did know something of importance? Embarrassing though it might be, he decided to place the dilemma before his colleagues on the delegation.

Most of them readily agreed that he was right in holding off Kerner.

"As you wrote him, Jim, we are in the business of conducting arms negotiations, not prying into some alleged secrets of the Kremlin," said Turnquist.

"We all met Kondratiev and know what a smooth, cold-blooded type he is," Hill supported him. "Suppose there is something unspeakable in his past. How could we use it? Make a Politburo member defect? Threaten to reveal his guilty secret, unless they make a major concession? Preposterous!"

But the deputy director of the CIA, who was sitting in on the session and whose judgment Doherty respected, shook his head. "I am afraid it was a mistake, Jim. We know so little about the Soviet bigwigs. It's not a question of scoring some sensational coup, or using the information as a bargaining chip. It would be absurd to think that. But any little thing that would have contributed to our knowledge about Kondratiev could have enabled us to have an insight into his personality, and helped assess what we might do if indeed he becomes the general secretary."

"It's still not too late. We can get him here in a jiffy."

The CIA man shook his head. "I'm afraid we can't. He's been

in an accident, is in a coma, and isn't expected to recover." He saw their expressions and shook his head again. "No, no. It *was* an accident. The FBI kept an eye on the professor—foreign-born, traveled extensively to the USSR—and they looked into the thing. He was trying to cross at a red light. The driver, who was going a bit too fast, stopped immediately after hitting Kerner and summoned help—it was just a high school kid."

The brief obituary notice in the *New York Times* did not spell out the details of Kerner's fatal accident. Instead of proceeding with his daily perusal of the *Frankfurter Zeitung* and *Le Monde*, Kondratiev reflected for a moment and then rang for an assistant.

"Get me copies or photostats of the following American newspapers from September 27." He named eight, including the *Indianapolis Star*.

"I assume, Comrade Kondratiev, you want the editorials and news."

"You are not to assume anything. If I wanted just one section, I would have said so."

The aide stammered out excuses and rushed out of the room as if propelled by some invisible force.

Having finished the full account of the "tragic death of a noted scholar and Soviet expert," Mikhail Alexandrovich felt first relieved, then annoyed with himself. Why should he care how the wretched professor met his end? He decided to push this thing out of his mind once and for all. But the next day, he received an envelope marked CONFIDENTIAL from the KGB.

In it were a Russian translation of the *Times* obituary and a handwritten note from Andronnikov: "Sorry to see you have lost an American admirer." Did the secret police chief want to titillate him, or had he assumed that he would find out the whole story by himself? Damn those people and their devious ways! He would wait until Andronnikov brought up the subject.

▬

One week later, after a Politburo meeting where it was decided to cut sharply the number of Jews to be allowed to leave the country during the coming year, Andronnikov asked for a meeting in Kondratiev's office. Once there, he announced he had to unburden himself of something he had not wanted to raise at the meeting.

He and his organization had been placed in an impossible situation. For years, thousands of Jews had been permitted to emigrate, and then recently and abruptly the Politburo had decided to turn off the spigot.

"Yet I am not authorized to take decisive measures against those who bewail loudly how unhappy they are here. All that riffraff remain at large, slandering the Soviet power to anyone who will listen, especially foreign visitors. You know me, Mikhail Alexandrovich, I am far from being an anti-Semite. But how long can this continue? Either let them go to Tel Aviv, New York, or hell, or let us put the worst troublemakers away. The way things are now, it is very bad for the morale of my people."

"You must be patient, Sasha. Someday we shall be negotiating again with the Yankees, and those Jewish malcontents could prove useful in the bargaining process. We should not only be able to get rid of them, but be handsomely rewarded for being so liberal, to boot. In the meantime, we must go easy on them. The Americans are very touchy on the subject."

"The Americans. Always the Americans. We did not use to be so careful about offending their delicate sensibilities. You, of course, know them much better than I do. But is it wise to get them used to meddling in what is none of their business? The more we encourage them, the more insolent they become in pestering us."

"Come, come, Sasha. We haven't done so badly in dealing with the Americans. As against trying to negotiate with the Chinese—"

"They *are* impossible. But what a fortunate country—no Jews." He was silent for a moment, reflecting, no doubt, on the unfair advantage enjoyed by his opposite number in Beijing. Then his official manner returned. "I assure you, Mikhail Alexandrovich, we shall scrupulously follow the instructions."

"I have no doubt you will. And please warn your subordinates about that anti-Semitic trash they've been purveying. It is harmful, quite apart from anything having to do with the Americans."

"You know me better than that." Andronnikov sounded genuinely aggrieved. "I have spoken about it, and quite sharply, to the people in our cultural section. Each time, they've told me the book or article in question has been authorized from above, more specifically, by Pavel Viktorovich Lisogor. I cannot take it up with him. You know why."

It was a ticklish situation. Traditionally, the Party's supervision of the security organs was exercised by the general secretary himself, but recently, for obvious reasons, Leontiev had increasingly delegated this task to Lisogor. Were the issue raised before the Politburo, the Chief might well take it as a reflection on himself.

"I realize that. Look, Sasha, I did not mean to criticize you. The way things are, we've all been working under a great strain and will continue doing so until the situation is clarified one way or another."

Andronnikov was understanding: "The devil knows what gets into Lisogor when it comes to the Jews. Not only them—I don't think he has forgiven me for having Greek ancestors. I also have a very hard time with him when it comes to appointing a Georgian or Armenian to a responsible post." He sighed. "Yes, I do hope the situation gets clarified, and you know which way I hope it does. My respects, Mikhail Alexandrovich." He got up, then suddenly tapped his forehead in a convincing imitation of a man who has just recalled something of little consequence. "About our dear departed American friend—I was going to bring you a longish article about him from his hometown newspaper. It will be on your desk tomorrow."

"Oh yes, the professor. I read the *Time*'s bit that you so thoughtfully sent on to me; would have missed it, otherwise. But unless the article has something related to the business we talked about, don't bother. It is not as if he had been an intimate friend."

"No, there is nothing of importance in the piece. Just tributes from his colleagues and students and a detailed description of the accident."

"Dear Sasha, I have no doubt it was an accident. I know only too well the humanitarian traditions of your organization."

Andronnikov responded in the same vein: "But you underestimate its powers. I snap a finger here in Moscow, and poof!—a man seven thousand miles away drops dead. In any case, it should teach the Americans that it is not safe to engage in—I believe they call it Sovietology?"

"Kremlinology."

"Whatever it is. You become so engrossed in trying to penetrate those sinister secrets of ours, you don't notice the light is red and so you step in front of a speeding car. Let them mind their own business."

"I am beginning to think you don't like the Americans, Sasha. We shall have to send you as ambassador to Washington. On closer acquaintance, they can be quite charming."

"I'd rather go to Kabul. I understand streets there are much safer."

Once the door closed behind his visitor, Kondratiev pushed aside his notes from the Politburo session, pulled out a copy of the Indianapolis paper, and proceeded to reexamine its story about Kerner. As he had thought, the account of the accident mentioned nothing about the professor's being struck while trying to cross against a red light. When he first scanned the obituary, it had appeared of no special significance that one of the colleagues quoted as paying tribute to the deceased had a Russian-sounding first and last name—the man was identified as a lecturer in the university's Slavic department. But now it came to him: this had to be the KGB collaborator who, as Andronnikov told him on a previous occasion, had been befriended by Kerner. Of course this had not been an accident. Quite meticulous, the manner of execution: no hit and run, a teenager at the wheel (the very fact that the latter did not panic and try to flee should have aroused the suspicions of the police, but evidently it hadn't). But how the murder was arranged, while intriguing, was less important than why. The KGB's professional concern to tidy up a potentially messy situation? Or did Andronnikov want his patron to guess at the truth—the slip about the red light might have been intentional—thinking this would give him an additional claim for preferment from the future general secretary? If so, it showed poor knowledge of human psychology. But then, after several years in that line of work, strange things happened to the minds of those people. No wonder so many secret police bigshots tripped on their own intrigues.

All of a sudden, Mikhail Alexandrovich realized that once he became general secretary, he would have to get rid of Andronnikov. Fifteen years as head of the KGB was much too long. No one should be allowed to hold that position for more than five or six years. Perhaps Kuliabko could be persuaded to take the job, and after a year or two Gorbunov could be eased into it. Why wasn't he being honest with himself? The truth was that he could not stand the man. Somehow, of late, looking at and listening to his old friend made him recall the features and voice of Major Nikiforov, who had grilled him in Leningrad in 1934.

A bizarre coincidence, thought Kondratiev. Thirty-one years before, he had been thrown by a horse and suffered a contusion in the lower part of his back. After several weeks, the pain disappeared and he put the accident out of his mind. But in recent months he had been suffering from intermittent backaches—nothing harrowing, but quite bothersome when sitting down—precisely in the same spot. His doctor could not account for this reemergence of trouble after so many years.

"We really don't know how our memory works, but I've heard it argued that the body may remember things the mind has repressed. We may forget and forgive an injury suffered in the past, but our nerves never do, and a fresh trauma can make them act up."

He was not suffering from any trauma, Kondratiev said irritably, but from pains in his back. The doctor had known and attended him too long to be offended or put off the subject.

"Then it might be overwork. Your general condition is that of a man twenty years younger, dear Mikhail Alexandrovich. Still, all that activity and responsibility would strain the constitution of a thirty-year-old. Why don't you take a rest once in a while? I believe you have not had a vacation in two years. But true, this business with the back may have nothing to do with stress. A man bangs his knee, and that somehow makes nerves in the location of an old injury react. Keep on with massage and hot baths. I could prescribe some pills, but I know it is hopeless to try to make you take them."

He had not banged his knee, and the stress he was under was nothing compared to what he had experienced at various other times in his life. So it had to be something else. Right there and then Kondratiev had a moment of inspiration. No, the problem could not be resolved just by firing Sasha. If he became the general secretary, he would (of course, after a suitable interval) abolish the KGB altogether. It would not be easy, but it had to be done. Its foreign intelligence side could be handled by an appropriate branch of the Defense Ministry. As to political police work, it should be assumed by the Ministry of the Interior and, most important, those charged with it would, as a rule, be transferred after a number of years to other duties. How could national security conceivably suffer from such an arrangement? At the same time, this ancient curse of Russian life antedating the Revolution—the secret police being a state within the state—would be lifted off. Now you appoint perfectly decent, normal people to the organs, but if they stay with them too long, something happens to them: they become transformed into megalomaniacs, intriguers, sadists. "My people," Andronnikov referred to them—what gall. Of course, this turbulent and anarchy-prone nation had to be ruled with a firm hand. But those entrusted with enforcing order and obedience to the Party must no longer be allowed to be, as it were, a separate caste.

▬

The elation with which Kondratiev had gone to bed gave way the next morning to sober second thoughts on the whole KGB business. He was not superstitious, but still, was it not foolish to think now what he would do when and if . . .? And it would be worse than foolish—fatal—if his colleagues got as much as a whiff of suspicion that he contemplated major changes in the traditional ways of running things. Whatever their other qualities, the members of the Politburo, even the least perspicacious ones, had by now developed a veritable sixth sense when it came to spotting a potential troublemaker. For most of them, a troublemaker was anyone who would tamper with the order of things which had prevailed all those eighteen years since Leontiev's accession. One need not propose or say anything. These men had sat and debated with each other for so long that a mere intonation of voice, a changed expression while an issue was being discussed, could convey to them a portent of danger: this man might become a dangerous innovator. "Oh, but isn't he a 'reformer'?" (with a sardonic intonation) from one of the senior members of the Politburo was enough to end the most deserving activist's chances for membership in the Central Committee.

As young men under Stalin, they had lived in constant fear for their lives. Middle-aged, they could never be sure that some new harebrained scheme of Khrushchev's would not cost them their jobs and appurtenances. Now, they wanted to live out their old age in peace. They could still be quite venturesome when it came to foreign affairs: the invasion of Afghanistan had been decided on the spur of the moment. But even the most logical and beneficial innovation insofar as domestic social policies were concerned would encounter anguished protests.

"We reduce the number of centrally imposed norms that the directors of the industrial enterprises have to meet from thirty-three to twenty-four, and then what? Very soon they will demand no rules at all, so that they may hire and fire as many workers as they fancy, produce what and as much as they please. It would mean an end to the planned economy—chaos, utter chaos. Is that what we want?"

That from Viktorov, once the boldest and most innovative of economic administrators. And as for anything having to do with the structure of power and its prerogatives and privileges, to change that in the slightest, in the opinion of his dear Politburo colleagues, would simply be sacrilegious—only a rabid *counter*revolutionary would even dream of doing it. Even the slightest lift in the veil of secrecy surrounding their decision making? Several months back, Leontiev had astounded them by proposing that the Politburo issue regular communiqués about its weekly sessions.

"We would not mention, of course, the most delicate subjects we discuss. Just the general stuff about economic plans, our government's peace initiatives, and so on. It would be good for the morale of the people."

There were raised eyebrows around the table, and it is doubtful that the proposal would have passed except for Gabayev's coming out with one of his usual idiotic remarks.

"But what if the people become curious about what we really do and discuss?"

That put everyone in such good humor that Leontiev's suggestion was passed on a trial basis. And now Soviet citizens could read (Kondratiev was sure that few bothered to) how, at its weekly session, the Politburo had approved further measures for strengthening the economy and raising the standard of living of the population, discussed the dangerous portents inherent in recent increases in the U.S. military budget, noted with satisfaction the strengthening of the bonds of friendship between the USSR and India . . .

So the KGB business would have to be handled with the utmost care. First install new people in the top positions, prepare the ground carefully, and then strike quickly and decisively. In the meantime, nobody must suspect that Kondratiev would turn out to be a "reformer."

These thoughts were still on his mind in the Politburo offices as he was going over the agenda for the forthcoming meeting of the Defense Council. A telephone ring interrupted his meditations. It was the general secretary's personal assistant: the Chief was suffering from sciatica; Comrade Lunin was also indisposed, so he would have to take the chair. Sciatica—my eye! As of late, Leontiev was increasingly unable to recall or keep straight the various technical facts and figures bearing on defense matters. At the last session of the council, it had become painfully obvious that he did not understand the difference between short-range and tactical nuclear weapons. The military men around the table sat with impassive expressions as the distinction was explained to the general secretary, but what must have been going on in their minds! How long could this last?

Unlike "restricted" (attended only by full members) Politburo meetings, where, for all the underlying personal antagonisms, there was, on the surface at least, a sense of camaraderie, meetings of the Defense Council almost invariably, even when there were no contentious issues on the agenda, took place in an atmosphere of strain. The generals did not feel at ease in the presence of their political superiors. Accustomed to command, to think and talk in the straightforward soldier's idiom, they did not find it easy to affect a tone of supplication and reverence while addressing the leaders; they grew perceptibly upset and impatient at the obfuscating circumlocutions when what they considered as commonsense military imperatives and arguments were fended off by the civilian bosses.

The latter, in turn, viewed the soldiers with a mixture of condescension and suspicion. They, the Politburo believed, did not have much political sense and could not be expected to appreciate the need for subtlety in international affairs.

"We should really consider marching in and putting an end to that Solidarity nonsense," declared Marshal Levandovsky, at the height of the Polish crisis in the summer of 1981.

"What would your ancestors say to that, Roman Vinkentovich?" jeered Kuliabko, who, impolitic though it was, could not resist an opportunity to stick a pin into one of the generals.

The marshal, who hated to be reminded of his family's origins, bit his lip and said nothing. It fell to Vorontsov in his capacity as both a Politburo member and professional soldier to remind the choleric chief of staff that he himself had previously held that, in all likelihood, there would be armed resistance, and that to pacify Poland would take four to five hundred thousand Soviet troops.

"No, we must try everything else before we decide on armed intervention."

And now at this session, Levandovsky was complaining, though circumspectly, that political leadership was hampering the efforts to put an end to the insurgency in Afghanistan.

"Under the current instructions we are not allowed to raid those bandits' camps on Pakistani soil. Their armed gangs go back and forth across the border at will. American and Chinese arms are being delivered to the rebels, practically in broad daylight. We don't have enough troops in Afghanistan to seal off the border. It is the opinion of our people in Kabul that under the present conditions, it will take five to six years to put an end to this wretched business. If the Pakistanis were impressed with the danger of trifling with the Soviet power, and stopped acting as a conduit of help to the rebels, we could wind up the affair in a few months."

"The Politburo," said Kondratiev in his most official voice, "has decided that for the present no steps are to be taken against Pakistan. I trust, Roman Vinkentovich, that you keep reminding General Pavlichenko that he must not allow any armed incursions or air strikes across the border. We are wearing out the rebels and keeping up diplomatic pressure on Pakistan. When and if the general international situation warrants it, we shall authorize further measures."

Levandovsky shrugged his shoulders. "Sure we are making progress, even with our present limited arms contingent. But the overall situation is not good for the morale of our armed forces in Afghanistan or, for that matter, elsewhere. Our losses are, well, tolerable. Still, Soviet lads are dying because the Afghan government cannot do its job properly."

"May I then repeat that we are committed, also subject to a possible change, to maintaining the present crew in Kabul, unsatisfactory as some members of it are. There are other than just purely military considerations that must govern our policies."

Levandovsky surveyed the faces of the other military men, but none of them chose to intervene in the dialogue. He then turned again to Kondratiev and said softly, "I fully realize and accept that. I just wish I knew what those other considerations might be."

"The Politburo's decisions—" began Filimonov, but Kondratiev cut him off.

"I know that General Secretary Leontiev wants our military leaders to be fully informed concerning anything and everything that bears on their responsibilities. That is what this council is for. But I think it would be best if he himself, possibly at our next meeting, were to survey the full complexities of the Afghan problem. I am sure he will do so with his customary lucidity and succinctness."

The last thing they wanted was to create the impression that the generals had the right to expect answers to any questions they chose to ask. The Defense Council—consisting of all the full Politburo members resident in Moscow, some alternate members, and a half dozen of the highest military figures—existed so that the military might brief the political leaders and not vice versa. Levandovsky should have learned that by now.

Yet it would have been tactless to state explicitly, as Filimonov with his stupidity was about to do, that even the chief of staff had no right to ask the Politburo the reasons for its decisions.

But when it came to the next and most important item on the agenda, military plans and prospects for the next two years, questions could not be avoided. The defense people could not be expected to say what their manpower and weapons needs were without being told how the Politburo viewed the international situation. In Leontiev's absence, it fell to Kondratiev to present a *tour d'horizon*. When he finished, he could sense that the listeners had been impressed by the clarity of the picture he had drawn, so different from the rambling and confused exposés they had been hearing of late from the Chief. But that did not mean that the military bigwigs had been appeased. Levandovsky led the charge.

"Comrade Kondratiev's survey has been most illuminating. As I understand, the Politburo does not preclude the possibility of a military intervention in Poland during the period, nor the need for doubling our contingent in Afghanistan if the counterrevolutionary movement there is not suppressed by the end of 1985. At the same time, it is not proposed to reduce our forces along the Chinese border. I did some quick calculations. I submit respectfully that in view of such potential emergencies the 4.5 million figure authorized for our forces for 1984 could prove grossly inadequate. To be on the safe side, we ought to increase it by at least 700,000."

"And where do you propose we find them, dear Roman Vinkentovich?"

The word "increase" had brought Viktorov out of his near slumber. "Every year a million and a half of our young people are taken into the army. The farms are becoming depopulated—look at the figures for our agricultural production. Our factory managers complain of the shortage of younger workers. We simply cannot afford to have our labor pool depleted still further."

Levandovsky looked imploringly at Vorontsov. But the minister of defense had to remember that in this setting, he was a Politburo member first and a professional soldier second. If an emergency did arise, he said, they would call up the reserves; there was no need to increase the size of the standing army.

Levandovsky hesitated, then decided to forsake caution. "Begging your pardon, Ivan Yakovlevich, that could be only a partial answer to the problem. The Polish operation, for instance, would require highly skilled and specially trained troops. We don't have such in abundance. Also, they would have to be rotated at fairly frequent intervals. There might be simultaneous trouble in another socialist country. I would be failing in my duty to the Party and the government if I did not offer as my considered opinion that the present size of our armed forces is already too low. I think my colleagues here could throw additional light on the subject of our preparedness and needs."

This was a signal for the others to vent their grievances. Chief Marshal of Aviation Melchuk repeated his long-standing complaint: because of financial stringencies, only a small part of his force was being kept on alert.

"The Americans at all times have one-third of their strategic bomber command in the air; we, one-fifth."

Yegorichev of the Rocket Command also latched onto the financial angle: "We've been criticized for always being behind the Americans when it comes to weapon technology and innovation. Well, our research and development funds have not been increased for the last three years. Like Roman Vinkentovich, I would be failing in my duty if I did not report that the morale of the people in my command is not what it should be. Their pay and living amenities are not commensurate with the hard, monotonous, and supremely important duties they are performing."

"They are not like the infantrymen and airborne troops in Afghanistan who are facing bombs and bullets. They sit at the missile sites and wait," Filimonov thought fit to interject.

"Precisely, Comrade Foreign Minister. For a professional soldier, sitting and waiting is the hardest part of the job."

Admiral Alikhanov pointed out the potentially unfortunate consequences of the sailors' low pay. "They visit and go ashore in foreign ports, where they are inevitably drawn to make comparisons that are not flattering to our socialist society. It is only through the most strenuous efforts of our propaganda and education administration that we have managed to keep desertions and other troubles at a minimum."

The two groups were arrayed separately, facing each other across the table. Kondratiev would change this arrangement, he mused—it was a bit too suggestive . . . Despite frowning glances from Smirnov and a couple of other Politburo members, he did not cut short this recital of grievances. Better to let it all come out into the open. Finally, the military chiefs subsided, some trying to read the expressions of the political bosses: had they said too much? Mikhail Alexandrovich gave them an assuring smile.

"I am sure that I am speaking for all of us on this side of the table in thanking our military comrades for their frankness. The security of our Fatherland, the preservation and enhancement of its armed might, is the uppermost consideration in the minds of the Party and government leadership. The problems you have raised will be brought to the attention of Comrade Leontiev." He looked at his fellow Politburo members. "If it meets with your approval, I shall propose to our Chief that we invite all of our higher military personnel to a general session where the issues raised here, as well as any others, can be freely discussed with the Politburo and other appropriate officials."

There was an approving murmur on his side of the table, but the faces of the marshals betrayed mixed emotions. They were not enchanted with the idea of the political bosses questioning and probing their subordinates and encouraging them to speak their minds.

"How large a group would it be?" asked the chief of staff.

"That would be up to Comrade Leontiev," he nodded toward Vorontsov, "and Ivan Yakovlevich to decide. I should think . . . from lieutenant generals up."

"That might be too large a gathering to allow for an effective discussion," Levandovsky began hesitatingly, but then, noticing a warning frown from Vorontsov, added hastily, "On second thought, I believe Comrade Kondratiev's suggestion as to the participants is quite right. We should solicit the opinions of those who are actually in direct touch with the rank and file of our officer corps."

"Precisely, Roman Vinkentovich. And I know that Comrade Leontiev will expect that everyone present, no matter what his rank, would feel completely free to express his opinions. As to the date, if practical, we should hold the session before the November meeting of our Central Committee. The discussion at the session might well enable our leadership to formulate concrete proposals to be laid before the committee. Do you have any other observations and comments, Comrades?"

"Then let us turn to the last item on our agenda. Comrade Filimonov will report on the international situation, and I shall then note what—in the view of the Politburo of the Central Committee—that situation implies for the tasks and the state of readiness of our armed forces."

The minister of foreign affairs launched into his survey: They did not expect any major crisis during the next two years. The present Washington administration began with and continues a very provocative language vis-à-vis the Soviet Union, but finds itself incapable of translating this opprobrious rhetoric into actual aggressive moves against the socialist camp. The pressure from America's allies, U.S. public opinion, and the growing strength of the worldwide peace movement have stayed the hand of the hotheads in the White House and the Pentagon.

"As our Ukrainian proverb has it, 'A cow that bellows much gives little milk,' " interjected Kuliabko.

There was a brief outburst of laughter, but Filimonov appeared at first puzzled, and then said, "Oh yes, I see," and his face creased into the semblance of a smile.

"They not only bellow, but sow mischief. It is with Washington's complicity that the Israelis are devastating Lebanon," declared Smirnov, who, even in the presence of outsiders, could not restrain his irritation with Kuliabko's levity.

"And the world wonders that our Syrian allies, though we provide them with the most up-to-date weapons, are doing such a miserable job against the Israeli air force," added Remizov.

Marshal Melchuk's face reddened with anger. "Our planes *are* first-rate, as good as or better than the American ones the Israeli aggressors are using. But with those Syrian riffraff flying them . . ." He waved his hand contemptuously.

"I remember Comrade Melchuk objecting strenuously to the idea that we lend Syria our own pilots. The Zionists would not then be able to gloat that they destroyed more than eighty MIGs without losing a single plane of their own." Smirnov was not going to let the military have the last word.

"It is bad enough to waste our equipment, but to sacrifice the lives of our Soviet lads as well? Those people have no idea about proper maintenance and technology. Sometimes I wonder what possessed us in the first place to get so heavily involved with people who have no idea of modern technology, no discipline, no—"

Kondratiev felt he had to stop Melchuk and what threatened to become a clash between the military and civilian components of the council. "Forgive me for interrupting you, Kondrati Pavlovich. But the decision to help our Arab friends against Zionist imperialism was reached by our government after all due deliberation. The Israelis may be gloating for the moment, but the time will come when they and their American protectors will realize that no matter what they do militarily, they keep getting into deeper and deeper political trouble . . . Let Comrade Filimonov proceed."

The foreign minister, somewhat disoriented by the interruption, resumed his report. He fully endorsed Comrade Kondratiev's last and very perceptive remarks. American imperialist schemes usually backfired: take Central America, where for all of its vast resources, the United States seemed completely incapable of prevailing over the national liberation movement in El Salvador. This was yet another example of how even a great capitalist power like the U.S. could not stop the forces of history and progress . . .

Kondratiev suppressed a yawn and consulted his watch ostentatiously. Filimonov, with his long-winded ways, tended to ignore the distinction between a propaganda and a business meeting.

The foreign minister hastened to conclude his recital. They would all, he was sure, join him in paying tribute to the wisdom and steadiness with which the Politburo and the Central Committee, guided by Comrade Leontiev, have directed the ship of state.

"For several years, our general secretary has advocated patience and conciliatory policies toward the People's Republic of China. Despite all the intemperate, and even occasionally insolent, reactions from Beijing to our friendly overtures, the general secretary has not wavered in this endeavor. There were some," he glanced at Levandovsky, who had assumed a stony expression at the mention of China, "who came close to advocating rather forceful and risky measures in regard to the People's Republic. But as usual, Comrade Leontiev's judgment and patience have been amply justified. The Chinese government has recently conveyed to us strong intimations that it desires normalization of state relations between our countries. In time, this normalization might well lead to the restoration of close and friendly ties between Moscow and Beijing, and the capitalists would lose their delusions that they could exploit for their own perfidious scheme those temporary dissonances between two fraternal countries."

How fortunate they all were in having at the helm a man with the wisdom and experience of Comrade Leontiev, Filimonov concluded, and looked around the table as if expecting applause, but there was only a sputtering of "Hear, hear."

How silly of the foreign minister, thought Mikhail Alexandrovich, to lay it on so thick. No reasonable man could entertain the slightest illusion that the Chinese had had a genuine change of heart concerning the Soviet Union. They simply found it expedient to normalize relations with the USSR, so that they could have a breathing spell to repair their economy from all the disasters inflicted on it by Mao's follies.

That was the theme with which he began his own observations. They all wished they could share Comrade Filimonov's hopeful outlook on future relations with China. True, as the foreign minister so aptly observed, they had to go along with the effort to normalize relations with Beijing. "As Comrade Leontiev once said, we cannot go on grappling with the capitalists while having China, so to speak, on our back." They must gain time to break up the Western alliance, to achieve a decisive superiority in nuclear and conventional weapons over the Americans. When that happens, there is at least a chance the Chinese will genuinely (he emphasized the last word) reappraise their attitude toward our country, accept once more our leadership of the socialist camp, and agree to limit their own nuclear armaments. If they do, we could help them with their economy, for there was no question in his mind that Beijing's present efforts to get out of the economic rut by aping the capitalists were bound to fail.

"For the military side, the implications of everything that has been said here are clear. We must be strong, become ever stronger. We must be prudent, avoid any confrontation either with the capitalists or the Chinese, and trust that, even more than in the past, the Soviet Union's growing might in all its forms will continue to impress the world so that no one will dare to challenge the legitimate interests of our Fatherland and its friends. We must continue to build up our strategic and tactical nuclear forces at a rapid pace, so that when we sit down to negotiate with the Americans we will have room for bargaining, and still be able to retain our superiority. Those then, Comrade Commanders, are the directives of the Politburo. We have full confidence that you will continue to carry them out in a spirit worthy of the glorious tradition of our armed forces."

"And for our part," declared Marshal Levandovsky, "you may assure Comrade Leontiev and the entire Party leadership that we shall spare no effort to justify the trust of the Party and the government, and to carry out to the utmost of our ability the lofty responsibilities with which they have entrusted us."

After the meeting broke up, Mikhail Alexandrovich thought it advisable to say a few words in private to Levandovsky, and drew him aside.

"We may differ on some points, Comrade Marshal, but you know you have in me a strong advocate of the army's views and needs."

"We fully appreciate that, Comrade Secretary of the Central Committee. Apart from everything else, we treasure the memory of your late father, and we are mindful of those." He pointed at the row of military decorations on Kondratiev's chest.

▬

"And where is the money going to come from for all those new weapon systems, dear Mikhail Alexandrovich?" asked Viktorov, with whom Kondratiev was having dinner the same night. "Konstantin Leonidovich keeps pressing me: 'We must have more consumer goods. Look at what is happening in Poland.' Yet we keep pouring more and more into arms. Last year it was 38.5 percent of our total budget; next year military appropriations are scheduled to rise to 43 percent. I don't have to tell you what it does to consumer industries. I am not a magician."

"But you are Alexander Ivanovich," laughed Arkadi Remizov, the only other guest. "The things you did after the war. I was a young instructor in the Secretariat at the time, and I remember Stalin saying, 'If our other industrial ministers and planners had half of Viktorov's ability, we would catch up with the Americans in a decade.' That was when he hardly had a good word for anybody."

Viktorov waved his hand deprecatingly: "I still have great doubts that I would be here today if he had lived a few months longer." He poured more vodka for his guests. "Tatiana Maximovna is still in the south taking a cure." Viktorov's wife suffered from recurrent bouts of arthritis. "You will have to excuse me if the household cuisine is not up to its usual standards."

His guests knew that he missed acutely, even for a short separation, his life companion of fifty-eight years. Their only two sons had died during the war. But with Politburo and government meetings, he could not stay away from Moscow beyond September 1.

When in a relaxed mood, over brandy and cigars, Alexander Ivanovich liked to discourse on the experiences of his long and rich past. But during the dinner he kept up his criticism of what he considered the exorbitant military budget: why did they need the crash program in intermediate nuclear rockets, cruise missiles, and the rest? Kondratiev kept patiently repeating his argument that had carried the day in the Politburo: if you don't push the capitalists, they start pushing you.

"Of course, we do already have enough long-range rockets to dispose of not only the U.S. but other NATO members, as well. But our intermediate missiles are *political* weapons. They are not targeted at London, Paris, and so on, but at the political links that hold NATO together. The average Englishman or West German has gotten used to those giant missiles, and believes they are *all* aimed at America. But when he sees what they call Soviet SS-20s multiplying like mushrooms, he respects us more and, increasingly, is having second thoughts about his country being tied to the U.S. And this sudden interest of Beijing in being friends with us is also not accidental. They can count too and know that some of those mobile missiles along their border could make short work of their puny nuclear facilities. Khrushchev skimped on arms, and look what happened to us in 1962 in Cuba."

Viktorov sighed: "For a man of my years, all those new weapons are terrible, and it is incomprehensible how anyone could ever think of using them. Sometimes when I think of my two boys who were killed, my only consolation is that Tatiana Maximovna and I have no grandchildren."

Remizov tried to turn the old man's thoughts in a more cheerful direction: "Come, come, Alexander Ivanovich. You were once a military man yourself."

"And so I was, at fifteen in the Red Guards when we took the Winter Palace. You should have seen the faces of Kerensky's ministers when we entered the room where they were trying to pretend to hold a cabinet meeting. 'We protest this unheard-of outrage against the legitimate government of the Russian Republic. Shoot us if you will, but you will never kill Russian democracy.' Some of the lads were indeed for shooting them out of hand, but one of the smarter sailors said, 'You are quite a speaker, but we would be wasting bullets on the likes of you. You may think you look like martyrs, but what your faces really show is that you badly need to go to the bathroom. After that, we will put the whole lot of you under lock and key for your own protection: the masses don't realize what farts you are and want to tear you to pieces.' "

Kondratiev remembered his father's shamefaced account of the ineptitude of the Kerensky government and how many professional officers had decided in November 1917 that they would rather have the Bolsheviks than that bunch of professors, bankers, and, as he put it, "all that intelligentsia riffraff who first brought the tsarist government down, but then did not have the guts or the slightest idea how to rule the country."

"But later on you had more trying experiences, Alexander Ivanovich," Kondratiev urged him on, enjoying Viktorov's reminiscing, no matter how often he had heard his tales before.

"Yes, at eighteen I was in the Civil War—a political commissar with a Red Army battalion. Those were exhilarating times—we were fighting against overwhelming odds, but I had not the slightest doubt that our cause would win. When we took prisoners, if they were officers, it was usually 'Against the wall!' And the Whites did the same to us. It all seemed so natural to me. I was the son of a worker, grandson of a serf. They were the accursed class enemies. Until one day . . ." Viktorov paused, poured himself a drink, and looked away from his listeners. "It was a kid, seventeen or eighteen. He cried, and swore that if we spared him, he would enlist on our side. I was ready to spare him—he was my age. But my commander said, 'You are too soft, Viktorov, he is just an ensign. What good would he be to us, and at the first opportunity he would run over to them.' And to the soldiers: 'Take the young gentleman and give him the usual treatment.' And that was perhaps why, after the war, I decided that the army was not for me and chose another profession."

He laughed sadly. "I could not have foreseen that in the thirties it would be as dangerous to be an economist as an officer. But I'll never forget the poor boy's face as they led him away. It no longer showed fear, just disbelief and wonder: why? I remember vividly when I received the telegram about my Kostya's death—he was about the same age. Well, at eighty, even an old Bolshevik can be allowed to wax sentimental."

How could a man like this have served Stalin? Kondratiev wondered. The old man must have divined his thoughts.

"You must think that all that slaughter in the Civil War at least made some sense, as against what was happening in the thirties; and how could old sentimental Viktorov have gone through all those years doing much worse things than not objecting to—and I could have stopped it—the shooting of the White Guardist. Well, you young fellows [seventy and sixty-five, respectively] have read but do not really know what it is to be an old Bolshevik. I am a hereditary proletarian, apprenticed to a factory when I was eleven; I remember my grandfather's tales of life under serfdom. I would have served the devil if convinced that by working for him, I was helping build socialism. And Josif Vissarionovich, monster though he may have been, was doing it. Well, enough of that."

The talk turned again to government and Party affairs. Remizov bewailed his problems as Moscow's boss. There was a steady, though covert, grumbling among the population over the recurring shortages: no coffee one month, lack of fresh vegetables throughout the winter, complaints from the medical administration that some of the hospitals lacked essential medications and supplies.

"I tried to draw the attention of the relevant ministers to the situation: the minister of health blames the minister of the chemical industry; people from trade tell me they are not allotted enough foreign currency to purchase the necessary supplies abroad. Can you imagine that we don't produce a reliable birth-control pill in adequate quantities? Things would be much worse except for your efforts, Alexander Ivanovich," he added hastily.

"I do what I can," said Viktorov wearily. "But as you know, Arkadi, when it comes to budgetary allocations, my powers are limited, to put it mildly. You don't have to tell me how bad things are. Lisogor, of course, is in charge of the consumer industries, and he should attend to these matters, putting the fear of God into the ministers, enforcing higher productivity norms and labor discipline in factories. But he is busying himself with everything but that."

They all kept silent for a moment, each having the same thought. This could not help but continue, with the man at the top incapacitated and unable to impart a sense of direction to the ship of state.

Remizov got up. "If we go on like this, we will start talking about something we should not. Remember me to Tatiana Maximovna when she gets back. Tomorrow morning I have to address the Moscow Party Bureau and should read the speech Loktionov has prepared for me. He is a good lad, but occasionally he gets careless. I did not check the last report before reading it, and it led to an embarrassment. I came to the bottom of the first page and was declaiming, 'Thus we see that the worldwide might and prestige of our Socialist Fatherland are . . . *Over.*' I stood there for a minute like an idiot, not understanding what it could be I was reading. They were beginning to titter in the audience, and then it dawned on me that I was supposed to turn the page over. So now I have to read my speeches before delivering them. Quite a nuisance."

"A good man, but a loafer," said Viktorov after the Moscow Party boss took his leave. "At least Remizov can laugh at himself. You write your own speeches, Mikhail, don't you?"

"For the most part. But honestly, what difference does it make?

Considering what we are saying in public, they all might be written by some hack from the propaganda department."

"It may be dull and repetitious, but believe me, it has a soothing effect on our people. They feel reassured that our leaders are united and speak the same language. When you hear of all the quarrels, scandals, and upheavals that go on in the politics of the so-called democratic countries, it must have a very unsettling effect on their people. That is probably why they have so much crime, terror, drugs, and pornography. For all their alleged and famous freedom, do you believe, dear Mikhail, that the average American or Englishman is happier than the Soviet man or woman?"

"Not from what I have seen, Alexander Ivanovich. We may occasionally stray from the path leading to a better and fuller life; they have no sense of going anywhere. Their 'freedom' is like one of those wooden idols our distant ancestors used to worship. They sacrifice to it and perform meaningless rituals to propitiate the democratic god, but it does not bring them happiness or endow their lives with meaning."

Was Viktorov pursuing this line of conversation to find out whether Kondratiev, in his heart of hearts, was not really a reformer and once on top, would turn out to be another Khrushchev?

But perhaps not. The old man's thoughts seemed to be lost in the past. "I am glad you agree with me, Mikhail. You know the Westerners much better than I do. But when I was very young, I came close to believing in that freedom of theirs—I thought we would have several parties in this country—no bourgeois ones of course—and a real parliament. Then when I listened to and read Lenin, I realized what nonsense that so-called democratic freedom was. But some of our young people—like my grandnephew Igor Lisitsin and your Pavel, Mikhail—why isn't it clear to them that Western democracy is but a sham and nonsense?"

"They are young. They will learn in time, as we did. I don't know Lisitsin. Pavel brought him but once to our house. But my son—he is not a dissident; he is, well, a private person. It is difficult for the youngsters to understand what socialism has meant to the likes of you and me. They have had such an easy life. And—"

"Go on."

"They cannot understand how we could have gone through everything we did under Josif Vissarionovich—how it could have happened."

"Ah, Nikita Sergeievich," Viktorov nodded. "He said either too much or not enough about that."

"We would not let him say more," Kondratiev reminded him.

"Sometimes I wonder whether we were right—not, of course, in getting rid of Nikita—he was turning everything upside down—but in not explaining how people like you and me could go on serving him. What would have happened in the twenties with Rykov, Trotsky, and Zinoviev at each other's throats? *He* saved socialism. And even with those dreadful things in the thirties, how could we have gotten rid of *him*, knowing that the war was coming? The country would have fallen apart—it came pretty close to it in the summer of '41."

Viktorov got up and paced around the room as if the recollection of Stalin made him imitate the tyrant's mannerisms. "No, don't go yet, Mikhail. Have another brandy. There is something I must tell you."

He poured himself a glass of vodka, something Kondratiev had seen very rarely during the last few years, and, even more unprecedentedly, drank it at one gulp.

"I know what you want, and if I am around, I shall certainly lend all my efforts to help you get it. You have some ideas I don't agree with, but I suppose we must move with the times. You understand our Russian people, and that takes more than being an efficient Party worker like Smirnov. You know the world. I think you'll make it, even without my vote. And I may not be around when the choice will be made."

"Absurd, Alexander Ivanovich. You are in the best shape of us all—"

"Without boasting, I have indeed felt perfectly well . . . until now . . . Tatiana Maximovna—it is not arthritis this time. The doctors give her six months. I've been able to work ten, twelve hours a day at my age, because I always knew I would find her home waiting for me. Without her, I'll be a lost old man, and that not for long."

"Doctors can be wrong, and medicine now moves with miraculous speed."

"Not in this case. You may say, 'You're an old Bolshevik,

Viktorov. It is your duty to go on serving, no matter what.' But this is not softness or senile sentimentality. Even though I took that extra drink, I am stating what I believe are the facts and figures about her and myself. I know I can count on your discretion. She herself does not know yet."

All of which was spoken in an absolutely even tone of voice. He might have been quoting the latest indexes of production.

Viktorov continued, "And I am telling you this for a very practical reason—something bearing on what we were discussing a few moments ago. If and when you become the leader, you will have to decide what to do with the image of that man; as the poet Tvardovsky wrote, 'like a dread spirit he hovered over us.'

For a long time, I believed what Leontiev used to say: 'Don't talk or write about him. In time, the memory of those horrors will fade away. What will be remembered will be the achievements, how he helped to make us a mighty industrial nation, how he held everything together to make victory possible in the Fatherland War.' But I no longer believe that: his ghost still hovers over us, and that is why our young people are cynical and lack the passionate faith in socialism that inspired our generation when we were young. You, as the leader, might have to exorcise this ghost. Whether and how you would decide to do it, I don't know. But perhaps it would help if I told you what I know about the events that preceded Josif Vissarionovich's death. Should I?"

Was there anything that really needed telling? wondered Kondratiev. He had heard a lot from Khrushchev, but had Nikita told all? He shrugged his shoulders: "I did hear that he was planning a new purge and other insane things, such as resettling Jews from the big cities in Siberia. But I never knew whether this was all true, or one of those fibs with which Nikita Sergeievich used to regale us."

"It was true enough. Whether he would have gone ahead with it is another matter. There were days when he was clearly demented, others when he was his old cruel but rational self. We, the senior members of the Politburo, decided that, for once, we would stand up to him. Take advantage of his resignation, proclaim Malenkov as the new general secretary . . . No, we were not planning to do away with him—our people, for the most part, still worshiped him, and any suspicion that Stalin had met with foul play would have convulsed the country. He would just be retired as Honorary Chairman of the Party, or something."

"It never would have worked," said Kondratiev with conviction.

"Of course not. One of us, that drunkard Bulganin, or Beria with his own schemes, would have given away the whole story. It probably would have turned into another 1937, only worse, because although he could still kill, he no longer had the stamina to hold the thing together. But most of us were desperate . . . We were planning the coup for March 15."

Mikhail Alexandrovich recalled his original reaction to the announcement of Stalin's death. "And then he saved you the trouble. He always had an excellent sense of timing."

"That he did. But before he died, I heard him say something that I must repeat to you."

Kondratiev sat up: "But how could he have said anything? He remained in a coma until—"

"Let me begin with the setting. I was in my office the night of March 1, when at 10:15 I got a call from Nikita Sergeievich. Would I pick him up immediately in my car? Could I drive it myself? Imagine that—a Politburo member driving his own car. Fortunately I was probably the only one of the bunch who could drive—I liked to take Tatiana for picnics without a chauffeur or bodyguard dragging along. But you can understand what must have gone through my mind. The jig was up! I kept a Smith-Wesson from my Civil War days in a drawer in the desk, and before I left I put it in my coat pocket. In the car Nikita told me we were going straight to the Boss's dacha. The commandant of his bodyguards had called him to say that something had happened to Comrade Stalin, possibly a stroke. We arrived there before other senior members of the Politburo. The commandant was almost incoherent, but somehow we got the details of the story. Alone, Stalin was in the habit in the evenings of ringing for his tea precisely at eight o'clock. When no call came, after another half hour or so, his favorite servant—she worshiped him and had free access to his study at any time—rushed in and found him lying on the floor between that wide sofa on which he used to nap or lie reading and the little round table with all those telephones.

"Just at this point of the story, the commandant was interrupted by the maid, Matryona Semyonovna, who burst in shrieking, 'He is dying! He is dying, and they won't call a doctor.' I asked the commandant why he had not summoned medical help. He stammered out that Comrade Beria had told him to do nothing until members of the Politburo arrived and decided on further steps. Honestly, I wished him dead, but something in me argued that this was not the way. I told the commandant that, Beria or no Beria, he would answer with his head unless he immediately called the nearest available physicians, and in the meantime I alone was going to stay with the sick man. I went in—he was still lying unattended in the same spot, unconscious, but breathing. I leaned over him: 'Josif Vissarionovich, can you hear me?' He opened his eyes and mumbled a few barely intelligible words, then passed out again. Two doctors came in and, though frightened to death, they managed to undress him and put him in bed, gave him some shots, and started an examination. I went into the hall where he used to hold those late-night dinners. The others were already there, and they looked at me as if I had taken leave of my senses. Beria said, 'I did not realize you were such a Christian, Alexander Ivanovich.' I did not bother to answer, but ordered the commandant to call several professors from the Academy of Medicine. Those two with Stalin were just local practitioners. We sat there silently until the doctors delivered their preliminary diagnosis: chances of survival, fifty-fifty, but almost inevitably a permanent impairment of brain and locomotion. Malenkov then suddenly found his voice and told them to stay with the sick man until the professors and the ambulance got there. He then proposed we go back to the Kremlin and discuss various contingencies.

"Once back, Beria turned on me again: 'What if he partly recovers? That would be the worst of all. You and your precious wife will go first.' Honestly, I myself was of two minds: I wished him dead but felt that not even a dog should be left unattended under those circumstances."

Viktorov paused and reflected: "It is probably because I really wished him dead that I pushed out of my mind the possibility of what actually happened after we left the dacha. The commandant placed the two doctors under guard in the guest house. Members of the Medical Academy were notified that Comrade Stalin's condition did not seem serious and that their services would not be required until nine in the morning."

"The autopsy showed he would have died in any case," said Kondratiev. "Frankly, Alexander Ivanovich, I don't know what I would have done in your place. Quite possibly I would not even have summoned the doctors. At the time, I was sure my days were numbered."

"I am not telling you the story because I feel any pangs of conscience. It was good for the country and for socialism that he died when he did."

There was another pause. Viktorov looked away from Kondratiev: "I have told you all this to explain how I happened to hear what his last words were when I was alone with him. Something that must have been in Georgian, then 'Nadezhda'—"

"His wife's name," said Kondratiev quite needlessly, feeling increasing agitation.

"Undoubtedly. Then again an unintelligible sound, followed by 'Mironovich.' "

"Kirov?"

"Probably. Then some more sounds I could not distinguish, and then—I could not swear, but it sounded like—'ask Kondratiev.' That was all. I may have misheard."

Viktorov glanced at Kondratiev, then looked again at the bust of Lenin on top of the bookcase. "Look, Misha, at eighty, having lived through what we have during all those years, one learns not to ask certain questions. If you have an explanation, please keep it to yourself. No one else has heard this story, or even knows that he recovered consciousness and tried to talk; no one ever will. I would not have told it tonight, except in view of what may lie ahead for you."

"And if the explanation touched on something that makes me unfit to lead the Party?"

"Having known you for forty years, that is something I absolutely would refuse to believe. None of us has completely clean hands. I countersigned Politburo resolutions that resulted in the deaths of men I knew were innocent. I wouldn't have been able to save them anyway, and it would only have doomed me and sentenced Tatiana Maximovna to rot in a camp. Nothing twenty-two-year-old Misha Kondratiev did could approach that. What is past is past. Let's observe its lessons and look to the future. You must."

Kondratiev got up. "It's past midnight. I am deeply grateful not only for what you just said, but also for what you've been to me for the last forty years."

"It would be un-Russian to end the evening with the bottle on the table still unfinished," smiled Viktorov.

Mikhail Alexandrovich had never before known him to stress that aspect of Slavic hospitality. But he understood that with what was happening to his wife, the old man dreaded being alone, so though feeling utterly exhausted emotionally, he sat down. They talked for another hour and a half: what one could really expect from the Americans; from the Chinese ("Another reason I am glad I have no grandchildren," said Viktorov with a sad smile); whether some of their marshals were not getting too big for their britches; and similar subjects usually covered by what Kuliabko described as "Politburo chatter."

Finally, Kondratiev definitely excused himself, and his host, again uncharacteristically, embraced him and kissed him on both cheeks.

He reached home at three o'clock and was amazed to find Irina waiting for him, something that had not happened on similar occasions for years.

"You knew where I was and that I would be late. Why aren't you in bed?"

"I wanted to remind you about flying to Kiev at eight in the morning," she tried to explain.

"Yes, and my secretary would not be here to fetch me, and my plane would take off without me! For Heaven's sake, Irina—"

"I sometimes forget about those things. I thought . . . Good night, dear."

At least she hadn't said what was obviously on her mind: "You haven't been yourself lately, and I was worried." Damn women and their intuition!

It was only in the plane that he felt clearheaded enough to try to make sense of Viktorov's tale. He thought back to what Stalin had said to him the last time they met: Didn't the Church teach that a single act of contrition might atone for all the evil perpetrated during one's lifetime? Could the dying man have been seized by a delusion that he was making a confession? Ivan the Terrible had been a very religious man, but those were different times and people then really believed in an afterlife. The idea was absurd to Mikhail Kondratiev, who had been brought up as a Communist and an atheist. But Stalin had gone to a church seminary and obviously had absorbed all that mumbo jumbo when he was young, probably even believed it until his early teens. Wouldn't Viktorov have been struck by the same thought: he was fifteen at the time of the Revolution and must have had religion drilled into him as a schoolkid. Just suppose—what a ludicrous scene it would have been: an old Bolshevik pretending to be giving absolution to *him*! Mikhail Alexandrovich could not quite remember whether the Orthodox Church allowed any layman—and an atheist to boot—to grant absolution in the absence of a priest and *in periculo mortis*. Undoubtedly a contentious question among the theologians.

"Ask Kondratiev." Did Viktorov guess what it was about? With his still phenomenal memory, he must remember the Solovyov Report. Would that have given him a clue?

The scraping of the wheels on the runway jarred Kondratiev's mind back into the present. When the plane had stopped, he went from his own cabin to the larger one occupied by his staff, and tapped his new private assistant, Firlin, on the shoulder.

"Denis, I would like you to call my wife's office right here from the airport and leave a message that I would be grateful if she could offer excuses for both of us for tonight's reception and wait for me at home. I should be back by nine, ten at the latest."

The young man hastened on his errand, reflecting to himself that he would never have suspected his boss was endowed with so much vigor and passion. He was evidently impatient for his wife's embraces, and to hasten the intimacy was ready to forgo what would undoubtedly be the high point of Moscow's social life this season: a great Kremlin reception in honor of the visiting president of France.

Kondratiev, in the meantime, bearing an expression combining an appropriate blend of hauteur and affability, was conversing with a group of Ukrainian Party and government leaders gathered on the tarmac, their faces displaying that attention and deference with which local notables are supposed to greet a visiting semidivinity from Moscow. Only Vishnevsky, in view of his status as the visitor's Politburo colleague, permitted himself a faint smile, looking at Kondratiev to his right as they stood amid the semicircle formed by the others. After the cameras stopped grinding, the whole party got into limousines to be driven to the seat of the Ukrainian Central Committee.

Once in the same car with Vishnevsky, Mikhail Alexandrovich dropped his pose of affability. There was no point in being civil to a man whom he despised and who, unless convinced of the inevitability of Kondratiev's succession, would be among his opponents. On the contrary, a rude and direct manner was the only way of impressing his kind.

"Dmitri Vasilievich," he went straight to the unpleasant matter, "this business of Catholic priests' being beaten or disappearing has got to stop. The news does leak out abroad, and we must be careful in our relations with the Vatican, not to mention other considerations. The Catholic church has been a moderating influence in Poland."

Vishnevsky spread his hands in a helpless gesture: "We do take measures against the Ukrainian Uniate church. We don't recognize its existence. Its underground priests are the main propagators of anti-Soviet Ukrainian separatism. But as to the violent incidents, believe me, Mikhail Alexandrovich, they have never been sanctioned by me. It has been the KGB."

"Come, come, Andronnikov has assured me he has instructed the local security organs to display the utmost sensitivity in dealing with the problem. You are the boss here, Dmitri Vasilievich. We no longer live in the times of Josif Vissarionovich and Beria. And if these and other abuses do not cease, I shall have to place the matter on the agenda of the Politburo and the Central Committee."

After a brief formal speech in which Kondratiev congratulated the Ukrainian committee, "so ably led by Comrade Vishnevsky," for their successes in combating "bourgeois nationalism, religious obscurantism, and all other attempts to sow dissension between the fraternal nations of our great country," he held a closed meeting with the top leaders, where he delivered a scathing disquisition in line with his previous remarks to Vishnevsky. Some, including the latter, protested feebly that much of the separatist unrest was due to the fact that the people in the western part of the union republic were able to receive radio and television broadcasts originating in Poland.

"When will we put an end to the continuing denigration of socialism that pervades some broadcasts from Warsaw and other Polish stations?" asked one of the officials. "Obviously, their own government is still not fully able to suppress that anarchic and anti-Socialist legacy of Solidarity."

"The Politburo of the Central Committee will decide on appropriate measures when they are indicated, and it will acquaint you with the proposed course of action when it sees fit to do so. For the time being, it behooves all of you, beginning with the first secretary," he nodded in the direction of Vishnevsky, who tried not very successfully to conceal his inner rage, "to show both more vigilance and greater sensitivity to your people's needs and feelings. Then you will not be getting into all those difficulties, no matter what happens in Poland or elsewhere."

"We are all grateful to Comrade Kondratiev for the directives he has transmitted to us on behalf of the Politburo of the Communist Party of the Soviet Union," said Vishnevsky in an almost normal tone of voice. "Comrades, let each of us be guided in his work by these wise precepts, and we humbly thank you, Mikhail Alexandrovich, for the incisive way you have presented them to us."

He will be among the first men I'll drop if I get a chance, thought Kondratiev.

There followed a sumptuous lunch, but the atmosphere was hardly relaxed. Mikhail Alexandrovich insisted on cutting down on the number of toasts with different kinds of vodkas and wines.

"I thank you for your truly Slavic hospitality, but an example must be set from the top if we are to combat that veritable curse of alcoholism that has gripped so many of our people."

Most present took it as an unmistakable reference to Vishnevsky, who had already undergone several "cures," after which he would invariably lapse back into the habit.

Then a brief visit to a factory where the visiting potentate addressed a few impromptu remarks to the workers, urging them to feel free to voice their needs and grievances and, if their petitions were not handled promptly on the local level, to address them directly to the Central Committee in Moscow.

"He is acting as if he were already the Chief," whispered Vishnevsky to his friend and boon companion from the Ukrainian government, as they stood smiling and waving at Kondratiev's plane as it started to taxi down the runway.

"Would it be so bad if he did make it?"

"You and I would soon be on our asses, if not in a worse place," replied the First Secretary of the Central Committee of the Communist Party of the Ukraine, in a gloomy tone of voice.

Once in the air, Kondratiev's morning impulse to have a serious talk with Irina as to whether he should strive for the top melted away. She really did not understand politics, and he still would not be able to bring himself to talk about the thing in his past. Besides, his sense of mission had been revived by what he had just seen and heard, not that it came as a surprise. The Ukraine was being run practically as a personal fief of Vishnevsky's. His son was a deputy minister of light industry; a brother-in-law was in charge of the housing construction trust for the city of Kiev. It would be interesting to examine those comrades' financial accounts. And most of the local bigwigs followed their leader's example.

He was home shortly before nine. Irina greeted him with a pleased but puzzled expression.

"But ought we not go to the reception? All of Moscow's most important people are supposed to be there with their wives. People will wonder if they don't see your name in the paper among those present."

"Not necessarily. My lightning Kiev trip was publicized. I might have been delayed, and we do get occasionally fatigued and indisposed. But I did not have a chance to see you this morning and apologize for my rude behavior last night. I wanted to do it right after I got back. And we should have a chat. Some of the things I've told you about myself are not true."

Her face expressed neither shock nor surprise, only compassion as he confessed that, in spite of everything he had adamantly sworn all those years, he had signed a false deposition in December 1934.

Irina kissed him. "How could you have let it torture you all those years? I am glad you did it. You would not be here otherwise. I was a toddler then, but I've had close relatives and friends who have told me what it was like and what they suffered. You would not have saved anyone by not signing . . ." She hesitated, then added, "But please, don't tell Pavel. It might push him to do something quite unreasonable."

She was so understanding that he almost felt like telling her the other, the main thing about the night of December 1, 1934. Instead, he said, "I know you have reservations on the subject, but I must go on trying for the top prize. I believe it is my duty. Does this still frighten you?"

She burst out laughing, flashing him back to the thought that it was silly to discuss politics with Irina. "Mikhail, you know that I really don't understand these things. If it would amuse you to be the general secretary . . . Do let's go to the reception. They might think that some Ukrainian beauty has detained you in Kiev. We can catch the end of the reception, and then, of course, there's *Swan Lake*. I must have seen it more than ninety times. Why can't they come up with some other ballet or opera on these occasions?"

He had been right: it was hopeless to try to discuss politics seriously with her. But she was right about the reception.

"We wondered where you were, Misha," said Leontiev, taking him to meet the president and his wife. "You are the only one of us who can speak French."

And indeed, the French leader greeted Kondratiev warmly, recalling their previous meetings: "We think of you as almost a Parisian by adoption."

His entourage was most complimentary about Irina's appearance and dress, and for all his myriad other concerns, Mikhail Alexandrovich could not help noticing once again how she stood out among the drab-looking wives of his colleagues, some of whom, with rather comic effect, were trying their rudimentary French on the visitors.

On the way back from the theater, he did begin to feel exhausted. Once home, his wife said rather too casually, "How do they expect men of your age to go through what you have during the last forty-eight hours? You must not have a single ounce of energy left."

"Let me show you whether I do," he said grimly, and followed her into her bedroom, ignoring Irina's protests that she wanted to undress in peace.

Afterward she patted him on the cheek. "I knew that was on your mind in the first place when you wanted to skip the reception." She fell asleep instantly.

He felt a strong temptation to wake her up and tell the other part of the story. No, he just could not. He tiptoed out of her room to his own bed. Sleep would not come. "Ask Kondratiev." Should he have spoken up when Stalin died? But he was in no position then. His own career had almost come to an abrupt end after that man's death.

CHAPTER 9

MOSCOW AND ABROAD, MARCH 1953–OCTOBER 1964

It was only in the car, being driven home, that Kondratiev began to think about the immediate future, and his own place in it. It was extremely odd that the Politburo had not been called into session immediately on the news of Stalin's stroke, which had evidently taken place on the night of March 1. Were the old boys taking over and shoving all the newcomers, elected like him last October, aside? By what right? Certainly, Beria had spoken confidently, as if he were expecting to run the show, even though in fact he had not been in charge of the security forces for at least a year. No, it was inconceivable that any single person, let alone Beria, could take over. If Beria were somehow to inherit power, Kondratiev's relief would have been much, much too premature. On second thought, he decided to stop at the ministry.

Instead of the single militiaman who had been on duty when Kondratiev left in the afternoon, a detachment of security troops now barred entrance to the building.

"I must ask you for your pass, Comrade," asked the lieutenant in charge, though seeing the limousine, he obviously recognized whom he was dealing with.

"Here is my pass," said Kondratiev, pushing the man so hard that he staggered and almost fell. The soldiers quickly stepped aside and let him enter. From his office he tried calling Ignatiev, and finally reached him at his home.

"I am as much in the dark as you are, Mikhail Alexandrovich. I was handed a decree of the Presidium of the Supreme Soviet which subordinates me to Comrade Beria, and he has relieved me of command of the security forces."

What a moron, thought Kondratiev, putting down the receiver. The Presidium of the Supreme Soviet had last met six weeks ago. He phoned Viktorov's office; Comrade Chairman of the State Planning Commission was attending the meeting of the Executive Committee of the Politburo, he was told. *What* Executive Committee? he felt like shouting. There was no such thing. And so it was a virtual palace revolution.

What was going to happen to him? Kondratiev rapidly calculated: fourteen new men had been added to the Politburo Presidium last October. What if he rounded them up and together they all demanded a meeting of the *full* Politburo, as they had every right to do? Hopeless! Most of the fourteen had been protégés of Malenkov's, and he undoubtedly was with *them*—Beria had always had some strange hold over him, even of late when Stalin had turned against the scoundrel. At any rate, Viktorov remained within the inner circle, and he would not let Kondratiev be thrown to the wolves, or more precisely, to Beria. He might become a plant manager somewhere. Which would be better than what had been clearly in the cards. He wondered idly what it might have been: probably curtains; in view of what Kondratiev knew, he would have hardly been sent to a camp where he might babble out the secret. Was Stalin really going to die? What if there was partial recovery? Mikhail Alexandrovich was in a foul mood as he left the ministry. The lieutenant approached him, but not too closely.

"I am sorry not to have recognized you, Comrade Minister. My instructions—"

"Get out of my way." On the way home he kept seeing security troops marching toward the center of the town and taking stations in front of public buildings. What did they think the people might do? Try to storm the Kremlin? If they had that much spirit, they would have done it long ago.

"Trofim," he said, "Comrade Stalin has been stricken and may not recover."

"It would be a great loss," replied his chauffeur, without any note of surprise or sorrow in his voice. "He has worked so hard for the common people and our whole country."

"Do you think that without him people might become confused and riot?"

"They know that he would not die before appointing a worthy man to succeed him, and the people would follow him as they now follow Comrade Stalin," proclaimed Trofim, firmly.

There you have folk wisdom, thought Kondratiev, irritably. What a nation!

Xenia was still up. Without any preliminaries, and curious of her reaction, he tossed out, "Stalin is dying. It will be announced tomorrow."

Stupefaction was followed by tears. "It cannot be, Misha. Misha, what is going to happen to us?"

"We shall survive." Of course, the joke was completely lost on her.

"I now understand why you have been so withdrawn and morose of late. He has always been so kind and considerate to us."

"I think you have met him, let us see, three times." He poured himself a drink, and began to feel ashamed of his enjoyment of the scene. The doctor in Xenia reappeared, and she began to ask about the details. He told her the little that he knew. The tears were succeeded by a look of horror on her face.

"They must have poisoned him," Xenia said all at once, "given him pills that stimulate high blood pressure."

"Who?"

"The murderer doctors. They evidently did not catch all of them."

"Nonsense." Still, Kondratiev sat up—who the devil really knew what had been going on of late; the charges against the doctors were absurd, yet Beria and some others were capable of anything. He added in a softer voice. "No one would have dared to try to harm Comrade Stalin."

"You would certainly think so. Who is attending our beloved Leader?"

"Practically the whole Academy of Medicine is sitting in—" Here he caught himself. They were told, God knows why, not to reveal that he had been stricken in his suburban dacha. "In the Kremlin. And now Xenia, I would like to have something to eat. We all must keep up our strength for the hard days ahead."

Later on, Xenia came to his bedroom. It would be a sacrilege at a time like this, he told her.

"What a mess. We are meeting and arguing practically all the time," said Viktorov on entering his office, where Kondratiev had been awaiting him for more than an hour. It was the day after Stalin's funeral. Malenkov was officially Number 1, but was he really? He had been named Prime Minister; at the same time, it was announced that he had resigned as a secretary of the Central Committee. Beria was again minister of state security. The Politburo was reduced to twelve, with Lunin the only newcomer from last October who had been retained.

"Quite a spectacle yesterday," began Kondratiev, realizing how platitudinous he sounded. After having been, formally at least, one of the most important people in the country, he was now among the legion of former bigwigs awaiting a decision on their fate.

"Yes, quite a spectacle," repeated Viktorov. "Two hundred twenty-nine people trodden to death in the rush to see the hearse. Even when he is no longer alive, he is still killing people. . . . Look, Mikhail Alexandrovich, I know what is on your mind. You will have to give up the ministry. I fought against it, but was outvoted."

"The Politburo now actually votes on appointments?"

"Yes, collective leadership is the word. But maybe not for long. Go and see Comrade Khrushchev. If nothing else comes up, there will always be a place for you on the Planning Commission."

Why Khrushchev? But it was embarrassing to go on asking questions, and Viktorov was clearly impatient to get back to his work.

As he waited in the secretary's reception room, Kondratiev felt a slight pinprick of nostalgia for the terrible old times: you couldn't be sure what would happen to you from day to day, yet while it lasted you did have a sense of power, and your fate depended on *him*, and not on votes and the whims of people like Khrushchev, a good man, but something of a boor. Then he felt shivers running down his spine—was he out of his mind? Only one week before, he had thought of shooting himself; and how about the poor, long-suffering Russian people?

"Come in, dear Misha, come in." Khrushchev was pumping his hand and practically dragging him into his office. There, he sank into his chair and spoke into the intercom: he was not to be disturbed. "Yes, even Comrade Malenkov." He turned to Kondratiev. "Ouf! Thank God it is over. But we have quite a job cut out for us. What was that place in ancient Greece full of horseshit?"

"The Augean stables."

"Yes, those stables. Our late beloved Leader referred to them a few times. He liked to show off that he had studied Greek in that seminary. Well, we have to clean up all that filth that has accumulated. The man was quite mad during the last two years; a few more weeks, and heads would have started rolling again."

"Very likely, my own among them."

"What makes you think so?"

Kondratiev told him that his last interview with Stalin had left him with a definite impression that his days were numbered.

Khrushchev studied his face for a while. "That is curious. Only two days before his stroke, he was telling Bulganin and me that he planned to resign as prime minister, and what would we think of you as a possible replacement? Never mind. He *was* mad. But unfortunately, some of my colleagues on the Presidium believe that you were one of those who gave him that absurd idea about the 'murderer doctors.' "

"That is absolutely false and preposterous!" shouted Kondratiev.

"Viktorov and I protested that we didn't believe it. We have known you as an honest Communist who would not dirty his hands with a vile intrigue. Of course, the doctors are completely innocent and will be released once they recover from the 'investigation.' But there is this very unfortunate letter."

"I have never written any letter concerning this wretched business."

"A letter to the procurator general saying that the writer has observed some of the accused doctors using impermissible methods of medication. It was signed by Xenia Yegorovna Kondratieva . . . You don't have to say anything, Misha. I can tell it all from your face."

There was a long pause. Then Khrushchev resumed. "Some, I don't have to tell you who in particular, wanted to clamp you down in jail. I said that we have done with punishing people for their relatives' real or alleged sins, and it was strange to hear such suggestions from Comrade Beria, seeing that he has recently become a champion of 'socialist legality.' There were voices urging that you be made to resign from the Central Committee. What do you say, Misha?"

"You can throw me out, but I shall not resign; that would be admitting I was an informer. I have served the Fatherland and the Party to the best of my ability."

"If you had said yes, you would resign, I would have no further truck with you. But now I agree with Viktorov. We cannot spare men like you. Give us some time. We will find a place suitable to your talents."

After a further pause, Mikhail Alexandrovich asked, "And my wife?"

"She will be called before the Party Control Commission and given a severe reprimand. It would be senseless to punish people harshly for mere stupidity, when those who have blood on their hands are still—" He broke off and began to laugh. "Eh, Misha, why do we need the Control Commission? You know what a Russian peasant would do to a wife who was giving him trouble. But I forgot, you are the son and grandson of *barins* [noblemen]. You would not dream of striking a woman. Let us have a drink. Just one to the better times. I wake up at night and still think it has been a dream; the telephone will ring and I'll hear that Georgian voice on the line. I have to pinch myself."

The better times did not come immediately for Kondratiev. On April 1, it was announced that "Comrade Kondratiev, M. A., has, at his own request, been relieved of the duties of Minister of Heavy Industry." The next day he was informed he must vacate his apartment and dacha by the end of the month. How did one go about finding a place to live? Ever since 1935—no, he corrected himself—since December 1, 1934, he had been *provided* with living quarters. Pride forbade him to inquire of friends, and immediately following the announcement, the number of those who could be qualified as such dwindled rapidly and prodigiously. Many who had previously fawned on him began to give him a wide berth. He had been heartened, but also ashamed, that the Perventsevs, whom he had seen infrequently since that scene with Xenia three years before, called him the very day of the dismissal to invite him to dinner.

At the Perventsevs he was introduced to one of the people who were now being released en masse from the camps, a biology professor whom he had met while in Kazan. The man barely acknowledged his greeting, and shortly after the dinner excused himself, saying that a lot of things had happened in biology during the thirteen years he had been away, as he put it, and he must study every night to catch up before he assumed his appointment at the institute.

"He looked at me as if it was I who had sent him away," said Kondratiev.

Pavel swallowed hard. "There are those rumors about you—"

"That I was one of the main instigators of the forthcoming purge, I know." He told them about Xenia's letter and that he was now determined to divorce her, but that he could not do it at a time when, among other unpleasantness, her medical license had been suspended pending the investigation of charges of unprofessional conduct, and she was in a state approaching a breakdown.

"Very few people in your position would have hesitated on that count," observed Valeria, and for the first time that evening looked at him with some of the old warmth.

He still repaired, on occasion, to the ministry; his successor, who treated him courteously—no doubt on Viktorov's instructions—required his advice on several matters. But when on one such errand Kondratiev sought to remove his remaining personal papers, an assistant minister barred his way to the safe.

"You cannot poke among official papers here, Comrade Kondratiev." When he explained that those were his personal letters and such, this formerly most servile creature had smiled venomously: "We still cannot release them. The Ministry of State Security may be interested in your correspondence. There have been great changes recently, Comrade Kondratiev, or haven't you heard?"

And indeed, Beria seemed to be in ascendance, his men being promoted to ministerial posts both at the center and in the union republics, spouting pieties about 'socialist legality,' playing up heavily to the non-Russian elements in the Party, clearly overshadowing both the colorless Malenkov and Molotov, now foreign minister again, but with no power base within the Party. Kondratiev wondered whether the hopes he had put in Khrushchev's protection might have been unrealistic. How could Nikita Sergeievich, well liked but always thought to be rather simpleminded by the more sophisticated members of the elite, prevail over a seasoned intriguer and scoundrel like Beria? And was the latter also responsible for the fact that Kondratiev had not heard from Viktorov about a job in the commission? He was still a member of the Central Committee—or was he? For two weeks now, he had not received the confidential weekly communiqué routinely distributed to its members about developments in domestic and foreign affairs. He might have to seek a job as an engineer, probably in the provinces.

And then came unmistakable signs that Mikhail Alexandrovich's pessimism had been premature. All of a sudden, a call came from the borough housing office: Would Comrade Kondratiev care to examine the new apartment being assigned to him and see whether it met his needs? It was in another building, housing high officials, though most of them below the ministerial rank, and was smaller than his present place, but in some ways it was more comfortable. The confidential bulletin of the Central Committee made its appearance in the small office he still retained in the ministry. And on what was to be his last visit there, he was not only handed a packet with his personal papers but informed by his beaming successor that there was to be a party in his honor.

"You did not think, dear Mikhail Alexandrovich, that we would let you leave us without showing the respect and affection in which the whole staff holds you, as well as wishing you Godspeed in the important job our government and Party are about to entrust to you."

The reptile who, on the previous occasion, had barred Kondratiev's access to his personal papers was profuse with apologies. It was clear that he had been working for the Security Ministry all along.

On April 21 came the announcement: The Presidium of the Supreme Soviet has appointed Comrade M. A. Kondratiev to be a deputy minister of foreign affairs and the representative of the USSR on the Security Council of the United Nations.

"It was something of a battle," confided Khrushchev when the new deputy minister called to express his thanks. "Beria kept bringing up this episode from 1934 and repeating, 'But what about the man's past?' Son of a bitch! One of these days we'll take a good look at his past! Molotov was worried whether, in view of your previous high position in the Party, you might not act too independently, and also whether your 'American background,' as he put it, would not make you vulnerable to the Americans' tricks. I said, 'Look,

Vyacheslav, on the first count, let us be done with those ambassadors who did not dare as much as let out a fart without getting a prior authorization from our dear departed Josif Vissarionovich. On the second, I know that you believe the capitalists would not respect us if we sent people there who know their ways and speak their language, rather than glaring and baring their teeth at them. But there is such a thing as scaring the West too much. The Americans are so mad about the war in Korea dragging on and on, they might go berserk. For now, we must speak more softly. Once we are strong enough, it will be a different story. Kondratiev fills the bill.' He finally let himself be persuaded."

"It does not look as if working with Comrade Molotov would be a bed of roses."

Khrushchev explained that Kondratiev's instructions would be coming from the Politburo—in fact, there was an unmistakable hint, from himself. ("Where was Malenkov in the whole scheme?" wondered Mikhail Alexandrovich.) Stalin's erstwhile closest collaborator was being kept as foreign minister, so the capitalists would not get the idea that Soviet foreign policy would change in a hurry.

"Give the old bastard his due: he knew how to scare the Americans."

Whatever Molotov told him, he was to be accommodating toward the Americans "without letting them imagine for a moment that we are ready to kiss their ass," and to make friends with the representatives of those new members of the UN from the Third World.

"Of course, they are mostly riffraff, but we must humor them: they could be useful in making trouble for the capitalists and distracting them from plotting against us."

Khrushchev took off his glasses and sighed. "The next few years are not going to be easy. The Americans are about to start arming their Germans. Our Chinese comrades have grown even more cheeky since Stalin died. Now they demand we give them fantastic sums in credits, and modern weapons free of charge, including the Bomb. It is sheer blackmail—they know we cannot afford to let the West know how things really stand between us and Mao. He is a maniac, just like our own late beloved Leader. And what a mess *he* has left us with at home. . . . We could use you here, Misha, but for the time being, it is better all around to be in foreign affairs. . . . You are still on the Central Committee. It is not going to be a rubber-stamp operation, as before. Beria and Malenkov will soon find that out, if they try any tricks."

"I am glad to serve the country in whatever capacity the Party thinks fit. And you may count on my support, Nikita Sergeievich, for your efforts to heal our society and guide it along the path prescribed by Lenin."

The interview with Molotov went off rather well. For most of it, the foreign minister was all business: The Soviet UN representative was to intimate to the U.S. that Moscow would advise the People's Republic to seek a truce in Korea, but of course the decision was up to the Chinese and North Koreans. They would begin, but cautiously, to be on speaking terms again with the Yugoslavs and Israelis. The latter presented an especially delicate problem, since they must not offend the Arabs. Molotov passed on those instructions in his dry, pedantic way, but then said in a different tone: "It is a great comfort to me, Comrade Kondratiev, to have a man of your caliber and knowledge of the West as one of my deputies."

"I am grateful that you chose me, Vyacheslav Mikhailovich."

"There were objections. No one questioned your qualifications. But some referred to that unfortunate incident in your past . . . That was, I believe, when we first met."

"I would hardly call it a social occasion."

"No, it was a most regrettable occurrence. I pointed out that Comrade Stalin had always had the highest opinion of you, and he could read men's hearts and minds."

There was a moment of uncomfortable silence, while Molotov took off his pince-nez and dabbed at his eyes.

"You must wonder, Mikhail Alexandrovich, how I can say this in view of what I . . . I had to go through during the last few years. Well, he no longer was himself then. But how much do our nation and socialism owe to him? We must not forget that."

"Yes, the Soviet people will never forget what he has done."

"I know you mean it, Mikhail Alexandrovich. There are those who want to blame him for all the hardships we have gone through. Maybe there were errors here and there, but in the main, he did what had to be done."

It was pathetic to see the tyrant's once chief accomplice, lately intended victim, grow excited and speak as if he were pleading before some unseen tribunal judging men and events.

"There are those who used to lick his boots, but now want to desecrate his memory, throw dirt on our glorious past. We must never, never allow it." He quieted down and smiled at his visitor: "Forgive me. There are certain problems, as you must know, that we are having with our Chinese comrades . . ."

Who could have believed that the old "iron ass," as he was irreverently known within the inner circle, was capable of such outbursts of sentimentality? thought Kondratiev, going over his notes after the interview. He recalled the ancient pagan rite where the dead leader's slaves were immolated along with him. It was too bad that those Molotovs, Kaganoviches, Malenkovs, and the like could not have been dispatched that way. But one way or another, Russia would soon be rid of them. It was going to be—in many ways, it already was—a new Russia.

And he had a new wife. To his great relief, it was Xenia who had taken the initiative about divorce.

"I know that I damaged your career, and you feel I am a millstone around your neck. I believed I was doing my duty as a Party member, but times have changed."

Mikhail Alexandrovich protested feebly: their small children; being an ambassador and deputy minister was hardly a disgrace. No, she knew he no longer cared for her. They had hardly spoken for the last few months. Things could only go from bad to worse. He felt stirrings of compassion for the poor woman; it was not magnanimity, but still her concept of duty to the Party, that urged Xenia to give up being a high dignitary's wife. She had erred; she should no longer be an obstacle to the Socialist Fatherland's making full use of Misha's gifts. So he felt at the moment, and it was only later that he would occasionally suspect there might have been another and more charitable explanation for Xenia's action.

An equally unsentimental set of reasons led him to decide to marry Irina. She would make a very decorative wife, and officials' wives were now beginning to be seen in public. There would be those long periods abroad, where a man in his position could not afford a casual affair. Besides, she had stuck by him during the interminably long weeks when he seemed to be not only in disfavor but in danger of something far worse.

▬

The next few years flew by in a whirl of activity. Mikhail Alexandrovich traveled to the four corners of the globe, speaking at international conferences, negotiating. At the UN, he was an instant success.

"For the first time, the Soviets are being represented by a man of sophistication and undoubted charm. His stone-faced predecessor's vocabulary consisted mostly of variations on *nyet*. The new envoy, even when attacking a resolution proposed by one of the Western powers, does it in a way that is not offensive, and often quite witty. There seems to be a new spirit animating Soviet foreign policy," wrote *Time*.

A conservative magazine warned the American public about Kondratiev's honeyed words: "The form and approach are quite different, but behind those smiles and phrases about 'peaceful coexistence' lurks the same sinister design to conquer the world for godless Communism."

He arrived in the States at the height of the McCarthy period, and was soon able to report to Moscow that the Americans were too busy trying to catch their own real and alleged communists to pay much attention to what the USSR and communists were doing abroad.

Despite the especially strong anti-Soviet atmosphere, Kondratiev had no trouble in establishing correct relations with American officials, who preferred to deal with him, rather than with Filimonov, the Soviet ambassador in Washington. The latter, Mikhail Alexandrovich was not surprised to learn, kept bombarding Moscow about the unseemly behavior of the ambassador to the UN: he was clearly succumbing to the capitalists' blandishments, attending parties at their homes where, as confidential reports indicated, he would be quite indiscreet about what was going on in Russia. Indeed, Kondratiev and his Irina ("Mrs. Kondratiev is a dazzling refutation of the myth that Soviet officials' wives are always overweight, shabbily dressed, and kept in almost total seclusion," wrote a women's magazine) became quite popular with Manhattan hostesses.

"But tell me, Mr. Ambassador, was your Stalin anything like that awful Senator McCarthy of ours?" the wife of the president of one of the largest U.S. banks once asked him.

He was not going to comment on U.S. politics, answered the ambassador readily. But Generalissimo Stalin had been too preoccupied with government and military affairs to chase in person after real or alleged spies or subversives. It should be kept in mind that the USSR has nothing comparable to the American congressional committees, where a witness can be grilled without any regard to the judicial safeguards.

"I shall be frank with you. Just before the war, when we lived in constant apprehension of being invaded, our courts were often overhasty in dealing with people suspected of disloyalty to the country, and in some cases the verdicts rendered were indeed unjust. But all such cases have been reviewed, and people found innocent are being released and compensated for what they have endured. And as you must have read in your papers, those people who were guilty of offenses against socialist legality have been stripped of their official positions and summoned to face the court."

Beria, it had just been announced, had been arrested. On Kondratiev's visit home, Khrushchev described to him with some relish the scene at the meeting of the Politburo of the Central Committee: "After a few routine items I said, 'Facts have come to light that necessitate the suspension of Comrade Beria as a member of this body and referral of the case to the Party Control Commission.' Instead of leaving, he began screaming at Malenkov, 'You have betrayed me. Wait till they do the same to you!' I pressed the button, and the three officers who were waiting in the antechamber rushed in and carried him out shrieking, 'I could have had you all shot!' He was executed the same evening—behaved in a most undignified way, tried to get on his knees, and begged the major commanding the squad to remember that he was a marshal of the Soviet Union. The officer said, 'Marshals of the Soviet Union don't get down on their knees. Let him have it, boys.' The officer was promoted. Beria was not only a scoundrel, but a degenerate and coward." Khrushchev spat.

"I see we still cling to the story that he is going to be tried."

"Yes—socialist legality. There will be a few live defendants thrown in—his almost equally disgusting pals. The military are very happy, but at the same time they are making a fuss over trifles. Zhukov insists that Beria be stripped of his marshal's rank before he is sentenced, and that shooting is too good for that scum.

They should all be publicly hanged. I told them not to be pedantic."

The meeting in August 1953 of the Central Committee confirmed Khrushchev as First Secretary of the Party. It was obviously only a question of time before Malenkov would be pushed out as prime minister, but the new Party leader was still having troubles with his colleagues in the Politburo. They would not let him make a speech denouncing Stalin there and then.

In 1955, Malenkov was finally forced to resign, but to general surprise, it was the old drunkard Bulganin who succeeded him as prime minister, while his pudgy predecessor remained on the Politburo.

Much as he enjoyed his foreign assignment, Kondratiev hankered after a more active role in domestic politics. These were exciting times: a period for cleansing Soviet society of all the filth that had accumulated over the last thirty years, and stirring up the vital forces within the country after that awful era of fear and lies. He was forty-two years old and did not relish the idea of continuing indefinitely in the diplomatic service. It was not like when he had been a minister: then, you had a sense of personal achievement each time a new steel or automobile plant was put into production; you made decisions, appointments. Now, for the most part, his job consisted of carrying out other people's instructions, arguing with foreigners, attending those silly receptions.

His frustration increased when, in 1955, he became an almost constant companion of Khrushchev's and Bulganin's on their travels in the West. At home, Nikita Sergeievich's coarseness was, up to a point, excusable: it contributed to his popularity among the Central Committee members, gross creatures most of whom were, like Khrushchev, of peasant background. But abroad it was a real handicap. Kondratiev, who, apart from being the Foreign Ministry's representative, was also often enlisted as master of ceremonies, and, when the language was English, as interpreter, was subject to continuous embarrassment, as well as an occasional outburst of temper by his easily excitable boss.

"No, I am not going to say 'filth' instead of 'shit,' and if your gentlemanly background does not allow you to translate my speech properly, you will be sent back to Moscow to teach etiquette in the Institute for Diplomacy."

On the state visit to England, Khrushchev would not even

listen to his suggestion that it would be advisable to order dinner jackets and wear them to the dinner reception at 10 Downing Street.

"Someone like me wearing one of those bourgeois contraptions? Good God, Kondratiev, it would look like a saddle on a cow. My peasant parents would turn in their grave."

It was only with the utmost difficulty that he was persuaded that it would not be proper, on meeting the Queen, to embrace and kiss her on both cheeks. Mercifully, the visit to Windsor Castle passed without a disaster, and on the way back Nikita Sergeievich appeared pleased and impressed.

"They are cultured people," he said. "They give you real drinks, not like it was in India, where all we got at receptions was . . . orange juice. Remember, Nikolai?" He turned to Bulganin, who was showing the effects of "real" drinks.

"Huh?"

"There was a minister who told us that he drank a glass of his urine every morning, and it was a marvelous way to keep fit. How could a people like that stand up to the Chinese?"

Kondratiev looked at the representative of the Foreign Office who accompanied them and who understood Russian: his face betrayed a considerable strain to keep from going into convulsions.

"That Queen of theirs," resumed Khrushchev, reflectively, "she is quite a dish. I would not mind—"

Here Bulganin, now fully awake, smirked. "You're boasting, Nikita. When was the last time you did it?"

"That is between Nina Petrovna and myself, but I get an erection at least once a month," solemnly declared the First Secretary of the Central Committee of the Communist Party of the USSR.

At that point, the Englishman had rushed out of the compartment, clutching his face. Sounds of wild laughter erupted from the corridor, and Kondratiev himself and Bulganin broke down, Khrushchev giving them a hurt look.

Mikhail Alexandrovich's supposed fastidiousness was possibly responsible for the fact that it was Filimonov, rather than himself, who inherited the ministry when Molotov was finally sent packing.

"I can well understand why you would not want to serve under him," said Khrushchev, when Kondratiev asked for another job. "To us, Filimonov's constant frown suggests that he probably is perpetually constipated. But for a foreign minister, that puss is an asset. One look at it, and the capitalists become frightened . . .

You would still report directly to me . . . Well then, how would you like to be Chairman of the Council on Cultural and Scientific Relations with Non-Socialist Countries?"

Kondratiev had hoped for something bigger, but under the circumstances the job was not bad: it carried with it a minister's rank, and in view of the growing intercourse with the West, the council's functions were becoming important.

Unlike most of the delegates to the Twentieth Party Congress, who sat in stunned silence when Khrushchev delivered his historic denunciation of Stalin, Kondratiev experienced a sense of deliverance: at last.

He felt quite lighthearted after the speech, as he went into the buffet room reserved for members of the Central Committee. The atmosphere was subdued, rather un-Russian: little knots of people talking in low tones, some standing by themselves, sipping tea or munching *zakuski*, a few at the table putting down one drink after another. Khrushchev had been talking to Molotov; he patted him on the shoulder and moved toward the door. Passing Kondratiev, he gave him a wink.

"Enough for one night. I am going to bed."

"Thank you, Nikita Sergeievich, from all my heart. There must be many in the whole country—"

"That was just the beginning," said the first secretary loudly, as he went out.

Talk stopped momentarily, then conversations resumed. Kondratiev poured himself a scotch and soda, and joined a little group surrounding Lunin, who introduced him to a stocky man in his middle thirties, a new member of the committee.

"Dmitri Pavlovich Smirnov, secretary of the Rostov district . . . I was just telling the comrades how what we just heard demonstrates the strength and vitality of our Party. What other leading group in all of history would have had the courage and magnanimity to acknowledge and correct such errors from its past? We are confident that the people will understand and approve, and we shall march on to further triumphs of socialism."

"It is still a shock," said a tall, swarthy man with a strong Central Asian accent. "So many of the activists from my area venerate Stalin's memory, and now we hear how he allowed honest Communists to be tortured and killed . . . licensed the cult of personality."

"Comrade Khrushchev," said Lunin severely, "explained that we must preserve a balanced view of the man. He had rendered great services to the Fatherland and socialism, before 1934, during the war . . . At other times he became so absorbed in the cares of state that he tended to overlook the excesses and violations of socialist legality."

"Surely," said Smirnov hesitantly, "we don't have to go into the details of those excesses when we talk to the rank and file, do we?"

"But how can you avoid it, when tonight some two thousand people heard the speech?" asked Kondratiev.

"A Politburo directive will explain what to say and how," announced Lunin curtly, and left them to join a group of higher dignitaries.

Molotov was still standing alone where Khrushchev had left him. It was with perhaps a slightly sadistic impulse, as well as curiosity, that Kondratiev walked up to him.

"Ah, Comrade Kondratiev. I hear such good things about your work on the council. Your knowledge of foreign lands and languages must be of great help." Molotov's face was pale, but otherwise he seemed to be completely composed.

"It is interesting work . . . Tonight must have brought painful memories to you, Vyacheslav Mikhailovich."

Molotov smiled with no sign of resentment or embarrassment. "I have been a Party member for fifty years. There have been quite a few painful moments during that period. But also moments of great exhilaration—the Revolution, the establishment of socialism in our country, the victory. I have also seen many changes; people who thought they knew what the Party wanted and needed would occasionally discover that they had been wrong. It may happen again. Of course, in the main Comrade Khrushchev was right: Josif Vissarionovich has been dead for three years. We had to assess realistically the errors in his style of leadership."

What a masterpiece of understatement, thought Mikhail Alexandrovich.

"But I knew the man better than most. Personally, he was far from being cruel or vain—just didn't believe you could rule our nation in any other way. Perhaps he was wrong. We shall see."

And he shifted the conversation to the international situation.

A tough old buzzard, the younger man observed: he is far from having given up.

Indeed, the next few months marked a sharp crisis in the Party leadership. Echoes of the struggle between Khrushchev and the Stalinist Old Guard reverberated beyond the Presidium's and even the Central Committee's sessions. Molotov and Malenkov pressed their attack: What had been the results of the first secretary's garrulity about the sins of the past? The rebellion in Hungary, near rebellion in Poland. And here at home, there was an alarming rise in lawlessness. They had had a couple of food riots, and the first industrial strike since 1928. Things could not go on this way. Khrushchev fought back cleverly, exploiting the hatred of Stalin's old henchmen among the local Party secretaries who constituted the core of the Central Committee: few of them had not been snubbed, insulted, or frightened to death by Molotov, Malenkov, or Kaganovich. At the February 1957 session of the Central Committee, Molotov categorically demanded an end to further denigration of the past and to "thus giving aid and comfort to the enemies of socialism at home and abroad."

There was considerable applause at his words, and just scattered cheers when Khrushchev got up. His face was grim: "I shall ask just one question: How many of you here had a wife, husband, brother, or any other relative repressed during that period of law and order that Comrade Molotov speaks of with such nostalgia?"

About three-quarters of those present raised their hands.

"If you want to go back to those times, it won't be under my leadership." And he sat down. But in a moment he was back on his feet, with both arms raised as the committee exploded into an ovation.

"That was a real triumph for you, Nikita Sergeievich." Kondratiev was seeing him right after returning from his unpleasant errand in Hungary.

Khrushchev waved his hand deprecatingly. "They know how to cheer, but have they really learned to think for themselves? How were things in Budapest?"

Kondratiev reported that the situation was still unsettled. The Hungarian comrades had promised to deal with the main instigators of the uprising with appropriate severity, but begged leave not to announce the death sentences until their people had calmed down.

"Yes, that is another part of the legacy of the Great Leader. He never thought of any way of keeping those countries in line, except by fear and terror. And so we must shoot perfectly decent, if misguided, men. For otherwise, what the Soviet soldier—not Stalin but the Soviet soldier—" Khrushchev banged his fist on the table, "has conquered would be grabbed by the capitalists." He paused. "Misha, I have another job for you, and this time I would be delighted if we could have some people shot, but no such luck."

Kondratiev was to go to China, ostensibly on a cultural mission, but in fact to try to persuade Mao and his colleagues to be more forthcoming in their denunciation of the cult of personality, and in their support for the USSR in general, and Khrushchev's leadership in particular.

"Of course, they'll name a price. Probably a trifle like a few A-bombs. Well, if there is no other way, promise them anything, but in very vague terms. Try to get some feeling for how strong Mao's position is and if there are others with whom we could do business. One almost wishes Chiang Kai-shek were still there instead of those conceited bastards."

The visit was a flop. He did not even get to see Mao. The Chairman, it was explained, was in his rural retreat, absorbed in writing poetry, but Kondratiev was also given to understand that China's leader felt it beneath his dignity to receive a relatively low-ranking Soviet official. The offer of a "sample" A-bomb was gratefully accepted. Not so the statement that he was not empowered to sign a written agreement to that effect. Yes, the People's Republic stood 100 percent behind the Soviet Union in its struggle against American imperialism, but the Chinese comrades were greatly surprised that the great and all-powerful USSR was not pressing the U.S. harder and was not supporting the wars of national liberation more vigorously. As to Stalin, they had criticized his errors, yet still considered him a great fighter for communism.

"He was 80 percent right, and 20 percent wrong."

"You know that his real feelings about the People's Republic and Comrade Mao in particular were not exactly friendly," said Kondratiev in exasperation.

His Chinese interlocutor smiled amiably. "We do know, and we realize that unlike him, Comrade Khrushchev is a true friend of the Chinese people. But why furnish ammunition to the enemies of socialism by dwelling on that 20 percent, rather than the 80?"

He had to sit and suffer through a five-hour Chinese opera, with its monotonous and unintelligible posturings and dissonant sounds, and endless banquets with their innumerable and interminable toasts to the "unshakable friendship of our two great peoples."

"I have never sensed such latent anti-Soviet sentiment—not even in Warsaw," reported Kondratiev to the Presidium on his return.

"How much is that feeling, in your opinion, Comrade Kondratiev, a consequence of our continuing the campaign against the cult of personality?" asked Malenkov, looking significantly around the table. But before Kondratiev could answer, Khrushchev exploded.

"You are like a child, Georgi, asking questions that have already been answered. We've had ample proof that the Chinese would resent us no matter what we do or say. They are rabid nationalists. They would start slandering us out in the open, except that they still hope to push us into a confrontation with the Americans. But we shall not go to war with the U.S. so as to please Mr. Mao and his gang."

No one said anything, but it was evident that most Politburo members resented having one of their number humiliated in the presence of outsiders.

The safe thing seemed to be to await the outcome of the inevitable clash between Khrushchev and the Old Guard. But was it, really? Khrushchev enjoyed wide support within the Party apparatus and the Central Committee.

"Yes," Leontiev, with whom he had become quite friendly, to the point where they could talk about the situation frankly, told him, "Nikita Sergeievich is certainly quick-tempered, and as to the language he uses . . . But it is better to be dressed down occasionally than to go through what we did in those years. You know that from December 1952 until the day Stalin died, I had my bag packed and woke up at night each time a car stopped in front of the house we lived in . . . Oh, if there only was a middle way. But can you, for the moment, think of anyone else who would be able to lead us?"

No, he couldn't. The only thing uniting the Molotov-Malenkov faction was their common fear that the continuing flow of revelations about the past would eventually bring to light their own roles in the "era of the cult of personality." What a euphemism that was for twenty years of mass murder and torture!

Any remaining doubts he had about taking a stand were dissipated in Kondratiev's mind by a talk with Perventsev.

"Your Nikita is certainly a vulgar and primitive creature. But let us be fair: he has opened the windows and let in some fresh air to clear away the stench we've lived in for so long. I don't think the people would stand for having the windows nailed shut again."

The idea that the perennially patient and obedient Russian people might react to a change in leadership did not appear very realistic to Kondratiev. But then, they just might. It all added up to many compelling reasons why he must not remain just an observer in what was about to happen.

Khrushchev's glum expression brightened when, at the end of a routine report, Kondratiev mentioned that he did not believe the rumors of an impending crisis in the Party, but in any case wanted to assure Khrushchev of his personal loyalty.

"There is going to be a clash, all right. Those bastards think they've pulled the wool over my eyes, but it is they who are in for a surprise . . . Here is what we must do."

And so, in June 1957, Mikhail Alexandrovich played a crucial role in the operation that assured the triumph of Khrushchev and brought about the final downfall of the Molotov-Malenkov group. He had just witnessed an effusive welcome given to Khrushchev and Bulganin on their return from abroad. But, as he immediately noticed, there were no preparations in the VIP lounge at the railway station for the reception customary on such occasions. On questioning the security officer who accompanied the travelers, he first got evasive answers, but finally the man admitted that the Politburo had to repair immediately to a special session.

"I think it is the new crisis in the Near East, Comrade Minister."

It was one of those rare moments when there was actually no crisis in that area, and on his return to the office Kondratiev made a number of telephone calls.

"They did not even trouble to cut off communications," he thought contemptuously.

Two hours later, a group of Central Committee members appeared at the Kremlin and demanded admission to the Politburo session, to sit in as observers, something that according to the Party rules was their prerogative, but one that for obvious reasons had not been claimed since 1922. The KGB officer in command of the Kremlin was as astounded as he was emphatic in his refusal.

"Comrade Bulganin's orders were explicit—no one but full members to be allowed in."

The minister of defense, Marshal Zhukov, who had just arrived, strode up to the commandant and struck him across the face. "You will tell Comrade Bulganin that I have ordered Moscow to be placed under martial law. I shall rescind the order only if we are told what is going on."

Within a few minutes, Bulganin and Voroshilov emerged and with strained joviality attempted to reassure the protestors that the Politburo was not seeking to put anything over on them. The result of the Politburo deliberations would be duly laid out before the Central Committee that was expected to be summoned in a week or so.

"Good God, Georgi Konstantinovich," said Voroshilov, turning to Zhukov, "you have known me for forty years. Would I, going on eighty, engage in any underhanded business?"

"That remains to be seen, Klimenti. You seem as full of vigor as when you led a cavalry charge in 1919. As to the Central Committee, it will meet tomorrow; military planes will be bringing the members from all over the country. You have five minutes to dismiss the KGB guards and let Nikita Sergeievich speak to us. Otherwise, I shall have soldiers take over the Kremlin."

The next day the conspirators humbly addressed the Central Committee, begging forgiveness for trying to remove Khrushchev. Only Molotov remained silent, and only he refused to vote for the motion that ejected him, Malenkov, and Kaganovich, now dubbed the Anti-Party Group, from all their Party and government posts. Khrushchev then moved that five of his partisans, including Zhukov and Kondratiev, be elected full members of the Politburo; the proposal carried unanimously.

"We shall throw out the other four traitors who tried to stab me in the back, one by one," the elated first secretary was telling Kondratiev at their conference later the same evening. "It would not do to reveal right away that the 'Anti-Party Group' had the majority in the highest Party organ, eh, Misha?" He suddenly frowned. "Would we have managed without Zhukov?"

Kondratiev replied that whatever had happened the day before, he was sure that the mass of the Party members would not have allowed their leader to fall victim to an intrigue.

"Hm . . . You are a diplomat, Misha. We shall have to deal with Zhukov, and rather soon. Our marshals must not get it into their heads that they can interfere with Party matters. And so Bulganin was in it up to his ears. And that old fool Voroshilov. He cried and begged me not to disgrace him—mumbling something about his grandchildren. We shall keep him on as chairman of the Presidium of the Supreme Soviet for a year or two. I have fired Sidorov as head of the KGB—the snake. How would you like to take over as head of our security? Most of their professional people are rotten to the core, and the whole organization has to be swept clean with an iron broom."

Mikhail Alexandrovich thanked him for the trust implicit in the offer, but begged off. He was not suited to that line of work. This brought out the proletarian in Nikita.

"I forgot, you're a gentleman and descendant of a long line of gentlemen! Just because we had some swine and degenerates foul up the organization does not mean that an honest Communist should turn up his nose at it."

Kondratiev explained that, far from considering the work of the KGB disgraceful, he felt it to be an honor to be entrusted with heading an institution charged with protecting the security of the state. But his own personal experience, of which Nikita Sergeievich was well aware, could make it difficult for him to display the hardness and, at times, the necessary ruthlessness that the position required. Better somebody younger and with no painful memories . . .

"Try to find someone without painful memories in this land of ours," said Khrushchev somberly. His anger subsided, and he smiled. "You are too sensitive, Misha, not a good thing in a leader. But then I may be too, being so lenient with those seven hypocrites who tried to ruin the Party and me . . . How about Karsavin for the KGB? He is thirty-seven and has been doing a good job as head of the Young Communist League."

Kondratiev hastened to express his approval: Karsavin was just the man for the job. Inwardly he had serious doubts about the young man, a typical bureaucrat and careerist. During Stalin's last months, Karsavin had gone beyond the call of duty in denouncing "homegrown Zionists, cosmopolites, and their Wall Street friends." With the despot dead, he had quickly sensed which way the wind was blowing and become unsparing in his denunciations of the cult of personality and in flattering Khrushchev. But there was no use objecting, because the first secretary had already made up his mind. The offer of the chairmanship of the KGB to Kondratiev had been just a ploy. Misha should not get any ideas on being promoted to the Presidium and becoming its youngest member: his social origins would always bar his ascent to the highest position. The erstwhile plumber's apprentice had displayed great generosity and broad-mindedness in advancing a former tsarist officer's son so high. Well, one had to run with the pack.

He knew what was expected of him. "You carried yourself splendidly, Nikita Sergeievich. Standing up to those hypocrites and then exposing their dirty game to the Central Committee. Made me think of Lenin when he fought for the Party's honor and unity."

"Now, now, Misha. Let's not start a new cult of personality." But despite his protestations, the first secretary was obviously pleased. To be flattered was a prerogative of the supreme leader, and as of June 17, 1957, Nikita Sergeievich was clearly much more than the first among equals.

Fulsome eulogies of Khrushchev were the order of the day, the following morning at the first meeting of the new Presidium. Weary and red-eyed from the strain of the last forty-eight hours, the oligarchs tried to surpass each other in paying homage to the man who, only a short time before, appeared headed for a catastrophic political defeat. Lunin, whose support of Khrushchev had at first been halfhearted, now applauded him for "bringing the Leninist style of work back into our ranks and thus thwarting the malicious designs of the few who would turn back the clock." Marshal Zhukov expressed his joy, both personally and on behalf of the armed forces, at having as the head of the Party a man "who during the great Fatherland War shared the dangers and hardships of the frontline soldier, and whose sage advice while a member of the Military Council of the Stalingrad Front contributed so signally to our victory over the Hitlerite gangsters." Viktorov, who, as Kondratiev knew, liked Khrushchev as a person but held him to be an ignoramus when it came to economic matters, chimed in with praise for the first secretary's trust in the people. "How courageously did Nikita Sergeievich battle those, happily no longer in responsible positions, who tried not only to cover up their own transgressions but also, through the use of fraudulent statistics, sought to conceal the true state of Soviet agriculture and impeded the needed reforms."

Throughout these tributes, Khrushchev sat with his head lowered, but now raised it and studied their expressions for a minute. "I thank those of you," he paused, casting a hard look at Voroshilov and Bulganin, "who stood by my side in the struggle against the Anti-Party Group. It was not personal ambition, but the sense of duty to the Party that required me to rebuff the arithmetical majority of the old Presidium when they sought to create dissension and chaos in our ranks. It is up to the Central Committee and *not*," here he raised his voice, "to a handful of old cronies of the late Josif Vissarionovich, to decide who should lead the Party."

"Comrades, I assure you—" Voroshilov tried to interrupt, but Khrushchev cut him short.

"No, Klimenti, no further excuses are in order. The Party, out of consideration for your years and past services, has chosen to pass over your recent and unseemly behavior. Try to repay this leniency with deeds and not words."

"I will. I will. Believe me, Comrades. I may not have much time left to me, but what there is will be spent in trying to repair the harm I've done to the Party, and to justify your magnanimity, Nikita Sergeievich."

"The devil knows what got into me." Bulganin sounded as if he was awakening from a trance. "But I sincerely promise—"

"Let's get on with the business at hand," said Khrushchev.

The first item, not surprisingly, was the future of the three main culprits in the recent drama. The first secretary began by relating a telephone call he had received from Kaganovich. The erstwhile "iron commissar" had begged in a shaken voice that he be forgiven and spared.

"It won't be the way it used to be done during the cult of personality, will it, Nikita Sergeievich?"

The room resounded with unpleasant laughter.

"He certainly should know how it was done," exclaimed Nikitenko, one of the newcomers to the body. "The bastard did not even lift a finger to try to save his own brother from a shameful death."

"Let him taste some of his own medicine," added Marshal Zhukov.

Khrushchev's frown stopped the commotion. "'Lazar Moiseyevich,' I told him, 'those days are gone, no thanks to you. You will have a chance to expiate your sins by doing honest work. But one more slip, and you'll be pleading not with me, but before a court.' Then I hung up." He stopped and looked inquisitively at the assembled.

"What, then, do you propose should be done with those three?" asked Leontiev.

"If it meets with your approval, Comrades, I shall ask Comrade Viktorov to find jobs in industry for Kaganovich and Malenkov. For years they lorded over our industrial cadres, bullying, firing, and destroying some of our best managers. Let them now find out what it really takes to run a factory. And, Alexander Ivanovich, make sure that their plants are far away from Moscow."

Some of the assembled, Kondratiev noted, could not conceal their disappointment. Obviously, they had entertained the satisfying vision of the erstwhile demigods getting their just deserts, being grilled by the KGB, and so on.

"And Molotov?" someone asked.

Khrushchev's face broke into a broad smile. "A petty bourgeois like him would be lost in a factory. He could not tell a lathe from a turbine. But he is a great expert on diplomacy. Comrade Filimonov has informed me that we need a new ambassador to Mongolia."

There was another eruption of merriment around the table.

"A capital idea," shouted Shevchuk. "He will be close to our Chinese comrades with whom he shares that great nostalgia for Stalin."

Only Viktorov shook his head. "You know how I feel about the man. But his wife is not well, and Ulan Bator's climate is brutal."

"She can remain in Moscow," allowed Khrushchev. "After all, Vyacheslav Mikhailovich hardly seemed heartbroken when his great pal Josif Vissarionovich ordered Polina sent to a labor camp, where she was kept for four years. Also, there are women in Mongolia, perhaps not quite as attractive as those ballerinas Molotov used to fancy, but at sixty-seven, his requirements should be more modest."

Bulganin began to laugh wildly, then abruptly stopped as everyone's head turned in his direction.

Returning home, Kondratiev tried to analyze his own reactions. No, he could not feel sorry for those scoundrels with the blood of so many on their hands. In fact, they should have been booted out of the Party, and granted that it would have been too embarrassing to have them tried and shot, they ought to have been exiled to some provincial towns, there to rot in inactivity. And why keep on the drunkard and lecher Bulganin? Only toward Voroshilov he felt a twinge of sympathy: he had been kind to Misha in his hour of ordeal. But then again, the old marshal had allowed his father to be arrested and ruined before he gathered enough courage to procure his release. More important than any moral compunctions, was Khrushchev wise in letting them get off so lightly? For the moment, he was clearly the boss. But would he be able to carry out his reforms, and excise the cancer of Stalinism from the body of Soviet society, if those who had something to hide came to believe that the worst they could expect was a demotion to a managerial or diplomatic position?

The next few months confirmed some of Kondratiev's misgivings about his chief. Whereas with Stalin, one had always felt as if one were standing on a trapdoor that might suddenly be sprung, working with Nikita Sergeievich could best be compared to a ride on a roller coaster: sudden ups and downs in the first secretary's moods, when it came to both policies and personalities; a dizzying sequence of administrative and economic reforms and initiatives, accompanied by his exuding ebullience at one moment, extreme irascibility the next. Under the tyrant, even his closest collaborators had lived in constant fear; under Khrushchev, you could not help experiencing fatigue and occasional exasperation. Would the frantic pace ever stop, and some stability be introduced into the Party and the lives of its oligarchs and officials?

At first, Mikhail Alexandrovich did not mind the new style of management: what were any of these discomfitures, compared to what had gone on before March 1953? And there was a new spirit throughout the land. People were beginning to be unafraid and relaxed. You even could talk about politics, of course within certain limits, to your wife or a friend without looking over your shoulder. Basically, he still liked and remained grateful to Khrushchev. But at times he could not help becoming irritated with his temperamental leader.

The Politburo members were now required, much more often than before, to address public meetings, to declaim the official line on the cult of personality and to explain the villainies of the Anti-Party Group. Kondratiev found this speechmaking as ritualistic as under Stalin, though in a different way, and increasingly burdensome. There was always the same question: How could the Party have allowed all those excesses to take place? At times, a simple soul in the audience might ask why the man responsible for bringing so much misery to his people was not disposed of in the manner in which he dealt with others. Kondratiev grew tired of having to repeat the same formula, to expatiate how Comrade Stalin's "errors" *after* 1934 should not make them forget his great services to the people and the Party *before* that date, that to have removed him would have played right into the hands of Fascists and imperialists, always eager for signs of weakness and discord in the Socialist Fatherland, so they might pounce upon the USSR before it was ready for war. Yes, the treaty with Hitler, monster as he was, came from a dire necessity: it had given the Soviets two more years of peace to build up industry and the armed forces.

At one of these meetings he was interrupted by a shout. "*He* certainly did nothing to prepare us for the war. Because of *his* negligence, millions of Soviet men and women died during the war's first months."

A hush fell over the audience, and Kondratiev asked if the heckler would identify himself. A sixtyish-looking man with several medals on his blouse stood up.

"Petrov, pensioner. I got this," he lifted the stump of his right arm, "on the Moscow front in December 1941. I was lucky. Most people in my militia unit did not last out that winter."

"You helped to save the capital of our great country, as much as did those other heroes in the regular army. But we must not be overhasty in our judgments, Comrade Petrov. The Central Committee has thoroughly evaluated the role of Josif Vissarionovich Stalin in connection with the war. During its first phase, he indeed committed some errors. But later on, as the supreme commander and chairman of the State Defense Council, he greatly contributed to the victory of our Fatherland over the vile German oppressor. And his wise diplomacy foiled the perfidious designs of Western imperialists such as Churchill and helped our fraternal nations to the west to establish socialist regimes. Believe me, our Party and military experts have analyzed all the data, scientifically and objectively, and Comrade Khrushchev personally approved the findings."

There were stirrings among the audience. Kondratiev was sure he heard some cursing, but he ignored the noise.

"And now about the future. As most of you know, the Central Committee, on the initiative of Nikita Sergeievich, has embarked on a grandiose scheme for rapid improvement of the level of material well-being of our people. Among other measures, millions of acres of hitherto virgin land are being put under cultivation."

This time, there was an outburst of applause.

When he recounted the episode at the next meeting of the Politburo, his colleagues testified to similar experiences.

"This indicates that we should talk more about the future and less about the past," suggested Lunin, looking inquiringly at Khrushchev.

The latter studied the faces around the table for a moment. "No," he said decisively, "one day we shall have to tell more about what went on, and not only after 1934. As yet, our people are not ready for it." He sighed, put on his glasses, and started to proceed with the agenda, but Marshal Zhukov was not ready to let the subject drop.

"There is one legacy of the sad past to which we should attend without delay. We, in the officer corps, find it difficult to understand why many of the accomplices in the 'crimes' of the thirties—Comrades will forgive me for not calling them 'errors'—have escaped being made to answer for them. There are those who tortured our comrades-at-arms, sent them to their doom, hounded their families—and they remain not only free, but living comfortably on their pensions."

"The procurator general has been instructed to investigate all such cases," said Khrushchev, with just a trace of annoyance in his voice.

"He is certainly taking his time about it," persisted Zhukov.

"My staff has collected all the names of those criminals and the relevant data. We are ready to turn the materials over to the procuracy. I shall expect prompt action."

The first secretary's face reddened, but his voice remained calm: "Do what you see fit, Georgi Konstantinovich. Let the guilty ones be punished with all the severity they deserve."

A few weeks later, Kondratiev learned that Zhukov had summoned the head of the political administration of the armed forces, called General Rostovtsev an "informer" and other names, and told him that from then on he would communicate with the Politburo only through him—Zhukov. Now it could only be a question of time. In some ways, Mikhail Alexandrovich sympathized with the choleric marshal—he recalled what had happened to his own father. But this time it was an open challenge to the authority of the Party, of the body of which he himself was a member.

It came, therefore, as no surprise that two days after Zhukov's departure on a visit to the fraternal countries, the Politburo was called into an extraordinary session. It fell to Leontiev to report "on the unhealthy situation that had arisen in the Ministry of Defense as a result of Comrade Zhukov's arbitrary acts and his violations of the principle of collective leadership of the Party and the state." There could be no question, he concluded, that the situation called for decisive measures.

"Might not there be some, well, trouble with our military comrades?" asked Lunin, hesitantly.

Khrushchev shrugged his shoulders: "We would be unworthy of being leaders if we hesitated to uphold the honor and authority of the Party, no matter what." Sensing that as much as his colleagues might agree with this lofty sentiment, they were still apprehensive, he added, "I have communicated with our ranking military commanders, including several marshals of the Soviet Union. Almost without exception, they have complained of Zhukov's high-handed conduct and pledged support to whatever steps we think are necessary. No, Comrades, we have not done away with the cult of personality only to tolerate a would-be Bonaparte in our midst."

One could sense the relief among those present, and now some were eager to close in on the kill.

"He is a brave soldier and was a talented commander during the war, but essentially the man is a brute. He used to order officers shot for the most trivial offense." Lunin was eager to compensate for his previous faintheartedness.

"In 1943, I was a member of the Military Council of the Twenty-first Army. Zhukov came to our headquarters and threatened to have me court-martialed for something or other," reminisced Shevchuk. "I told him I was a member of the Central Committee. He made an indecent gesture and said, 'That is where I have your Central Committee.'"

There was a murmur of indignation around the table, but before further storytellers could come forward, the first secretary tapped impatiently on the table. "We are agreed, then: dismissed as minister and expelled from the highest Party organs. I also move that Marshal Malinovsky be appointed as minister of defense."

They all approved. Kondratiev, though he realized it was not politic, felt constrained to say, "Georgi Konstantinovich must not be subjected to any indignities. We know his faults, but among the masses his name is widely revered."

Khrushchev at first misunderstood him. "Of course. I have asked Comrades Malinovsky and Karsavin to take appropriate precautions . . . Oh, I see what you mean, Misha. I keep forgetting you are a general's son. Well, if he behaves, he can keep his rank, villa, and pension, and since you are so tenderhearted, why don't you welcome him on our behalf when he gets back, and tell the marshal he will now have more time to attend to his young wife and write his memoirs."

It was not a pleasant errand, though Zhukov took the news calmly.

"I suspected something like this was brewing. You may assure your colleagues that they need not fear any trouble from me. Zhukov is a soldier, and whatever else some might think, also a loyal Party member. I am grateful that it was you whom Nikita Sergeievich delegated to give me the word and not Karsavin, or that ass licker Malinovsky."

"No matter what, your name, Georgi Konstantinovich, will forever remain associated with our victories in the Great Fatherland War."

"You are most kind, Mikhail Alexandrovich, but I suspect that those who during the next few years will write about the war will not stress the point. And now, you'll excuse me. I am now a private person and must not take the time of an important official."

He turned away from Kondratiev and walked toward a handful of his former subordinates, most of them retired, who had screwed up enough courage to come greet the fallen man who, in her hour of peril, had been Russia's first soldier.

Early in 1958 it was Bulganin's turn to bite the dust. There was some desultory discussion in the Politburo as to who should be his successor as prime minister, but throughout the group it was well understood who it had to be. After some perfunctory resistance on his part, Khrushchev let himself be persuaded that he must head the government, as well as the Party. Kondratiev was made one of the first deputy prime ministers, and it was assumed that in the chairman's absence, he and Mikoyan would take turns presiding over the council.

Khrushchev now had the two jobs once held by Stalin, but additional honors and powers seemed only to increase his restlessness.

"I wonder where Nikita Sergeievich gets his energy," sighed Lunin during one of his rare social calls on the Kondratievs. "This week he is traveling all over the southern regions, extolling the virtues of corn and how American agriculture is so efficient because they grow and eat so much corn. Next week he takes off to India, Burma, and Indonesia. Of course, all those trips increase our own authority and prestige throughout the world, but still . . ."

At this point, Irina excused herself, and after she left, Lunin resumed. "I mean, Nikita Sergeievich ought to pay more attention to what is happening right here in Moscow. Some of our writers and artists have taken the denunciation of the cult of personality as a signal that they may write, paint, and compose as they please, and pay no heed to the Party's guidance. I ask you, Mikhail Alexandrovich, are there no other subjects for novels and short stories about the thirties except what was allegedly happening in the camps and jails? We've had some art exhibitions featuring paintings and sculptures done in the disgusting and decadent Western-type manner. So much for what is done openly, but as you know, we have had some underground publications, scurrilous tracts, besmirching our Soviet system."

"But Pyotr Nikolayevich, it is up to you to watch over the cultural front, and as to those anonymous libelers, our security people know how to deal with them."

"Well, I've had a few of those exhibitions closed and sent packing some editors of the journals and heads of the publishing houses. But you cannot stop those . . ." he searched for the appropriate term, "harmful fads from spreading by such half-measures. We need a few arrests, a trial or two, to put, if you will excuse the expression, the fear of God into the unruly elements of our intelligentsia. When I suggested that to Nikita Sergeievich, he brushed it aside and said we must not make martyrs out of a few immature artists and writers."

Was he testing him about Khrushchev, or was there a real fear in his bigoted mind that a few scribblers and artists could undermine the Soviet power? Kondratiev wondered. He kept silent and looked questioningly at the Politburo's official guardian of ideological purity.

"Don't get me wrong," said Lunin, after a pause. "Nikita Sergeievich's instincts are usually right. It is simply that he is away most of the time and too busy to see and read as much of that potentially dangerous trash as, unfortunately, it is my duty to do. We must persuade him to take interest in the matter. And above all, let us stop harping so much on what happened in the thirties. It is all in the past, and our people do not have to be constantly reminded of this or that sad episode that took place then. Some in Nikita's personal entourage are pressing him to reopen the Kirov affair. Why stir up a hornets' nest?"

Kondratiev felt a sudden chill run down his spine, but managed to sound quite matter-of-fact. "As you probably recall, Pyotr Nikolayevich, I have personal reasons to wish that ancient business cleared up and an end put, once and for all, to the many rumors about it. But I realize how it could be awkward and might hurt the Party to rummage in what was clearly a mess."

Lunin sounded genuinely surprised. "I completely forgot that you were serving under Kirov when the dastardly murder took place. Of course you place the Party's honor above personal feelings. I am glad you share my views on the subject. Nikita Sergeievich puts great weight on your judgment. Oh, yes," he added, "he likes to tease you, but never dresses you down the way he does the rest of us."

For the moment, their apprehensions proved unfounded. Just as suddenly as he embarked on a new wave of revelations about Stalin's dark deeds, so did Khrushchev drop the subject. He now became engrossed in foreign affairs and would pay scant attention to any other subjects raised during the Politburo meetings. Time was growing short, he kept repeating—sometimes breaking in with this warning during a discussion of quite different topics—if they were to forestall the deadly dangers to the Soviet Union: West Germany on the one hand, and China on the other, acquiring nuclear weapons of their own. What, then, could be done? They had to force America to agree to a German peace treaty containing ironbound guarantees against the Bonn revanchists' ever getting their fingers on the nuclear trigger, and they must try to persuade, bribe, or browbeat their Chinese comrades into giving up their own program to produce A- and H-bombs.

The Politburo was fully persuaded of the urgency of both problems. But during the next three years, they watched with growing skepticism Khrushchev's foreign policy pyrotechnics aimed at achieving those objectives: his alternate bullying and cajoling of the Americans; his at one time publicly denouncing Mao and his clique as "dogmatic left-wing sectarians" and at another privately pleading with Beijing to give up its nuclear ambitions, in return for which the USSR would compel the U.S. to abandon Taiwan.

Nothing worked. The Americans, unable to penetrate Nikita Sergeievich's sublime stratagems, came to believe that the Soviets wanted to take over West Berlin rather than use it to make them more amenable to a peace treaty.

"But why don't we tell them what we really want, and make them see that it is in their own interests to go along with it?" inquired Shevchuk during one of the Politburo's discussions on how to deal with that impossible nation. Khrushchev gave the Ukrainian a pitying look.

"Tell the Yankees that we are afraid of a few A-bombs in West German hands, and they would start pushing *us*. 'What is it worth to you, if we don't give Adenauer the Bomb? How about you giving up East Germany?' Correct, Comrade Kondratiev? You know them better than most of us."

"Correct," replied Mikhail Alexandrovich, and he was sorely tempted to add, "But then we should not push them so brutally. They can get very stubborn when they feel they are being blackmailed."

The trouble with the Chinese was that they understood the Soviets only too well. They knew that the prospect of the 800- to 900-million-strong nation (the devil knew how many of them there were in fact) obtaining nuclear weapons and the means of their delivery haunted the denizens of the Kremlin. Without the Bomb, they would always have to depend on the USSR for protection. And so they would thank their Russian comrades for their solicitude about Taiwan, and for their assurances that since the Soviet Union protected them with its own nuclear might, they should not waste their resources on developing such expensive playthings. But no! In due time, Beijing was going to take care of Taiwan itself, and they were determined to produce their own deterrent. Mao, abandoning polite sarcasm, had started to attack the Soviets publicly: they were failing in their obligations to support the national liberation movements, and at home they were betraying the principles of Marxism-Leninism—witness their denigration of that giant of the proletarian movement, Stalin. They shrewdly suspected that Khrushchev was not averse to making a deal at their expense with the American imperialists. Soon the Great Helmsman and his gang were indelicately hinting at complicity between Washington and "the new tsars in the Kremlin"; socialism in the USSR was becoming a sham.

"Why do they distrust us so much?" bewailed Khrushchev on occasion. "If we had not helped them, they would still be fighting on the mainland. If the USSR had not stood by them during the Korean War, the U.S. would have bombed them to hell . . . Oh, I am talking like a schoolboy. We were stupid to let that megalomaniac Mao and his fellow bandits take over the mainland. It is another accursed legacy of Josif Vissarionovich. He got so engrossed in that idiotic quarrel with Tito—a petty Balkan chieftain—that he did nothing to stop those hooligans, who always hated us, from seizing the wretched country. Our children may have to pay dearly for that idiocy."

"They are already insolent enough to hint that not only Mongolia but our Soviet Central Asia and the Maritime Province should of right belong to the People's Republic. There is considerable apprehension of Beijing's long-range aims among my people," added Izmailov, head of the Uzbek Party.

"Let them but try," said the first secretary, grimly. "Oh, if only the Americans were not so obtuse."

"I once heard an attaché of the British embassy say when in his cups, 'You in the Soviet Union may be the last hope of the white race,'" interjected Kondratiev.

They all laughed, but then proceeded to approve the draft of another note to Beijing, proposing negotiations "to resolve the differences between the two fraternal nations and thus to put a stop to the dispute that benefits only the imperialists and other enemies of Marxism-Leninism." And, as usual of late, there was a prompt, and this time the most insulting yet, response from Beijing.

In his frustration, Khrushchev reverted to his hobbyhorse: he mounted a new campaign against Stalin's ghost, much more comprehensive and virulent than the one he had orchestrated between 1956 and 1958. At the Twenty-second Party Congress held in October 1961, each of the Politburo members was instructed to include in his speech a passage dwelling on the grim past. The first secretary tried to persuade Kondratiev to refer to his own imprisonment in 1934, but Kondratiev absolutely refused.

"Some might think I was boasting—the only member of the Politburo who had 'sat.'"

"While others like Khrushchev were extolling 'the greatest genius of mankind,'" said Nikita, bitterly. "But then tell them of another horror. There is plenty to choose from."

In his own speech, Khrushchev scrapped the formula "Good before 1934, bad afterwards" in regard to Stalin. The former divinity was depicted as displaying criminal tendencies from his early years, being a coward ("He was afraid to go anywhere unguarded") and a sadist, to boot. More than ever before, the speaker enlarged on the sinister mystery of the Kirov affair: thousands of listeners, among them foreign Communist guests of the Congress, must have left with a feeling that quite likely it was Molotov and Malenkov, if not indeed "the greatest genius of mankind," who were the real culprits.

Others picked up the theme.

"One wonders how Molotov, Malenkov, and Kaganovich can sleep nights, knowing that their hands are stained by the blood of so many innocent people," exclaimed Karsavin, whose slavishness to Khrushchev had been rewarded by a seat on the Politburo.

Kondratiev was assigned the role of disposing of the legend of Stalin's inspired leadership during the war: never went near the front, interfered with the experts' opinions on military strategy, thought that cavalry still had an important role to play in modern warfare. He did this with some reluctance: Stalin's leadership during the latter phase of the war was, to his mind, one of the few redeeming factors in his career.

Stalin's mummy was hustled, unceremoniously, out of the Lenin mausoleum. An aged Party member, halfcrazed after her years in labor camps, had been made to announce that Vladimir Ilyich Lenin had appeared to her in a dream and complained that he found it oppressive to have his earthly remains rest next to those of the man who had betrayed his legacy. Karsavin proposed that the mummy should be incinerated and the ashes spread in a potter's field, but by a majority of one the Politburo decided to have the remains reburied in the Kremlin Wall. This led, as should have been expected, to further confusion among the Party masses: if Stalin had done so much evil, why still commemorate him among the heroes of the Revolution?

▬

"And where do we go now, dear Mikhail Alexandrovich?" mused Viktorov, when he dropped by Kondratiev's office some time after the Congress. "You know my feelings about the late leader. Will this continuous bringing up dirt from the past help us to keep the Germans from getting their fingers on the nuclear trigger? Or help with the Chinese, who more insolently than ever before are reviling us before the whole world? The Americans are certain that we want to grab West Berlin, and as you pointed out before, Misha, when you push them against the wall, they can get dangerous. Ouf! This is the first time since the war that I've been really worried about international affairs."

Viktorov sighed deeply. "Well, Nikita Sergeievich will undoubtedly come up with some new trick. Let us hope it does not blow up in our faces, like this business of putting new lands under cultivation. We poured billions into the scheme, and most of that land is already turning into a dust bowl."

Kondratiev, though he shared most of these misgivings, was trying to sound reassuring. After all, Khrushchev could not embark on something really major without the Politburo's sanction. The Virgin Lands scheme was not a total failure; it had given them a few good harvests. And after the Congress, Nikita Sergeievich had heeded their remonstrations and agreed that by now enough had been said about the past.

"He agrees, and then starts in again. Take this Solovyov Commission. Let's hope you're right. I still like the man. His heart is in the right place. But his mouth . . ."

Misha laughed. "You would not exchange our present problems for the ones we had during the reign of Josif Vissarionovich, would you?"

He did not feel like laughing after his visitor left. The Solovyov Commission had been established by a secret Politburo resolution of November 4, 1961, "to investigate the background and full circumstances regarding the foul murder of S. M. Kirov." No, nobody in the present leadership would be called on to testify or otherwise be involved in the investigation, Khrushchev assured them, when he moved that the appointment of the commission and the report be made public only after it had been thoroughly discussed and approved by the Politburo. But in all likelihood, somewhere in the KGB archives there still must be a signed deposition and the record of the "trial" of M. A. Kondratiev. Was it just his imagination, or had Karsavin glanced pointedly in his direction as Kondratiev, along with all the others, raised his hand to vote for the resolution? He rubbed his left cheek. It had been twenty-seven years. Would he ever get rid of the nightmare?

That Khrushchev did have a new trick up his sleeve became apparent in late winter of 1961. First, he began to hint that if the Americans continued to be stupidly obstinate about Germany and the Chinese unreasonable about acquiring nuclear weapons of their own, there was a way to force both parties to see the light and agree to the Soviets' proposals. The matter required utmost secrecy: except for the full members of the Politburo, only the ministers of defense and foreign affairs were to be in on the planning of the operation.

"When we anticipate a possible crisis, we usually give a warning to the heads of the fraternal Parties in the socialist countries. Shouldn't we do it this time?" asked Leontiev.

"No, they might blab. Besides, there will be no crisis." Khrushchev smiled, slyly, obviously enjoying their puzzlement.

What could it be? Another blockade of Berlin? But they had decided that would be too dangerous. Was there some special information in the first secretary's hands indicating that Mao might be overthrown? There had been a flow of intelligence reports from China about sharp conflicts within its leadership, but hardly anything suggesting that the Great Helmsman would be deposed. Furthermore, how could the Chinese and the American-German problem be resolved by a single coup?

In June the first secretary dropped the other shoe: they were going to place Soviet missiles in Cuba. "Let the Americans learn what it feels like to have them right on their border. They've been doing it to us for years, with their . . . what do you call them, Malinovsky?"

"Jupiter and Thor rockets," said the defense minister, frowning, and he added, "Our intelligence sources are positive that the American military plans include a prompt response, should Soviet weapons be placed in Cuba."

"Who's talking about *weapons*? I mean launching pads and missiles. You don't think we are going to place any nuclear warheads outside the Soviet Union?" He noted their dumbfounded expressions, and smiled. "You must think old Nikita is losing his grip. Let me tell you what I propose."

The plan was to construct the launching pads and slip missiles in with the greatest secrecy and with the utmost speed.

"How long should it take for some thirty, forty launchers?"

"Depending on their intended range, five to seven months," replied Malinovsky, in a shaky voice.

"It must be done in three."

"But then we would not be able to camouflage them properly. The Americans, with their spy planes over Cuba, would catch on to what we are doing in weeks, if not days." The marshal wiped perspiration from his face and looked imploringly at the others. "I don't see—"

Khrushchev, disregarding him, went on with his plan. Once the pads and missiles were in place, he himself would announce to the whole world that the USSR had weapons capable in a matter of minutes of laying waste the entire Eastern seaboard of the U.S.

"But," his voice rang with determination and confidence, as if he were already delivering the ultimatum to an astounded and shaken America, "I shall also say: We offer to pull out those damnable weapons from Cuba, each and every one of them, and do it under international inspection, if your government signs a German peace treaty, guaranteeing that no such weapons be produced or stored on German territory. And let us also have a nuclear-free zone in the Pacific. The People's Republic would not proceed with development of their own Bomb if the U.S. abandons its protective shield over Taiwan and removes strategic forces from Japan."

He stopped and looked triumphantly at the others.

The Americans, he continued, should be only too glad to jump at the proposal now. They were not particularly keen on Bonn's having its own nuclear force, and were deadly frightened of Beijing's getting one. They would be vastly relieved that the USSR did not want their precious West Berlin.

"What do you think, Comrades?"

"It is a grandiose scheme, Nikita Sergeievich," began Leontiev, cautiously, "but there are some risks involved."

"What risks?" said the first secretary, irritably.

"Let us assume, as the marshal suggested, that the Americans discover our missiles are being deployed before you make this admittedly brilliant and generous offer. They would believe that the weapons are there to stay, and they might do something rash."

"They would think we are installing those ground-to-air missiles that we've publicly promised Castro in order to protect Cuba from American air piracy, something Washington is quite ready to put up with . . . I saw their president in Vienna. He is a pleasant young man, quite timid. He burned his fingers over Cuba once. It will take place in the fall, when his mind is on the congressional elections. If by bad luck the U.S. administration learns about this business prematurely, they'll keep quiet about it until after the elections, and then we'll be able to tell them what it is all about. Believe me, they will be grateful to us; we shall have solved not only our own most pressing problems, but theirs as well."

It was a brilliant stratagem, but somehow it sounded too easy, thought Kondratiev, and could sense that the others shared his uneasiness.

"The Chinese have told us again and again they would never abandon building their own Bomb, no matter what," pointed out Lunin.

"They are hardly in a position to be so snooty this time. Mao is in serious trouble. Several of the other bigshots, like Li——, God, how can you remember those f— Chinese names?—are blaming him for quarreling with us and for their industry going to ruin ever since we pulled out our advisers and stopped shipping them our technology. There is famine in large parts of China. . . . Well, if they still turn up their noses at our generous offer, we'll tell them we shall not lift a finger if they get into trouble with the U.S. The Americans are itching to teach them a lesson, but up to now they have been afraid to move against them because they fear us."

"Could we really let the Americans bomb North Vietnam, or attack Beijing and its nuclear installation? True, their leaders have strayed, but does proletarian internationalism allow us to sit idly by while the imperialists are wreaking havoc on fellow socialist states?"

Lunin's interventions had for some time annoyed the first secretary, and this latest one brought an explosion.

"I am grateful to you, Pyotr Nikolayevich, for instructing us in Marxism-Leninism, but save your preaching for when you address a Komsomol meeting. I say communism is the Soviet Union. Those bastards in Beijing—it is they who are betraying proletarian internationalism. Trying to push us into a war with the United States, intriguing against us with every Communist party in the world. Well, let them choose: either work loyally with us, help us to secure peace so that the socialist world grows stronger while the capitalist one goes on disintegrating, or go their own ways and see how long their ideological purity will protect them from American bombs."

"I would not dream of trying to teach you anything, Nikita Sergeievich, and no one here condemns more strongly than I do the evil machinations of Mao and his clique."

Even though his face had grown pale, Lunin's voice was steady; his tone deferential, yet not apologetic.

He is through if Nikita's scheme succeeds, thought Kondratiev, maybe even if it does not. He himself felt constrained to ask, "How much do we tell Castro? He and his people are hardly the soul of discretion."

"Of course we will not tell him what it is all about. As far as the Cubans know, we would be installing ground-to-air missiles to protect their island from the American overflights." He turned to Malinovsky: "Rodion Yakovlevich, I hardly have to tell you that the units to protect the sites will have to be chosen with the utmost care. There will be absolutely no contact with the local population for the duration of the project—no Soviet soldier is to stray beyond the compound."

To Karsavin: "The KGB units will man the perimeter of the area. Every construction team, each crew of the ships carrying supplies to Cuba, must have your men exercising strict supervision."

"The security forces will exert every effort to help assure the success of your brilliant plan, Nikita Sergeievich," declared the KGB head.

"Are we then agreed? Good. I propose that a special committee watch over day-to-day developments of the situation: myself, Comrades Leontiev, Kondratiev, Karsavin, and Filimonov. We shall call it 'Operation Persuasion.'" He paused and smiled shyly, "Our ancestors on an occasion like this would cross themselves. We are past such superstitions. I am sure that the spirit of the Great Lenin approves of our enterprise."

Leontiev went over and embraced him. The others followed his example.

On the ride home, Kondratiev felt his uneasiness turning into serious apprehensions: there were so many *ifs*. It was almost inconceivable that the Americans would not spot the unusual doings in Cuba before Khrushchev appeared in the United States, ostensibly to speak before the UN, and dropped his bombshell. Would they back away from a confrontation and wait for Nikita to explain what it was all about? He had seen their president at the Vienna summit, and although it was true that he had appeared unsure of himself and thrown off balance by Khrushchev's alternate bullying and cajoling, something about Kennedy suggested that if backed into a corner, he could be a tough antagonist and throw caution to the winds. Why couldn't they just tell the Americans: You don't want China to develop the Bomb. We don't like the idea of West Germany having one. Let's strike a deal. No, it would never work. How could such an intelligent people be so stupid when it came to foreign policy?

The first stumbling block they encountered was with the Cubans. Castro's brother Raul came to Moscow in July. He enthusiastically went along with the idea when told that the Soviets wanted an enclave for deploying antiaircraft missiles to protect them from American air pirates. But his face fell when informed that the missile sites would be manned exclusively by the Russians, and the local population in the area would have to be evacuated.

"Our national honor requires that we actively participate in defending our country."

It was explained to him that if the Americans discovered the installations being built and manned by the Cubans, they would not hesitate to bomb them.

"They would not dare to do it to our people," said Khrushchev, barely containing his impatience.

Why were the missile sites to be in a remote part of the island, rather than around Havana and other cities? wondered the Cuban. Marshal Malinovsky explained at length the imperative technical reasons for locating them away from the urban areas. It was only after he was promised some Soviet fighters and bombers for his own air force that Cuba's defense minister stopped his importunities.

"He is a good comrade; even if he suspects something, he'll keep quiet. I wish he were running the show there, rather than his blabbermouth brother," said Leontiev after the final session with the visitor.

Karsavin smiled: "We have our sources. We'll know what Raul said to the Cuban Politburo within hours after he lands in Havana."

No disturbing news came from that quarter. But throughout August and September, Soviet agents in the U.S. kept transmitting rumors about growing agitation within the American intelligence community. On September 4, President Kennedy assured his countrymen that "no Soviet bases or offensive ground-to-ground missiles" were being installed in Cuba, merely antiaircraft rockets and radar installations. As he noted the statement, the first secretary beamed at his fellow members of the Persuasion Committee.

"But Kennedy added, 'Were it otherwise, the gravest issues would arise,'" pointed out Kondratiev.

Khrushchev shrugged off the remark: "They like big words—'gravest issues,' 'massive retaliation'—I instructed our ambassador to inform the people in the president's entourage that we would do nothing to complicate his life before the fall congressional elections. They practically dissolved in gratitude, and assured him that the administration is looking forward eagerly to my visit there in November. They hope both sides can work out a realistic plan about Berlin. Boy, will they be surprised to learn that we have already solved that and several other problems."

On October 19, Khrushchev began to read to the full Politburo the draft of the speech he proposed to deliver in November. In the middle, he stopped. "Perhaps we are being overgenerous. Why not also demand, at least as a talking point, that *West* Berlin be internationalized?"

Just then Karsavin was called away. He returned, shaken. "The Americans know," he announced. "There have been repeated overflights over the most exposed sites. One plane was shot down, and what they found in the wreck leaves no room for doubt that their fliers must have been taking fairly accurate pictures for several days. Also, our American agents report several airborne and marine units are being moved to Florida."

Khrushchev turned on Malinovsky, who though not a member was present at the session. "How could we have allowed them to fly freely over Cuba? You told me our antiaircraft missiles could hit a fly at 35,000 feet."

"We were told to go on with the launching pads in a hurry. There has not been enough time to provide an adequate number of SAMs."

"You were told to do it in a hurry, but taking every care that they not be spotted. And now a plan that would guarantee our security for decades is jeopardized because some idiot there has failed to take the most elementary precautions."

The pudgy face of the marshal became beet red, but he remained silent.

"No," said the first secretary, after a pause, "I still think Washington will keep quiet; if Kennedy admits that he has been fooled, the Republicans will sweep the election. I know the Americans. They think they can scare us by moving a division or two. They will send some stiff notes, make noises in the UN. What else could they do? We're going ahead; speed up the shipments and construction. The missiles are to be in place by November 1. Now let me continue with what I was going to say."

What the Americans could do became apparent in the early hours of October 23. Hastily summoned to the Kremlin, Kondratiev listened to the shortwave broadcast of Kennedy's speech, while the others were following a simultaneous translation being flashed on a screen. When it was finished, Khrushchev remarked calmly,

"He's got more guts than I gave him credit for. It is still words, words."

"You don't think that they mean it when they threaten to blockade Cuba? What do we do when they stop our ships?" asked Viktorov.

"It's a bluff. Soon they'll be talking about postponing the blockade while we negotiate. Still, we must put our forces on the alert."

The same evening, to demonstrate the Soviet government's equanimity, all the members of the Politburo attended a gala performance of *Boris Godunov*. The tragic tale, couched in somber music, of the impostor-ruler haunted by the crime that had enabled him to reach the throne was hardly designed to soothe the nerves. But those of the audience, who, during the intermission, directed their glances at the former imperial box, in which the oligarchs were sitting, could only note that their rulers were chatting and smiling as if nothing unusual were happening or threatening. Kondratiev, more conversant with the Russian classics than his colleagues, had previously suggested to the theater's management that they ought to skip one of the minor incidents in the opera, the seizure and lynching by a peasant mob of a boyar whose name happened to be Khrushchev.

"That scene has been omitted for years," the director assured him.

Immediately after the performance, they all went back into session. The next day, the papers were to carry the official announcement about "America's piratical intentions in the Caribbean," and reveal that an alert was ordered for the rocket, air, and submarine forces, all leaves for their personnel being canceled. Measures had to be taken to avoid panic. They approved the text of the first secretary's personal message to Kennedy. Its tone was unyielding, but conciliatory. Khrushchev was still in full control of himself, but weary and clearly less confident than the preceding night.

"Perhaps you should come out with your proposals now, Nikita Sergeievich," said Viktorov, voicing what was also on Kondratiev's mind.

"It would not work. They'll say 'Take away the weapons, then we'll talk.' We would be negotiating on our knees, our fears an open secret, our bargaining chips all but gone. So far, none of our ships to Cuba have been interfered with. We must go on and show them that the Soviet people cannot be bullied or bluffed."

Mikhail Alexandrovich returned home only around noon to snatch a few hours of sleep. When he woke up, he was confronted by an anxious Irina and fourteen-year-old Kolya. The boy, with great excitement, related how at school they had gone through an air raid drill, the whole class going to an underground shelter. They all thought it was good fun, but their class supervisor was rather distracted and Kolya had heard her say to one of the fellow teachers, "This would not be happening if *he* were still alive and in charge." Whom did she mean, and were they going to have a real war that would bring capitalism down?

Somehow, the sight of his child, almost a man already, brought a change in Kondratiev's hitherto fatalistic mood. No, there was not going to be a war, he replied with such confidence and determination that he astounded himself. A war would be a terrible thing. As for the teacher, she was talking nonsense—no, he checked himself—she did not understand the situation.

"You'd better go back to your homework, Kolya."

When the boy, obviously disappointed, had left, Irina looked at him imploringly.

"Yes, I mean it. There is not going to be any war. And now I must go. Very likely I shall not be back for quite a while, but don't draw any wrong conclusions. War happens only if someone wants it, and neither we nor the Americans wish for such a calamity. It will just be hard on our nerves for the next few days."

In the car he sensed that Trofim also wanted to be reassured, but cut off any questions with, "I know there are a lot of rumors in the air, but I would not pay any attention to them. Comrade Khrushchev and the leadership know what they are doing."

"I would never think otherwise, Mikhail Alexandrovich."

"Yes, we are both old soldiers, Trofim." Kondratiev now felt a bit ashamed of his brusqueness. Was he really convinced that the whole business would pass off peacefully?

For the next four days the Politburo was in continuous session, though individual members would occasionally take off to attend public functions scheduled prior to the crisis, so as not to increase the general anxiety hovering heavily over the country. On the surface, the discussion was calm; they were waiting on the events, scanning the latest reports from Washington and the Caribbean.

But Khrushchev's confidence was visibly eroding. Increasingly, he would turn to Kondratiev. He knew those people. What did this latest editorial in the *New York Times* or column by Walter Lippmann mean? Were these signs of the Yankees' realizing the consequences of going through with the blockade? Kondratiev, alas, could not detect any realistic reasons to be optimistic. Obviously, there were people both in and out of the U.S. administration who were scared to death by this whole business, but the president and his closest advisers appeared possessed by a desperate fatalism: if we are to have it out with the Russians, let it be so. Whenever he voiced such an opinion, Khrushchev would declare irritably that he read the signs differently. But his protestations lacked conviction.

As if things were not bad enough, the Chinese had chosen that moment to start border warfare with India. The embassy in Beijing reported great gloating in the official circles there over the Soviets' predicament.

On October 26th, Karsavin and the chief of military intelligence presented their grim conclusions. Unless the crisis were resolved within a week, the Americans, not content with the blockade, would launch air strikes against the missile sites, following them with a full-scale invasion of Cuba.

"You are sure this is not American disinformation?" asked Khrushchev.

"Absolutely, Nikita Sergeievich. This comes from our American sources of utmost reliability. It is confirmed by the messages from the Pentagon to the various theater commanders, which our intelligence has intercepted during the last twenty-four hours."

"Might we not announce that any strike against Cuba would be answered immediately by a complete blockade of West Berlin, and propose at the same time an immediate summit meeting between the heads of the two governments?" suggested Lunin, breaking the silence that followed the intelligence chief's statement.

Several of them turned toward Kondratiev. He shook his head. "It might work, but then it might make the Americans go absolutely berserk."

Khrushchev had kept his eyes on a piece of paper in front of him. Now he raised his head and for a moment seemed to contemplate the ceiling. When he spoke, he sounded weary but determined. "We cannot stake millions of lives, the fate of our

Fatherland and of socialism, on what might or might not happen. The president's latest letter to me proposes that we pull out our weapons—we shall not disabuse him from thinking they were weapons—for an American solemn promise not to invade Cuba. I believe we should accept his offer."

Their careers had endowed them with considerable ability to hide their emotions. But now, one could see undisguised relief on everyone's face . . .

Two weeks later Khrushchev reported on the sequel to the crisis. There had been those painful meetings with the heads of the fraternal countries' Communist parties, who had descended on Moscow one after another to find out what had gone on. Castro, now that he knew, was behaving abominably, threatening to denounce the USSR publicly. Nothing said about the Soviet Union by the Hitlerite scoundrels surpassed in scurrility the vile accusations now being launched at the USSR and its leaders by Beijing.

There were some positive results. World public opinion gave the USSR credit for prudence and restraint, as against the U.S. government's adventurism and recklessness. And the Americans themselves, sobered by the experience, were ready to negotiate about nuclear nonproliferation. No, the Socialist Fatherland had not suffered any loss of prestige. It stood higher than ever, and that is why Mao and his gang were so furious.

"However, I would be less than frank, Comrades, if I did not acknowledge that the policy I recommended did not bring the expected results and placed our country in grave danger. It is not in my nature to shirk responsibility. I propose to resign as first secretary and head of the government, the public announcement to be made when you see fit."

"And we would be shirking our responsibilities, Nikita Sergeievich, if we as much as considered accepting your resignation," Lunin spoke up instantaneously and in great agitation. "Since when do we Bolsheviks abandon our leaders in moments of difficulty? How many such setbacks did Great Lenin suffer, and didn't his comrades, after each of them, stand by him unflinchingly?"

Not quite true historically, yet very moving, thought Kondratiev.

"It is your *duty* to continue to lead us, ours to rally around you more firmly than ever before."

The room resounded with shouts of "You're right," followed

by prolonged applause. For once, Khrushchev was at a loss for words. He began, "Comrades—" Then, wiping his tears, "Let us go on with the agenda." They all, Kondratiev was sure, shared his own sudden surge of affection toward the man who, for all of his bombast, vulgarity, and madcap ideas, had led them away from terror and fear.

Affection in politics is seldom a reliable guarantee of concord and loyalty. Within weeks of this moving scene, the atmosphere began to change. Khrushchev's proposals increasingly encountered objections from other Politburo members. He usually carried the day, but clearly the missile crisis had wrought a subtle transformation in intra-Politburo relations. One felt that Lunin's authority had been enhanced, Nikita Sergeievich's self-confidence heavily bruised. The strain of the past weeks was taking its toll now that the danger had passed. Shevchuk, the head of the Ukrainian Party, always somewhat unbalanced, became mentally ill and had to be relieved of his post. Early in December, Lunin suffered a heart attack. The doctors' prognosis was for a complete recovery, but he would require a lengthy period of recuperation.

It was during his absence that the first secretary startled his Politburo colleagues with an announcement that they could not go on postponing a definitive verdict on the period of the cult of personality.

"I know we thought we had done with it, but the problem will not disappear of itself. Wherever I go, on whatever topic I speak, people in their questions revert to the damnable issue. 'Nikita Sergeievich, how could it have happened? My father spent seventeen years in the camp, though completely innocent.' 'Why are *his* former accomplices still in the Party?' We must exorcise this evil once and for all, if our people are to be convinced we are following in Lenin's path."

What concrete steps did he propose? asked Leontiev. They had already rehabilitated all the top military leaders, unjustly condemned during those years. The procurator general was reviewing other cases, and several of the repressed people's families had been awarded pensions. What more could they do, without . . . He did not finish the sentence, and the first secretary did it for him.

"Without undermining the people's faith in the Soviet system? No, it is the other way around. Unless the truth is told, our people will grow cynical. You can see it already among the intellectuals and artists. Concrete measures? For the beginning, I propose a commission to study the violations of socialist legality between 1936 and 1940. The procuracy has been diddling with all those cases. We must once and for all excise that cancer eating at the entrails of our society."

The commission was duly appointed, and to Karsavin's obvious anguish, it was Kondratiev who was designated as its chairman. The KGB, the procuracy, and the Ministry of Defense were instructed to place all their files at the commission's disposal.

"Once the report is ready, as well as that of the Solovyov Commission, the nightmare of the past will be put to rest," declared Khrushchev. "Capitalists and our own domestic enemies will no longer have any opportunity for jeering at us and for slanderous fabrications. I don't remember much of the mumbo jumbo the priest taught us in my village school, but one phrase has stuck in my mind: 'And the truth will make you free.' Yes, truth will make us free, will lift from us that burden that we, along with our whole nation, have borne. Nothing, then, will impede the grandiose process of our society's passing from the socialist phase to that of communism."

The next day, Mikhail Alexandrovich was about to conclude his day at the office with his customary cursory glance at *Pravda*, something that, as a rule, took him five minutes. The first page was what could be expected: Khrushchev's reception of a Danish parliamentary delegation, an appeal for Komsomol volunteers to work in Siberia, the achievements of a textile plant in Gorky. Ditto the second: a sentimental depiction of life on a collective farm in Byelorussia, a scathing article about how the "left wing sectarians and dogmatists" in Beijing were ruining China's economy with their doctrinaire policy. What was this—a poem on the third page? The author, a writer currently in favor with the first secretary; its title, "On Stalin's Heirs." Awful poetry, but that was beside the point. The rhymester presented Stalin stirring in his tomb:

"No, Stalin has not given up. We threw him out of the Mausoleum, but how to root Stalin out of the minds of his heirs . . . [who] condemn Stalin from the platform, but at night pine for the old days. Evidently, not without reason do Stalin's heirs nowadays suffer heart attacks."

Phew! This was not likely to help Lunin's recovery. On second thought, it might very well speed it up . . . And the comical plea:

"I implore our government: double, triple the guard at the burial slab, so Stalin may not rise again, and with Stalin, the past."

On further thought, not funny. One did not have to think long to realize where the idea behind the poem, indeed some of its phrases, had originated.

"The Party ordered me not to be quiet. Let some repeat over and over again that enough has been said. I cannot remain quiet as long as Stalin's heirs exist."

Now they were in for it. Nikita had not really been chastened by the Cuban business. Perhaps even a politician cannot change his ways at sixty-eight. Still impatient, incautious, still itching to rush headlong at the enemy without first testing his defenses or assessing the forces behind him. Kondratiev's sympathies were with Nikita—since his political fortune was bound up with that of the first secretary. But could they afford to tell the Soviet people the *whole* truth about the terrible past? Could Mikhail Kondratiev, about his own?

▪

"I shall leave you two alone, since obviously politics is coming up. But Pavel, don't let Misha drink and smoke too much." Irina kissed both of them, and with her graceful step, was gone.

Perventsev looked after her admiringly. "She is quite right. And you were just telling me how smoothly our ship of state was sailing."

They had been discussing the recent assassination of the president of the United States. Kondratiev had used it as another example of the foolishness of America's political system and the growing rot of Western society.

"Say what you will about our politics, it would be inconceivable here . . . Oh, I know what you're going to say. We've done with it. It has been ten years since his death, and now there is not so much as one political prisoner in the entire country."

Pavel smiled incredulously.

"Yes, but that does not mean we don't have growing worries: China; that new man in the White House. Kennedy had just begun to see the importance of maintaining good relations with us. His successor does not know anything about foreign policy—the way the American system works, it takes two or three years to break in a new president. The idiotic process of running for the presidency virtually disqualifies a man for the job. So, we may soon be in a mess in the Middle East, or in Southeast Asia. And our friends in Beijing would love to see the U.S. and us at each other's throats. They are stirring up troubles in Indonesia and Vietnam, all in order to provoke the Americans to do something foolish." He could have added that all was not well within the leadership.

As often was the case, Perventsev could read his friend's mind. "I read the newspapers. But if a non-Party man may be indiscreet with a Politburo member, I hope that our temperamental leader has things under control."

Mikhail Alexandrovich poured himself another scotch and soda. He had no compunctions about discussing Party affairs—up to a point, of course—with his old friend.

"Oh, our Nikita does get us into an occasional trouble, but he has a knack of getting us out. I thought your intelligentsia friends did not particularly fancy him."

Perventsev sighed. "I don't blame the young ones, like my daughter and her husband, for thinking him vulgar and intolerant, but I cannot stand the ones who had groveled before Stalin now saying the same thing. I am seventy, and I still don't believe in this system of yours . . . ours," he corrected himself. "But I don't expect to see it changed. Frankly, I would not know how to go about changing it. And so, for all my griping about the way things are, I've reached the reluctant conclusion that they would only get worse with someone else on top. Unless it were you."

Kondratiev laughed. "We both know it is most unlikely. But believe me, Pavel, he is firmly in the saddle, and things will not get worse."

He said it with conviction, but he began to wonder whether his friend might have a better sense of the situation than he himself, with all his knowledge of the inner workings of the Party and the government. Curious, that Perventsev should so suddenly have developed this positive attitude toward the head of the regime from which he had always felt so alienated. Well, no man, even as idealistic as his friend, remains unmoved by official favors and honors. Perventsev was now a full member of the Academy, quite unusual for a non-Party man. He had been sent on several missions abroad, and had recently been decorated with the Order of Lenin.

Kondratiev knew that Perventsev felt keenly his estrangement from his daughter. A fervent Komsomol member and Stalin worshiper in her teens, Yelena then used to reproach her parents for their refusal to share in her enthusiasm. Now a talented research biologist, she shared in the current intelligentsia fad of viewing the regime as both oppressive and ridiculous. Her mother's recent death had brought her closer to Perventsev. Still, she had felt embarrassed at Perventsev's accepting the Order and would not attend the ceremony.

He himself, once "Uncle Misha," was nowadays treated with reserve by the young woman—quite likely the influence of her Jewish husband, a brilliant mathematician but unable to obtain a position commensurate with his achievements in the field. And so poor Perventsev, all his life an opponent of Marxism and Leninism, was seen by Yelena and her friends as a member of the Establishment, all the more unseemly in a man who considered himself a Christian (and that itself was rather old-fashioned). He, in turn, could not understand the mentality of this new breed of dissenter.

"They haven't lived through what we have, don't know what they really want, and can't realize things cannot be changed overnight." Perventsev professed in mock despair: "What have I done to deserve this, Misha? I've stuck to my principles and worked honorably for my country all my life. Yet the person dearest to me suspects her father of being a timeserver, and my closest friend considers me an unregenerate reactionary."

"On the contrary, I've felt for a long time you belong with us, in the Party."

Yet there was a bitter truth behind their joking: a man of Perventsev's personality and achievements did not lack friends, yet felt curiously isolated. He had never believed in socialism, yet could not share in the illusions of the young fools who thought, when they did think at all, that the system that was breaking down all over the West could somehow be implanted in Russia.

Kondratiev poured himself another drink and, for all his affection for Pavel Perventsev, felt a twinge of irritation with his old friend. Why didn't people like him realize that if you wanted things to get better, rather than worse, you had to work within the system, and not stand scowling on the sidelines?

Khrushchev had recently started a practice, which Kondratiev, after some initial reservations, had decided was salutary. *Some* meetings of the Central Committee would be open to outsiders: Party and non-Party specialists in the subject under discussion. A session devoted to agriculture, for example, would be attended by a sizable number of agronomists and collective and state farm chairmen. This innovation was strongly opposed by Lunin and, strangely enough, Viktorov; others, though not with great enthusiasm, concurred with the first secretary.

Mikhail Alexandrovich understood only too well Nikita's chief motivation: in the presence of outsiders, the oligarchs would be inhibited from criticizing or opposing his policies. Such criticisms, though usually in a veiled form, were now not infrequent at the Politburo meetings. Still, Kondratiev supported the initiative. It would lead, he declared, to greater understanding and support of the Party by the masses and counteract the trend toward political apathy and even cynicism among the young. The people would see their government at work. This would refute the absurd accusations that decisions affecting the people's welfare were being made in secret by a small clique. It was the Leninist way. Privately, he thought giving the *qualified* people a sense of participation in governing the country was a much better way of strengthening links between the Party and the population at large than continuing the stream of revelations about horrors of the past. Well, Perventsev, when invited to a session on heavy industry, had refused on grounds that he was now retired. But to Misha, he confided that he thought the whole thing a charade: "In principle, a good idea. But what happens in fact? The leaders announce their decisions, then the Central Committee approves them unanimously, then all those present vote for them, also unanimously."

"But at least the public is let in on what is going on. And noncommittee visitors are encouraged to speak up. You could repeat what you told me about the flaws in our automotive industry."

"I am too old to change my ways. You might ask how, then, I could have accepted the Order. I did because it was the *state* that bestowed it on me."

But he obviously would feel sullied by participating in a Party function, thought Kondratiev bitterly. As if there were any real differences between the government and the Party. Oh, how fastidious our intelligentsia have grown since Stalin's death: some like

Perventsev with their silly scruples; others like his daughter with their even sillier rebelliousness and daydreams; while the great bulk observe conformity, for careerist reasons, but sneer privately at their government and its uncouth leader. If this continues, they'll have nobody but themselves to blame when Lunin and his like get their way and the Party comes down on them, and hard.

This made him reflect once more about Khrushchev's leadership. Why should Perventsev have doubts about the first secretary's position? Probably another faulty conclusion of the Russian intelligentsia: if the ruler does not crack the whip, he must be in trouble. Kondratiev's own peculiar public opinion poll on the question was not particularly reassuring. Marfa, his house servant, volunteered, "Oh, Nikita Sergeievich, he is a good man." Trofim had said, "Comrade Khrushchev does not put on any airs. He is like one of us."

Did the Russians really want their ruler to be just like one of them? Anyway, how could it matter? Well, it might. What the people thought somehow, as if by osmosis, affected the lower and middle ranks of the Party hierarchy. And if those elements felt that the masses were losing their respect for the boss, it might affect the Central Committee's attitude when and if it came to a clash between Khrushchev and Lunin. But then a real clash that would bring the issue of leadership again before the Central Committee was most unlikely, unless something verging on the inconceivable *were* to happen.

But there was no one in sight to replace Khrushchev. Lunin himself realized he did not have what it took. Leontiev? He was a firm supporter of the first secretary, and on a few occasions when even Kondratiev had hesitated on whether to support some new proposal, he would lecture him in private about the inadmissibility of challenging Nikita.

"It can only encourage the renegades in Beijing, make us look weak in the eyes of our people and ridiculous before the rest of the world."

The inconceivable happened a few weeks later. Khrushchev announced out of the blue that it would be a good idea to split the local Party apparatus into agricultural and industrial sectors. Viktorov hung down his head.

"Would that mean," asked Lunin, trying to keep incredulity

out of his voice, "that, say, the Moscow region Party organization would have two first secretaries, one for agriculture and one for industry?"

"Precisely. This should have a beneficial effect on the entire economy."

"And which one would have the ultimate authority over matters like personnel, propaganda, and the like?"

"Those are details to be worked out at our next meeting . . . And, incidentally, I thought our deliberations would greatly benefit from the presence of a number of Party activists, economists, and other experts."

"I move that we approve this creative initiative of Nikita Sergeievich," broke in Leontiev.

And so it was approved. Members of the Central Committee, when in turn presented with the plan, were somewhat dazed, but also voted for it unanimously. There was a tragicomic incident during the session. Gabayev, who for reasons mysterious to Kondratiev had just been appointed by Khrushchev as First Secretary of the Uzbekistan Party and co-opted into the Politburo, announced that the working masses of his region had greeted enthusiastically this brilliant, truly Leninist plan of Comrade Khrushchev's. This provoked a gale of laughter, and the Uzbek looked around in confusion.

"Your working masses must be endowed with a remarkable power of clairvoyance. The plan to restructure the Party has not been made public." Khrushchev tried to sound sarcastic, but his face was purple. He had disregarded his colleagues' hints that Gabayev did not have the intelligence to run a village soviet, let alone an important Party organization.

The unfortunate man launched into an incoherent explanation: after the Politburo decision, he had thought it permissible to prepare his countrymen for such a momentous measure; it was a peculiar quality of Comrade Khrushchev's leadership that he could discern in concrete terms the ideas already sprouting in the people's minds. Some continued laughing. The more compassionate cheered.

In July the Politburo discussed—this time, thank God, without outsiders except for the minister of defense and chief of staff of the armed forces—the menacing developments in Southeast Asia. Indonesia was now clearly leaning more and more toward

Beijing. Pressure from the same source was making Hanoi intensify the Vietcong activities in the South. The Soviets' advice to the North Vietnamese to be cautious and prudent and their prediction that the Diem regime would soon fall of its own weight and rottenness were being ignored.

"The Mao gang is clearly intent on setting a trap for us. The Americans are quite likely to respond to the increased pressure on the South by aggression against the North. The latter will then suddenly realize that all the Chinese will do is to cheer them on, and they will expect *us* to protect them from the Yankees."

Khrushchev turned to the military men. "You have the information."

Both the minister and the chief of staff declared that, barring some new development, there was no doubt that after the presidential election the Johnson Administration was going to initiate systematic bombing of the North, perhaps even follow it with an invasion.

"These are the same sources that kept us so accurately informed during the Cuban crisis," added the marshal.

"What do we do, then? Warn the Americans? They'll think we are bluffing. Sit idly by while a Communist state is being devastated? Then quite possibly we would have an explosion in Warsaw, Prague, or all over Eastern Europe! NATO is again talking about giving West Germany access to nuclear weapons."

Never before had the first secretary sounded so indecisive, asking rather than telling them what should be done.

"Inform the Vietnamese comrades that since they keep rejecting our advice, they should seek help from Beijing if they get themselves into a mess with the Americans," suggested Leontiev.

"They would not listen. And no, this would not be like Korea. I remember Mao telling me in '59, 'You'll never again get us to pull your chestnuts out of the fire.' *Our* chestnuts, that son of a bitch!"

"We must not allow ourselves to be provoked." Lunin had evidently forgotten his erstwhile strictures about ideological solidarity. "The Americans are way ahead of us in rockets, and—"

"And what difference could it make if we were ahead three, four times as strong? Our Fatherland would still be left crippled for decades, while those criminals in Beijing—"

Khrushchev was now sputtering with rage. "You have all read

about Mao's latest swinishness—that interview with Japanese journalists where he brands us as imperialists, says we stole Mongolia and large areas of Asia from China, robbed Poland and Rumania of parts of their territories during the war. Why can't the Americans get it through their thick skulls that the real danger to peace comes from Beijing, not some beggarly guerrillas in Vietnam? Their grandchildren will curse them!"

"There are highly placed Chinese comrades who recognize the folly of Mao's anti-Soviet policies and are trying to change them."

The first secretary would not be consoled. "I wish I could believe that, Konstantin. They *all* hate us, the only difference being that he wants to have the pleasure of seeing us bleed before he croaks; the others prefer to wait until they build up their economy and military power."

His extreme agitation made it difficult for him to concentrate on the actual problem before them. It fell to Leontiev to steer the discussion toward concrete measures. It was agreed that Hanoi should be advised that if it clashed with the U.S., Soviet aid would be confined to military supplies and economic assistance. Articles in the press should stress the rumors that America is about to embark on warlike ventures in Southeast Asia.

"Should such rumors prove true, the USSR government will not fail to take the appropriate steps to rebuff the forces of aggression and imperialism."

The majority rejected Kondratiev's suggestion that Poland's ambassador in Washington be instructed to drop an "indiscretion": Moscow strongly believed that any American move against North Vietnam would play right into the Chinese Communists' hands. There was an almost fatalistic feeling that another dangerous crisis was in the offing. They were about to conclude the meeting, when Gabayev, who as a rule kept silent on foreign policy, suddenly spoke up:

"I don't see any reason to be depressed. The Americans would never be able to subdue the heroic Vietnamese people. The Hanoi comrades will have to realize that the Soviet Union is their true friend. And Mao and his gang will come to rue the day when they embarked on this perfidious game."

Nobody bothered to take notice of his remark, with its idiotic optimism; how could you argue with a man whose mentality was that of the rawest Komsomol recruit?

Years later, a newcomer to the Politburo would often confide to Kondratiev his amazement that someone as stupid as Gabayev could continue as a member of that august body, not to mention the most recent scandals in his Uzbekistan. Mikhail Alexandrovich would try to keep a straight face as he explained to the questioner that, dumb as he was, Rashid Gafarovich had the gift of clairvoyance: "Here is what he told us in July 1964 . . ."

At the time, Kondratiev emerged from the meeting shaken, and not only because of the impending crisis in Southeast Asia. Had Nikita lost his grip, or was it a temporary aberration such as had happened occasionally during the past ten years? He shared this concern, in circumspect terms, with Viktorov, when spending a weekend at the latter's dacha.

Alexander Ivanovich was lost in thought for a minute. "I've thought of that, too. And one of our colleagues—I don't have to tell you who—has sought my opinion on the question of whether the burden of being both first secretary and prime minister is not proving too heavy for a man of Nikita Sergeievich's years . . . There was also just a hint that the latter job, having to do mostly with economic matters, ought to go to someone like myself."

"Of course you would be ideal in it," exclaimed Kondratiev. "But . . . but, Nikita would never agree. He would see it as a repudiation of his leadership. He would fight, or resign altogether."

"That's what I also said. I am ready to serve in whatever position is entrusted to me. I have had serious reservations about some of our most recent policies and practices. But I told our friend I would not lend my hand to precipitating a leadership crisis at a time like this."

But he had *not* definitely said no to becoming chairman of the Council of Ministers. Things had gone pretty far. Who was Lunin's candidate for first secretary? Himself? Hard to believe.

During the next few days, Mikhail Alexandrovich pondered his own position. He rehearsed his speech for when and if the issue came to a vote in the Politburo, or if Lunin attempted to enlist him in his camp . . . There was an American proverb, 'You don't swap horses midstream.' All the storm clouds over Asia! How could they afford to appear divided at a time like this? The majority would undoubtedly see it in the same light. Then, in most people's minds, his own career had been linked ever since

1953 with that of Khrushchev. If Lunin took over, he would very likely be dropped from the Politburo and become a mere minister or ambassador.

For the moment, the commotion over Vietnam subsided, even though intelligence reports kept insisting that, for all the denials in his campaign speeches, Johnson when reelected (and that was taken for granted) planned a major move in Southeast Asia.

There was a ray of hope concerning China. Confidential reports confirmed that the majority of Beijing's Party oligarchy were bracing for a confrontation with Mao, who had clearly grown senile and was increasingly under his wife's thumb.

"They could very well have a civil war." Leontiev voiced what had been the unspoken prayer of many of them for quite some time.

"If they do, let's hope that the healthy elements within the Chinese Party would prevail in that struggle," said Lunin, piously.

"But pray God, let the struggle be lengthy," added Kuliabko, the new head of the Ukrainian Central Committee, whose wit and vivacity had favorably impressed Kondratiev.

Buoyed by such possibilities, Khrushchev appeared to have recovered his spirits. He sketched his travel plans before the Politburo. If the comrades agreed, he proposed to go in September to Prague.

"The Czechs are dragging their feet with de-Stalinization. If they keep following the old ways and don't rehabilitate the victims of the period of the cult of personality, they'll come a cropper one of these days."

In November, if the present secret negotiations with Bonn succeeded, he would visit West Germany.

"Now that the old devil Adenauer is gone, we can make the Germans realize they have a lot to gain by having friendly relations with us. If that works, I'll propose to the American president to hold a summit meeting in December or January. Perhaps we can get some sense into the Americans' thick skulls. Johnson sounds like a man with whom you can do business. It is his advisers who are pushing him into that Vietnamese trap set up by Beijing."

Announcements of Nikita Sergeievich's travel plans usually aroused apprehension among his associates. This time there were no objections about the itinerary or the issues he would take up with the West: Soviet guarantees about free access to Berlin in return for a formal recognition of the German Democratic Republic, a nuclear nonproliferation treaty, increased trade between East and West. This was again the sober, purposeful Khrushchev, and Kondratiev felt assured. He was clearly in charge once again.

And then the first secretary dropped a bombshell. "We have a Central Committee meeting scheduled for the middle of October. By that time, Comrade Solovyov's commission on the Kirov case will have completed its report, and it will be placed on the agenda."

"Am I correct in assuming that we would be able to discuss the report before it is placed before the committee?" asked Lunin.

"Certainly, Pyotr Nikolayevich, you will be getting the draft within days."

One week later, having declined an invitation to an embassy dinner, Mikhail Alexandrovich sat in his library—three thick typescripts bound in soft red covers stacked in front of him. He leafed impatiently though File One. It contained the original official version of the assassination, and the deposition of Nikolayev and others sentenced for planning and committing the murder. The second volume bore the heading *Testimony of the Witnesses and of Others Inculpated in Connection with the Crime.*

There it was: his own signed deposition, word for word. He turned back to the beginning of the volume. In his agitation and haste to look under the letter *K*, he had skipped the introduction, which stated that since most of the "testimonies" presented in File Two had been obtained under duress and were palpably false, these materials were being distributed only for the private and confidential information of the members of the Politburo and would not be included in the final report to be presented to the Central Committee. Who else was here? Yes, two other full members of the Politburo, then young men, testified that they had heard from their acquaintances (who were subsequently tried and condemned) that Zinoviev and Trotsky had nourished special hatred against Comrade Kirov. Some relief. Still, why circulate the damnable thing in the first place? The third volume was entitled *New Materials and the Commission's Conclusions.* Evidence suppressed at the time clearly indicated that the confessions of Nikolayev and his alleged accomplices had been obtained through the accused's having been drugged and tortured. There was clear proof that during the months preceding the murder, the culprit had had contacts with "individuals, now deceased, who at the time were in the entourage of V.

M. Molotov and G. M. Malenkov, then high officials, currently retired, having been expelled from the Party in 1961 for their long-standing factional and anti-Party activities." He put down his glasses. It was very bright in the room. He looked at his watch. It was seven o'clock in the morning.

"No, it is necessary, Misha." Khrushchev was watching him intently. "The Solovyov Report must see the light of day."

It was the fourth of October. Khrushchev was about to set out on his belated Crimean vacation. The meeting of the Central Committee had been scheduled for the sixteenth. When assembled, its members would find on their desks that somewhat shortened and expurgated version of the third part of the Solovyov Report.

"As I said at the Politburo meeting, I simply don't see the point, and the consequences—"

"I wasn't born yesterday. You think I may be putting my head on the block. I know what Lunin is up to. He won't get anywhere. You saw how quiet he was at the meeting. Well, he is not going to remain a Central Committee secretary much longer, and in a year or so we will ease him out completely. He will make a tolerable director of the Institute of Marxism-Leninism, dried-out dogmatist that he is. Or an ambassador to China. He would feel at home there."

Nikita Sergeievich chuckled in obvious relish at the thought of his antagonist's discomfiture.

"But the effect on the Party, throughout the world . . . Besides, those people are dead, and there is no tangible proof that Molotov and Malenkov—"

"Of course they were behind the killing. At one time I thought it was the old bastard himself who arranged it. And now we have clear indications . . . Molotov was Number 2 then, Malenkov rising rapidly, and here they saw Kirov, whom they loathed, getting ahead of them . . . You have some special reason to think they did not instigate the murder? Then who? That half-wit would not have done it on his own."

Kondratiev remained silent. He later on wondered what he would have done had Khrushchev continued looking into his eyes, but the latter suddenly got up, went to a file cabinet, and came back carrying a thick sheaf of correspondence. He tossed it on the desk.

"Here, just one week's collection. You can read them."

But then, impatiently, he pulled out a letter himself and began to read. The writer, a worker from Kalinin, expressed his disappointment and outrage that "those villains whom you, Comrade Khrushchev, have denounced so justly for their complicity in the crimes of that unhappy era have hitherto not only escaped answering for their deeds, but are living comfortably on their pensions."

"It is not easy to answer such letters. But more painful are the ones that simply ask, 'Why?' Why was their father, mother, son, suddenly snatched away and made to rot or die in a camp?"

He turned his head away from Kondratiev and slowly, in a voice that did not seem his own, said, "But those are not the hardest to take. This is."

And, still not looking at Kondratiev, he handed him a sheet. It was from the widow of a prominent Ukrainian Communist. The woman expressed her gratitude to the Party and to Khrushchev personally for rehabilitating her husband, shot in the purges. "And so, for restoring my dear Volodya's good name, I thank you, Nikita Sergeievich, from the bottom of my heart."

"Thanking *me*. I signed the resolution excluding him from the Party in 1938, which was then the equivalent of a death warrant. That man . . . he turned us all into swine. But he could not have done it without those Molotovs, Malenkovs, and others who fed and abetted his suspiciousness and lust for blood. And you are trying to tell me they've been punished enough."

It was the most difficult decision he had had to make since that day in December 1934, Kondratiev kept telling himself as he left the first secretary's office. Of course, Nikita was right, absolutely right. But it was equally clear that Nikita's days in power were numbered. He was so wrought up emotionally that his political instincts were failing him. He thus overlooked that the very fact that the proposal to present the Solovyov Report passed the Politburo with so little discussion was a sign of major trouble brewing. He had told them that Molotov and Malenkov would not be put on trial: "Let them live out the rest of their miserable lives in shame."

But from what he had just said, it was obvious that indeed a trial was very much on his mind. How could one be certain that File Two would not also be made public? Was it inconceivable that Mikhail Alexandrovich Kondratiev could be summoned to testify?

Did Molotov or Malenkov know the truth about the Kirov affair? Given their positions at the time, it would be odd if they didn't. But he remembered Stalin's words to him in 1943, "You and I share a secret," and his last audience with the tyrant. No, he was almost sure that no one alive, save himself, knew what *must* have happened.

Waking up in the middle of the night, he realized that his silent soliloquy of the preceding afternoon had been pointless. The report would never reach the Central Committee. Khrushchev would go down before the meeting. Was there any sense in sacrificing his own career, his dreams of what he would do for the country, for a lost cause? It was probably too late anyway—otherwise, by now he would have been approached by Lunin or someone else in on the plot. Still . . .

The first part of his premonition was confirmed on the ninth of October. He was discussing the forthcoming visit to Moscow by the president of Indonesia with Karsavin, now a Central Committee secretary but still in overall charge of the security apparatus, when the latter sighed.

"He could not be coming here at a more inappropriate time."

Kondratiev immediately understood, but thought it best to say jocularly, "You mean, it coincides with the Central Committee meeting. But one does not have to interfere with the other. Your people can surely find some feminine company for the president, who much prefers it to lengthy discussions with government leaders, anyway. He'll be able to amuse himself while we are busy."

"I don't mean that, Mikhail Alexandrovich. Comrade Lunin and some others would like the committee to begin its deliberations on the thirteenth, rather than on the sixteenth. We wonder whether you would go along with the idea?"

Kondratiev smiled—Karsavin, one man whom Khrushchev trusted implicitly. "Why not? On second thought, a state visit might interfere with our business . . . When would Nikita Sergeievich be notified?"

"After the committee votes on a resolution proposed by Comrade Lunin on behalf of all the remaining members of the Politburo . . . that is, if you and Comrade Viktorov decide to support it."

"I support it," said Kondratiev, after a pause. Even if he decided to warn Nikita, it would be much too late—a useless self-sacrifice.

"I am sure that if he sees your signature under the resolution, Viktorov would add his."

Karsavin was obviously greatly relieved, but the dislike that Mikhail Alexandrovich had felt toward him turned into instant loathing when the youngster (as Kondratiev thought of him, despite his forty-one years) saw fit to add, "Nobody regrets this tragic necessity more than I do. Nikita Sergeievich has been like a father to me."

Next day, the notables gathered in secret to distribute the offices that would be vacated. Lunin primly refused to consider becoming first secretary, but was visibly rather disappointed that nobody tried to press him. Viktorov genuinely, and Leontiev much less convincingly so, tried to resist, but finally agreed to be the successors, as Prime Minister and General Secretary, respectively.

On October 14, Khrushchev was summoned from his Crimean retreat. He was met at the airport by Karsavin, who gave him the news that the Lunin motion was bound to pass with an overwhelming majority, if not unanimously, and that it would be only seemly if he were to volunteer his resignation. Nikita's response was to slap the face of his erstwhile favorite. For two hours he ranted and raved before the committee, removing any lingering doubts of his would-be defenders. Then, in the middle of a sentence, he suddenly stopped and sat down. A few minutes later, he walked out of the room.

The motion carried unanimously: The committee "acceded to the request of Comrade N. S. Khrushchev that, in view of his age and ailing health, he be relieved of his Party and state offices."

"He certainly was a vulgar man," declared Irina in one of her rare pronouncements on politics. (The use of the past tense was characteristic; for the mass of Soviet citizens, the man who had fallen from such heights was dead.) "Imagine, he told an artist acquaintance of mine whose work he did not like that only a homosexual could paint like that. And the language he used! He once asked me whether it was true that my friend Tamara was 'screwing' Leontiev."

A few years later, Kondratiev was informed by Nina Petrovna, with whom he kept in touch concerning her husband's health and needs, that her husband would appreciate his visit. He drove to Khrushchev's suburban villa, much as he knew that his colleagues would twit him for misplaced sentimentality. It did turn out to be a melancholy occasion. Mikhail Alexandrovich was reminded of the French proverb, "Old age is like a shipwreck." Nikita Sergeievich was visibly failing. He talked plaintively about having nothing to do.

"Believe me, Misha, for a politician not to be in the midst of things is like having his balls cut off."

He rambled on about the international situation. Kondratiev carefully skirted any subject having to do with domestic politics. As he got up to leave, the fallen leader took his hand and for a while did not let it go. "Thanks, Misha." There was a flash of the old shrewdness in his eyes. "Tell me one thing. It was the Solovyov Report, wasn't it?"

Taken by surprise, he could only stutter, "No, I mean, that was not the main thing."

"I don't hold it against you. I understand it was you who persuaded the others to allow my recollections to be sent abroad without too many deletions. An old man's vanity. I want to be remembered as having done some good for the Fatherland, for peace."

"Of course you have, Nikita Sergeievich, and it will be remembered. The record of history cannot be erased."

The minute it came out, he realized how silly it must sound to a man whose name had not been mentioned in print, as much as once, during the past six years. Khrushchev's loud, cackling laughter was only stopped by a coughing fit.

"Forgive me," he said, dabbing his eyes, "but I don't think most of your colleagues would endorse that statement." He gripped his visitor's hand again: "I thought I would live to see you lead the Party, but now I doubt I shall make it. I hope you will. Good-bye, and God be with you." Sixty years of belief in a rival creed had not obliterated the habit of speech acquired at home and in the village school of his childhood.

Chapter 10

MOSCOW, OCTOBER 1982

The first frosts brought with them a preview of the grim Russian winter. Muscovites wondered if it was going to be grimmer than usual. Already on some days, coffee and meat were unobtainable, except in restaurants and factory canteens. There were stories of bread being rationed in several provincial towns. With the summer barely over, it was already difficult to obtain fresh vegetables.

There were the usual attempts to blame the deficiencies on the derelictions of the lower and not-so-low officials. The minister of food industry was dismissed on charges of "maintaining a lackadaisical style of work and tolerating serious abuses in the agencies subject to his supervision." Two of his deputies were not only fired but thrown out of the Party. The chief of the vegetable and fruit trust for the city of Moscow received a stiff prison sentence "for his criminal negligence in safeguarding socialist property and allowing a large quantity of produce to be spoiled because of inadequate provision for proper storage." Finally, the manager of the city's largest store was sentenced to death, guilty of "diverting a sizable quantity of foodstuffs for his own and his relatives' use and profit."

"And why, pray tell," asked Smirnov of Kondratiev, when they found themselves at some distance from other guests at a reception in the Bulgarian embassy, "doesn't our dynamic secretary for agriculture receive as much as a slap on the wrist? He is certainly more responsible for the whole mess than some store manager with sticky fingers."

"This is neither the place nor the time for such talk, Dmitri Pavlovich," replied Kondratiev, noticing that the others, as usual when Politburo members were engaged in private talk, were eyeing them surreptitiously while pretending to carry on conversations of their own.

Smirnov, however, seemed incapable of letting up on Kubiak, unpolitic as it was to allow even the slightest hint of a private vendetta between two such potentates to leak out. The text of the speech he proposed to deliver to the Party officials in Kuibyshev contained a passage stating that in the sixty-fifth year of the Soviet power, "our people enjoy material and cultural amenities of life that were undreamed of before the Revolution and are now the object of impotent envy by the capitalists as they struggle to quell the rising wave of protests by their working class against the poverty and unemployment that has gripped the West. But we Communists never rest on our laurels. Our citizens are entitled to a greater variety and better quality in consumer goods than that which they are presently getting, especially when it comes to food. It behooves our Party and government officials charged with those sectors of the economy to improve their style of work, or if incapable of effecting improvements, to give way to those who are."

The text, when circulated to the members of the Politburo for comments, aroused violent objections. He would be quite interested to know, declared Kubiak, what practical suggestions Comrade Smirnov had in mind for improvements in his department of the Central Committee. Perhaps he could come up with some ideas on how they could control the weather that had been responsible for the poor harvests of the last few years. But it would help if the local Party secretaries selected by the Personnel Department for the main agricultural regions were people with some knowledge of the subject who paid some attention to what was happening in the farms in their districts, rather than dozing over their desks.

Smirnov was about to say something in reply, but Leontiev stopped the discussion.

"Enough. You had better eliminate that last sentence from your speech, Dmitri Pavlovich. We do not wash our dirty laundry in public. And as you know, Valentin Valentinovich, Comrade

Smirnov's Personnel Department does not *appoint* the local secretaries. It nominates them subject to approval by this body: you have as much right to object to individual names as anyone else."

The incident did not enhance either man's standing or chances for the succession. But Kondratiev was aware that his own position was still not invulnerable. The story of his behavior in Kiev had strengthened the lurking suspicion that, once general secretary, his hand would weigh quite heavily on the local bosses, especially the non-Russian ones.

"If you will forgive me for saying so, I think you were too harsh there," Kuliabko told him. "A boor like Vishnevsky does deserve a kick in the ass. But why show your hand prematurely? One of the people who was there told me, 'He carried himself like a tsarist minister addressing some benighted provincial officials.' I told him I have been a friend of yours for thirty years, in good and bad times, and I've never detected the slightest touch of condescension or prejudice against non-Russians. He only shook his head as if he still had doubts on that point. And this is an honest Communist, not one of Vishnevsky's gang. For Heaven's sake, Misha, must you be so high-minded *now?* Save your sermons and ammunition for when the power is yours. You Russians are reputed to be prudent and calculating. I, as a Ukrainian, am supposed to be emotional and impulsive. But honestly, at times it is the other way around."

"Maybe one of my female ancestors was guilty of an indiscretion with a Ukrainian steward on her estate," Kondratiev said, trying to parry what he recognized as a fair criticism with a joke.

But Kuliabko was not amused. "Misha, this is the time to be serious and prudent. You have no right to be impulsive or frivolous with so much at stake."

Mikhail Alexandrovich doodled for a time on a pad in front of him and then raised his eyes; his friend was still looking at him censoriously and questioningly. "I realize, Mykola, I laid it on too thick in Kiev. Something took place the night before that—Well, believe me, it will not happen again."

Alleged haughtiness toward local dignitaries was not the only complaint being brought against Kondratiev in what was clearly preliminary sparring for the succession. A rumor, obviously contrived, was circulating that Mikhail Alexandrovich had misled the leadership about the probable reaction by the West to the USSR's breaking off the arms control negotiations. He had, it was insinuated, virtually guaranteed to the Politburo that the Soviets' walking out would throw the Western European governments into a panic, make them refuse to deploy U.S. intermediate and cruise missiles on their soil, and thus practically force Washington to beg Moscow to renew the negotiations, and on the latter's terms. And here were the Germans, British, and the others—reluctantly, to be sure—preparing the bases for installation of the deadly weapons, some of which would be capable of wreaking destruction on Moscow and other points in the European USSR in a matter of a few minutes. Where, it was asked in some Party circles, was that intuitive grasp of the Western capitalists' mentality and politics which, according to his partisans, was such an outstanding attribute of Mikhail Alexandrovich's and would thus make him particularly suitable to lead the country and the Party through these perilous times?

An unsigned *Pravda* editorial spoke scathingly of certain unnamed Party activists "who unwittingly tend to lull the vigilance of our people by underestimating the cunning and malevolence of the warmongering faction in the Washington administration. For all the clearly expressed wishes for peace and friendly relations with the USSR on the part of the great majority of the people of Western Europe, the U.S. military-industrial complex has succeeded, with the assistance of the German revanchists, in forcing Bonn to prepare installations for weapons that could strike into the heart of our country. The same warmongering gang is now trying similar blackmailing tactics on other NATO governments."

There were other hints in the article, incomprehensible to the vast majority of readers, but easily decipherable to those in the upper Party ranks—how some "even in fairly high positions" minimize the danger arising from the current machinations of the U.S. government and are too ready to dismiss as mere rhetoric slanderous statements about socialism and brazen threats against the USSR emanating from the White House. "But the Soviet people may rest assured that those charged with the protection of our Socialist Fatherland realize that there is only one thing the imperialist warmongers understand, and that is strength and the constant readiness of our glorious armed forces to rebuff any provocations against the USSR and its allies with an instant and crushing blow."

"But this is simply outrageous!" exclaimed Gorbunov after ascertaining that Kondratiev had read the article. "I don't see how you can take it so calmly. It is a vicious, thinly veiled attack on you. How could it have been authorized by the Propaganda Department?"

"I suspect that it came from another source. But don't worry. It will backfire."

And indeed, at the next session of the Politburo, Viktorov asked leave to take up the matter of the article in question. It was a fairly transparent attack on a member of this body, something quite inadmissible, quite apart from the fact that the views attributed to the anonymous "man in a fairly high position" were grossly distorted.

"How could a scandalous piece of trash like this have been allowed to appear, Pyotr Nikolayevich?"

Lunin, with obvious embarrassment, explained that the piece had been authored by one Afinogenov, until fairly recently a section head in the Agricultural Department of the Secretariat. Since he himself was indisposed at the time, it had been authorized for publication by one of his deputies, who had read it hurriedly and missed the insinuations. Afinogenov had been fired and barred from journalistic work for three years. His careless deputy had been relieved of his functions. Both would appear before the Party Control Commission, which would consider further sanctions.

"Not enough," exclaimed Kuliabko. "The writer should be put away in a camp."

"We shall move on to the regular agenda," announced Leontiev.

After the session, the general secretary invited Kondratiev to his office to take tea. "I hope you'll appreciate why I didn't want to have more fuss made over that disgraceful episode. This is hardly the time for us to have clashes, mutual recriminations, and similar unpleasantness within the Politburo. What do you think?"

"My own feelings should not be the uppermost consideration in this case," answered Kondratiev slowly. "But the article in question has been taken up by the foreign press, and is seen abroad as an indication that we reject the very idea of negotiating with America, and that our leadership believes that a nuclear clash is almost inevitable."

"Pyotr Nikolayevich has instructed the editors to correct any such misunderstanding. There will be several authoritative pieces repudiating that idiot's article. And Lunin is taking special care that the contents of our leading journals are scrutinized more scrupulously, so the little misunderstandings that may arise among ourselves do not get out."

They sipped in silence, and finally the general secretary, a mischievous twinkle in his eye, said, "We wouldn't be having all these problems if I suddenly dropped dead, or if by some miracle my health should get much better."

"I shall vote for the second part of the motion," Kondratiev reacted instantly, "provided 'should' is changed to 'will,' and 'by some miracle' is omitted."

Konstantin Leonidovich threw back his head and laughed. "Oh, Misha, you do have the knack of saying the right thing at the right moment. That already has been noted—guess by whom?"

Kondratiev looked surprised. Leontiev did not usually like to refer to Stalin. The general secretary understood his puzzlement: "Yes, it was him. He was uncanny in his ability to size up people, often with very unfortunate results for the person in question. But you he liked.

"As a matter of fact, I do feel better. I am going to give those speeches in the south, next week. That will put the rumors to rest. Also, an American congressional delegation is coming to Moscow, and believe me, talking to those senators for one hour is worse for my blood pressure than the most strenuous speaking tour. You will deputize for me, and you know what to say if they become a nuisance about the dissidents, Jews, and similar stuff."

"Zdrastvuite, ya Senator Stuart z, z, Kalifornia," stammered out the oldest of the senators, a lanky, gray-haired man in horn-rimmed spectacles. "Good afternoon. I am Senator Stuart from California," translated the interpreter instantaneously, as they all burst into laughter.

"Thank you, Lukin, but I do know Russian," said Kondratiev to the young man, who blushed deeply. "As a matter of fact, I would propose that we speak English. It would save time."

"Did I say it correctly?" asked the senator, timidly.

"The accent was perfect; a very minor error—the name of the state should have been in the genitive. We once had a philologist who claimed that English was a more progressive language than Russian. You do not have all those cases, aspects, and other peculiarities that bedevil foreigners." (The man, he remembered vaguely, who was foolish enough to propound that thesis in 1938 or 1939, had been stripped of his professorship, and sent to a camp.) "I certainly would not go that far, but I enjoy speaking your beautiful language. You just take notes, Lukin."

The ice was broken, and Senator Stuart launched into preliminary civilities: how enchanted they were with the historic sights of Moscow and Leningrad, how many more cars he saw now in the streets than on his last visit here some years ago.

"We should really have more Americans visiting your country, and vice versa. I am sure it would have a most beneficial effect on relations between the two nations. Even though I'm sixty-five, I plan to start seriously to learn your language, genitives and all."

"Yes, we have all enjoyed the sights," his colleague broke in somewhat impatiently, "but there are some serious issues we would like to discuss, Mr. —— how do we address you?"

Mikhail Alexandrovich smiled (didn't they brief them in the embassy?). "People here—who are, as you would put it, stuffy—would say 'Comrade Secretary of the Central Committee,' but that would sound as artificial as my calling you 'Mr. Assistant Majority Whip' or 'Senior Senator from Minnesota.' So let it be Mr. Kondratiev and Mr. O'Dell, OK?"

The American refused to be mollified by his affability. "We had hoped, Mr. Kondratiev, to discuss these issues with Chairman Leontiev. Do we understand you can speak for him?"

It would not do to show irritation at the man's atrocious manners, thought Kondratiev. "Comrade Leontiev, who, by the way, expresses his regrets—his speaking engagements had been arranged some months ago—has authorized me to express the views of the Soviet government on some issues that may be of interest to our countries. There are others on which only he, the leader of our state, can give the authoritative answer."

The discussion went on as it might have been expected: the arms limitation talks, Afghanistan, the Helsinki Declaration. On the first, Kondratiev professed that he did not understand some of the technical terms used, called for the interpreter's help, and finally threw up his hands in mock despair.

"As you see, I am a civilian. I do not understand what those acronyms stand for and all those technical issues with the SS-18, SS-20, and so on."

"But you were the head of the delegation to the strategic arms limitation talks only three months ago," the odious senator pursued his point relentlessly.

"Oh, in Geneva I left all that mysterious business to our scientific military experts, and our soldiers do not always share their secrets with us civilians. Isn't it the same in your country?"

"Generals are the same everywhere. They always want more weapons, more men, more money," Stuart chuckled. "Couldn't we civilians on both sides say to them: Enough, let's stop at what we have now?"

O'Dell gave him a furious look.

"Yes," said Kondratiev reflectively, "what you are saying comes close to Chairman Leontiev's proposal: a mutual freeze on the production of both tactical and strategic nuclear weapons. Our countries are about equal in both categories. So why waste money and resources on weapons of destruction rather than devoting them to constructive uses for the welfare of our two nations?"

O'Dell opened his mouth, but then shrugged his shoulders and said nothing.

Other subjects did not prove more amenable to discussion. Kondratiev purported not to know too much about Afghanistan. He could only repeat what the official policy of his government was: a friendly state bound to the USSR by a treaty of alliance had requested Soviet help to fight foreign-inspired and foreign-sponsored subversion of its sovereignty. As soon as foreign incursions on Afghanistan's soil ceased, the USSR would withdraw the limited contingent of troops it had sent there to help a fraternal nation.

"You could not deny, Mr. O'Dell—why, your own press speaks openly about it—that the CIA sends weapons and other equipment to the so-called freedom fighters?"

Again O'Dell was about to say something, but thought better of it. There was a moment of silence, broken finally by Senator Neuwald of Pennsylvania, who had hitherto not participated in the discussion.

"I guess all these ticklish problems will have to continue to be explored by our governments. But may I ask you something, Mr. Kondratiev, which bears on the obligations your government has freely and solemnly subscribed to under the Helsinki Accords?"

"You can ask me anything and everything. We have nothing to hide."

Neuwald, who appeared a bit nervous, began, "There is a considerable interest in our country"—but then stopped and blurted out, "Why don't you let those Jews who want to leave the USSR emigrate?"

"We do. In the last decade we have permitted about a quarter of a million people, Soviet citizens mostly of Jewish nationality, to emigrate legally. In my frank opinion, most of those people have been beguiled by Zionist propaganda that has painted life in Israel as a veritable bed of roses. Many of them have, since then, repented of this foolhardy step. We have received numerous requests by people disillusioned by the conditions there who want to be allowed to return to the Soviet Union. If the appropriate organs decide that the person in question is genuinely determined to resume the duties and rights of a Soviet citizen, we let them."

"But there are many others who are being refused permission to leave."

"Each case, insofar as I know—again, this is not my department—is considered on its own merits. Some of these misguided people have aged parents and simply want to shirk their obligations. Yes, Mr. Neuwald, we consider the family a bulwark of our Socialist society, and feel its members have obligations toward each other, as well as to society at large. Others are people who want to avoid the consequences of their crimes and other antisocial acts—"

"Isn't this 'crime,' in most cases, simply that they consider themselves Jews, feel discriminated against, and want to go to what they believe is their own country?" broke in O'Dell.

Kondratiev raised his eyebrows. "You know as well as I do that for all their alleged love for Israel, many, perhaps most, very soon leave it to move to the U.S., or even go there directly, once out of our country. We have made considerable progress in improving the standard of living of our people. But I shall not deny, as some of our overzealous propagandists do, that in some respects we have not yet caught up with America. In time, we will. Again, some of those unfortunate persons fall for the tales that in the U.S., the streets are paved with gold and one does not really have to work strenuously to make a living. They go to New York and Boston and find a different picture: there you also have to work hard, and as often as not, you will not find a job.

"A man who repented and came back told me a joke current among our former Soviet fellow citizens: One émigré asks another, 'Have you gotten established already?' 'No,' is the answer. 'I still have to keep working.' Such people, indeed, we don't need in our country, where the vast majority of the Soviet citizens of *all* nationalities are proud to work hard, knowing that they are contributing to a better life for all."

Senator Stuart sighed audibly, and there was a period of uncomfortable silence. Mikhail Alexandrovich, who by now wondered how his visitors had ever managed to impress their constituents enough to be elected, resumed.

"Anti-Semitism is punishable under Soviet law. I am sorry to admit that sixty-five years of socialism have not *completely* eliminated that stupid prejudice among all our people. And so one encounters an occasional boor who might say, 'Those Jews, they shirk work and seek an easy life.' If he says it publicly, he is liable to criminal prosecution. But the great majority of our people of all nationalities have entirely discarded such vulgar prejudices.

"Discrimination? My chief scientific adviser at the arms limitation talks, a very sensitive position, was a Jew. Some of the most crucial posts in our state apparatus are occupied by persons of the same ethnic background. Read the names of members of our Academy of Sciences, and you'll see that the percentage of Jews there is way out of proportion to that in the total population of the USSR. And by common sense, how could a state and movement that claims Karl Marx as one of its progenitors tolerate discrimination against our Jewish fellow citizens? Such slanders are simply grist for the mill to those who want to poison relations between our peoples.

"Some of my countrymen when confronted with the charge of anti-Semitism would say impulsively, 'And how do you treat your Blacks?' I shall not, because I know that all enlightened Americans have been striving toward the goal of racial equality, and I wish you complete success in achieving it. So let's not cast aspersions on each other: our two great nations comprise many ethnic groups and races, face many problems on that score, but are fighting successfully to overcome them. We live in the twentieth century."

"You would have been great on my college debating team,"

said O'Dell, and for the first time smiled. The rest of the session went on more amicably. Yes, they were free to look up any dissidents they wished. Neuwald wondered if he would be permitted to visit a town in the Ukraine, once the home of his grandparents. He understood that it was now in a zone barred to foreigners.

"Oh, I think we can make an exception in your case," said Kondratiev nonchalantly. "Personally, I don't see why, with all the satellites we fly over each other's territories, that can spot the most minute object on the ground, we need these 'forbidden' zones. I suppose it titillates some bureaucrats."

"Would you change the system if you had a chance, Mr. Kondratiev?" asked Stuart.

Mikhail Alexandrovich did not miss O'Dell and Neuwald's disapproving frowns at their colleague's indiscretion, but answered without the slightest note of disapproval or embarrassment in his voice, "Now, now, that *is* a state secret." They all laughed.

Most of the tension that had accompanied the encounter was now gone. What could have been the thorniest part of the meeting—the senators' mentioning several names of those incarcerated for expressing dissident views or for wishing to emigrate—did not lead to any clashes. Kondratiev promised to look into some of the cases, but added, "You must not imagine that I can just say a word, and lo! the man or woman is released. Our judicial organs—you won't believe it but it is a fact—are quite obdurate, and my colleagues on the Politburo take a dim view of attempts to interfere with them."

"What a smooth character," said Stuart when they left the office. "He wouldn't do badly running for an elective office in the States, either."

"Smooth and slippery as a snake," retorted O'Dell. "But I'll grant you, unlike the others, he is a man of a certain refinement and some sense of humor. Who knows—maybe things would change with him on top."

Mikhail Alexandrovich was, meanwhile, looking through the list left by the senators. Most of the names on it were of people sentenced for trivial offenses. No great harm in pardoning them, and after a suitable interval, letting them emigrate. But he had not been entirely fibbing when he had told the Americans that it was not within his power simply to order their release. That case with

Yelena Perventseva—God, had it really been fourteen years since then!—the only occasion on which he had come close to giving up his career . . .

▬

It was the last day of August 1968. Kondratiev was perusing the latest confidential reports on the Czechoslovak operation—he preferred to think of it as such to avoid that ugly term, invasion. Things were working out quite satisfactorily. No armed resistance, as the more nervous members of the Politburo had feared. There was a lot of fuss and noise being made about it in the West, even among the Communists, but that would soon die down. To be sure, the mass of Czechs and Slovaks were greeting their uninvited Soviet guests with undisguised and sullen hostility. But that too should pass in due time and give way to a sober recognition that the Warsaw Pact forces' intervention had saved their country from much greater troubles. He himself had no compunctions about supporting the operation: a few more months of Dubcek's madcap reforms, and the entire country would have been plunged into utter anarchy, and then you would have had bloodshed.

He put the documents in the safe, and rang his assistant on duty that night to tell him he was leaving and to have his car brought to the entrance.

"There was a telephone call for you, Comrade Kondratiev. Someone named Perventsev. I told him it was too late for you to accept calls. What are your instructions if he calls tomorrow?"

"You will put him through, whatever I may be doing at the time." He hesitated. Pavel had never before called him at his office. His health, if not mood, had been excellent when Kondratiev saw him two weeks before—but then, he was seventy-five years old. He dialed Perventsev's home number.

Half an hour later he was in his friend's apartment.

"I should have waited until morning," began the latter apologetically.

"So what is the story about your daughter, Yelena?"

"When I called you two hours earlier [it was now past midnight], all I knew was that she had been suspended from the institute for refusing to sign the resolution approving the action of the government in regard to Czechoslovakia, and then after making a speech at the meeting of scientific workers denouncing the intervention, she was summarily dismissed. A quarter of an hour ago, I received a call from one of their neighbors: Yelena and her husband had been taken away by agents. Their apartment is sealed."

Pavel spoke calmly until he came to the words "taken away." Then his voice broke. He looked at his friend as if gauging his expression and then added, "I still would not have called you, but she is six months pregnant."

Kondratiev took his friend's hand in both of his. "She will be released, I promise you, Pavel. Maybe not tomorrow, but soon."

"But how can even you . . . I just wanted your help in enabling me to see her and make sure that, in view of her condition—"

"I do think I carry a little authority, and these are not Stalin's times."

The next day Kondratiev set aside his regular appointments and made a number of inquiries. A call to the prosecutor's office revealed that Mikhail Bernstein would most likely be released, though he might be brought before a court later, on charges of possessing and distributing subversive literature. Yelena Perventseva-Bernstein was being detained. She freely admitted making speeches characterizing the action of the Warsaw Pact states in coming to the aid of the Czechoslovak working class "as a barbarous display of brute force unworthy of any civilized, let alone socialist, state." She would be charged with slandering the Soviet state, "a criminal act as defined by the following provisions of the Penal Code . . ."

From Andronnikov, whom he summoned to his office, Kondratiev got more pertinent information. Yelena was one of a group of eleven arrested for publicly protesting the invasion. In all likelihood, the majority of them, "and this woman appears to be the most brazen of all," would get sentences of three to five years' imprisonment or detention in a labor camp.

"In her case, it would be a relatively easy camp regime because of her approaching motherhood."

"Is there any chance of separating her case from those of the others and having her tried when things have quieted down?"

"Mikhail Alexandrovich," said Andronnikov earnestly, "believe me, if it depended solely on me, she would be set free at once. I know of your ties with her father. But the directive for the arrests and guidelines for the eventual sentences have come from the Secretariat of the Central Committee. More specifically," he lowered his voice, "from Pyotr Nikolayevich Lunin. All I can do is to make sure that the woman gets the best medical attention we can give her. She is thirty-eight, and it is her first pregnancy, I understand."

"Possibly," said Kondratiev, as if he hadn't quite heard the question, or as if his mind had suddenly become preoccupied with an idea. "Oh, many thanks, Sasha."

"You yourself, Mikhail Alexandrovich, have been one of those who argued most strongly for taking tough measures against those who defame our state and who publish scabrous libels in the same vein," said Lunin that afternoon, looking sharply at Kondratiev.

"I haven't changed my mind on that score. I am frankly pleading for indulgence in this particular case."

Lunin's face assumed what for him was the closest approximation to a smile. "I am not fond of quoting Nikita Sergeievich. In many ways, he is responsible for all these troubles we are having. But one of his frequent sayings is appropriate to this case: 'Friendship is great, but duty ranks higher.'"

"In peace and in war, Pavel Perventsev has rendered services of the highest importance to this country. Is our socialist state so vulnerable that it cannot overlook a piece of foolishness on the part of a woman who is most likely in an unstable emotional condition because of her pregnancy at a rather advanced age? Can't we soften the rigor of the law for the sake of a distinguished state servant who is not far from the grave? We have shown great leniency toward people who committed much greater crimes under the cult of personality."

Lunin's face hardened. The reference to Stalin's times had been a mistake, thought Kondratiev.

"As you know, Mikhail Alexandrovich, you can place this matter before the Politburo, and ask for my directives to be reversed. I have no personal stake in the matter. I am simply doing what I believe is my duty."

"I shall do so, Pyotr Nikolayevich. But then, let me be frank. If your decision is confirmed, as I believe it would be, I should be obliged to offer my resignation from the Party's leading organs."

The last words clearly startled Lunin. He sat for a while eyeing his colleague, as if trying to gauge whether he was being serious, and finally said, with less than the usual self-assurance in his voice, "No one, on account of personal feelings, has the right to leave a post entrusted to him by the Party."

"This is not as much a matter of my personal feelings as of a principle."

This time, the Central Committee secretary in charge of propaganda did not try to rebut him. Instead, he picked up the folder in front of him and began to leaf through the pages. He raised his head: "The woman is a troublemaker. If she gets a suspended sentence, is it likely that she and her Jewish husband would seek to emigrate?"

"I know very little about her or her husband. I've known Pavel Perventsev and his work for thirty-four years."

"And I have known you for, let's see, twenty-three years—long enough to realize the Party cannot dispense with your services."

And, as at the conclusion of their first meeting—it now seemed ages ago—Lunin came out from behind his desk and embraced Kondratiev.

▪

"And so that is the story, Pavel," concluded Kondratiev.

"I daresay you haven't told me everything." Perventsev was shrewd enough to know that someone like Lunin was unlikely to be moved by humanitarian or sentimental considerations. "You must have used a special argument to get Yelena freed."

"Let's say that I applied some pressure."

"And put your own position in jeopardy."

"Perhaps, but that's beside the point. I am afraid that your daughter will have difficulties in finding a research position with the same status and salary as before. It would be easier for her to get a teaching post, at least to begin with."

Pavel sighed. "Both she and her husband—in his case, the only job he could hope for currently would be that of a laboratory assistant—are determined to emigrate. My grandchild will grow up to be an American or an Israeli."

"Not necessarily. They are both Russians to the core, no matter what her political views or his ethnic origin. Some day they may decide to come back, and be welcomed. Think how this country has changed since Stalin's days. Who knows what things will be like in five or ten years?"

Pavel shook his head slowly. "Forgive me for saying so, but it would have to be the kind of change you would not like or tolerate. And it would take much longer than ten years. But I don't want to sound maudlin or ungrateful. At least my child won't have to rot and give birth in a camp or prison. Let's have a modest celebration."

Perventsev would die in 1970, while visiting his daughter, son-in-law, and grandson in Canada. His last request was that his remains be shipped back and buried in his native country. As a Politburo member, Mikhail Kondratiev found himself in the incongruous position of arranging and attending an Orthodox funeral service for his friend.

Yes, Perventsev had been right. Things hadn't changed very much during the last fourteen years. Mikhail Alexandrovich put the list of names left by the American senators in a drawer—tomorrow he would send it to the procurator general with the recommendation that each case be reinvestigated and those not guilty of major transgressions be included in the amnesty to be proclaimed on the occasion of the approaching sixty-fifth anniversary of the Revolution.

▬

It was evening. Irina would not be home until quite late. Something—was it that he had just been thinking about Perventsev and all the associations his longtime friend evoked—was making him feel both restless and lonely. Perhaps he would invite Gorbunov and a couple of his assistants for a drink and supper with him. Whatever their other engagements or family obligations, they would feel honored and perhaps even be pleased to come along. Or would it be selfish of him? He just didn't want to be alone this evening. Just then, the special telephone connecting the highest Party and government officials began to ring . . .

▬

"I thought it best for just the four of us to take counsel at this point." Lunin appeared calm and collected, but to one familiar with his characteristically rapid and self-assured delivery, it was significant that he spoke slowly, trying to choose the right words. He hesitated before "to take counsel" and "at this point." Then, instead of going on to explain, he stopped and looked questioningly at Viktorov. The latter understood.

"I am afraid that we all have guessed why you summoned us so urgently, Pyotr Nikolayevich. It is something about the Chief, isn't it?"

He now resumed his usual manner of speech: "Yes. His assistant called me from Baku. Konstantin Leonidovich had complained in the morning of having an upset stomach. The doctor wanted him to cancel his speech, but he insisted on delivering it, and afterwards said he felt fine. He took a nap in the afternoon and got up for tea. Then it happened. Preliminary diagnosis—a cerebral stroke, no immediate danger. Specialists are flying to Baku, and if they think it is safe, they will bring him here for treatment. That is all."

After a pause, he resumed: "In a situation like this, the responsibility for taking appropriate measures, until the meeting of the full membership of the Politburo, devolves on me. But as you know, Vorontsov is in India, Remizov is in Paris at the French Communist Party Congress, Kubiak just left for his tour of North Caucasus. And, of course, Vishnevsky, Georgadze, and Gabayev are, as usual, away from Moscow. To call them back immediately would undoubtedly send a shock wave throughout the country and the world. So, what is your advice?"

"Are we the only ones within the leading organ who know, so far?" asked Smirnov.

Lunin nodded in the affirmative.

"Then why not leave it that way until Konstantin Leonidovich's condition is clarified?"

Both Kondratiev and Viktorov shook their heads. "I am afraid that is impossible, Dmitri," said the former. "Though the doctors are sworn to secrecy, some rumors are bound to get out. Were any change for the worse to take place, we would be accused, and justly so, of usurping the authority of the Politburo. All of its full and alternate members, as well as the Central Committee secretaries who are not in the Politburo, ought to be notified forthwith."

"But they should be told to go on with their usual activities as if nothing has happened," added Viktorov. "Let us see: Remizov should be back in two days; Vorontsov in three. We shall then be able to hold a meeting—that is, unless in the meantime—"

"No, it will not happen," Lunin cried out. The guardian of orthodoxy, the "dour ideologue," as he was often described in the Western press, became for a moment an ordinary human being, despondent over what was happening to a lifelong friend.

Could it always have been just friendship? was the thought that flashed through Kondratiev's mind, but he immediately dismissed it. Still, it was astounding to see a veteran Politburo member so emotional, crying out in distress over what was essentially a political problem.

But almost immediately, Lunin resumed his usual manner. "I am sorry. What do you say, Dmitri Pavlovich?"

"I've been persuaded by the arguments of Comrades Kondratiev and Viktorov."

"We shall act accordingly." He paused and again spoke with some difficulty. "As you have just seen, it is hard for me . . ." and turning to Viktorov, "Won't you take temporary charge, Alexander Ivanovich, and also maintain liaison with the doctors?"

The old man shook his head: "No, you three as secretaries should jointly be in charge. There would be all kinds of rumors and misunderstandings if old Viktorov, always a government person, suddenly pushed himself to the fore. And don't be embarrassed because of your feelings, Pyotr. Whatever the outside world thinks of us, we are not automatons."

Andronnikov was summoned, and after having been told the news, received the appropriate instructions. He listened intently, looking at the senior secretary, but when Lunin began to read the names of the people to be notified, the KGB chief stole a quick glance at Kondratiev.

"Shouldn't we also warn our principal foreign missions to prepare for an important announcement?"

"There may not be a need for any announcement," retorted Lunin angrily, and again the others in the room exchanged anxious looks. "It's your job to prevent any rumors from flying around."

Smirnov had caught Andronnikov's inquiring look at his rival and said irritably, "Baku was the final stop on Konstantin Leonidovich's tour. It is only natural that he should be taking a prolonged rest."

"I know my duties, Dmitri Pavlovich. Are any further instructions to come from this group?"

Lunin understood the thrust of his question. "Yes, if Comrade Kubiak were in Moscow, he would be here with us. But since he has scheduled speeches in the south, he must go through with them. Nothing else would make rumors spread like wildfire so much as if he canceled them and flew back."

"Then I would ask that you communicate this to him personally, Comrade Lunin. I am in no position to issue orders to a full member of the Politburo and secretary of the Central Committee."

"I shall do so," said Lunin curtly.

After Andronnikov left, the four leaders sat in silence. "Shouldn't we call Baku?" asked Kondratiev.

"Would you please do it for me, Mikhail Alexandrovich? You can call from the adjoining room."

Kondratiev returned in five minutes. Lunin's face bore an imploring look.

"Yes, he can be flown to Moscow. This is an encouraging sign."

For the first time in the evening Lunin smiled, and then rang for sandwiches and drinks to be brought in. Usually abstemious, he quickly downed two sizable shots of vodka. Then he started talking about the international situation as if that had been the subject that brought them together in the first place.

"Pyotr Nikolayevich," Viktorov said finally, "it is very late. We are going to have a lot on our hands in the next forty-eight hours. Those two youngsters," indicating Smirnov and Kondratiev, "can take it. We must get some rest."

"Yes, of course," said their host and then added, "Kostya [Mikhail Alexandrovich had never heard him refer to Leontiev thus in front of others] had a heart attack three years ago, but was himself again in a few weeks. Let us hope. We shall stay in touch."

They walked downstairs in silence. Viktorov's limousine left first, and while waiting for theirs, Smirnov nudged Kondratiev, whispering so the guards would not hear, "Who would have thought that about Lunin? My God."

Kondratiev just shook his head and got into his car. On the way home he thought over the whole situation. Lunin was probably finished as a Party leader, and yet his vote would be crucial in deciding whether he or Smirnov . . . Once again, he recalled the talk he had had with Lunin about Perventsev. What was that saying? "Friendship is precious, but duty ranks higher." Would Lunin remember that conversation when it came to casting his vote? He was under no illusion that in Lunin's eyes, he, Kondratiev, was rather "soft"; one would expect him to support Smirnov. But now? Strange how one could suppress those basic human emotions for so long, and yet they would suddenly break out and take over. Perhaps over the years, each of them had built up an immunity to what most ordinary people felt—pity, the need for companionship and love—all their energies and thoughts preoccupied by one passion: power. Yet could one suppress those other feelings indefinitely, completely?

He arrived home just ahead of Irina.

"A very dull affair," she announced. What do you suppose has brought about this new fashion of organizing women's soirees? Until a year or two ago, we were left to our own devices. Now we are supposed to accompany our husbands to official functions, and have all those silly all-hen affairs with models displaying the latest fashions, lectures on women's roles in socialist society, and all kinds of other foolishness."

"As usual, someone gets the idea we should ape Western trends. What do you talk about?"

"That's it. I have precious little in common with the others. They are not interested in literature or the arts. All you hear is the trouble they're having with their grown-up children. Mitya drinks too much. Sergei got it into his head to become a sculptor rather than follow a diplomatic career. I like Olga Smirnova, but each time we have a conversation, the others stop chatting and start gaping at us. Ugh. Good night."

Irina kissed him, but with her hand on the door of her room she hesitated and said over her shoulder, "You seem to be more preoccupied than usual. I don't suppose you could tell me what it is about? Something about Pavel or Nikolai?"

"You know very well I never keep anything about the boys from you. No, it is something I could not tell you, but I suspect you'll learn about it soon enough. Nothing unexpected. Good night, my dear."

He had intended to go to bed, but Irina's questions chased away his sleepiness. He sat down and picked up a cigarette from a box on the table and lit it—his first in several days. What was it with Irina? She seldom showed any interest in politics. No, this was hardly the time to start pondering his marriage.

The next day brought no startling developments. The general secretary was now in a special wing of the Kremlin clinic, attended around the clock by a team of doctors from the Academy of Medicine. One of them timidly suggested bringing in a foreign consultant, but of course that was ruled out by Smirnov, to whom liaison with the doctors on behalf of the Politburo was delegated.

"Better not tell it to Pyotr Nikolayevich," he told Kondratiev after conveying the news. "I am sure he would have said yes."

But Lunin, with whom Mikhail Alexandrovich kept in touch by telephone, seemed to have regained his composure. He was emphatic in insisting that the members of the Politburo and those others who were now in the know should not besiege the medical people with inquiries about the stricken man.

"Let Smirnov notify them daily, but not more often . . . That also goes for ourselves," he added after a long pause. "We'll have a meeting in two days and will then get the full picture. Also, we'll decide whether and what public statement should be issued."

If he lasts that long, thought Kondratiev. There were slight encouraging—should he really think of them as such?—signs. The sick man recognized his surroundings and made a few intelligible sounds. Anna Leontieva proved to be no problem.

"I am a Party member as well as a wife," she said simply when told about what had happened, and kept up a brave front.

Andronnikov assured them that the news had not leaked out, though by now, counting doctors, medical attendants, and the like, there must have been about forty people who knew what had happened to the head of the regime.

"We keep constant watch over outsiders, monitor their telephone calls and their conversations at home. Of course, they've been told in no uncertain terms what would happen if they blab . . . Experience shows, however, that seventy-two hours is usually the maximum time you can hope to prevent rumors from starting on an occasion like this."

By that time, Lunin assured him, they would have had a Politburo meeting, and if the situation warranted it, would issue a public statement.

"It is not the outsiders who worry me," said Kondratiev slowly.

"Just between us, it is some of our colleagues who might be tempted to babble."

The next forty-eight hours indeed passed without rumors of any kind. Luckily, the general secretary's calendar for the week was free from publicly announced engagements. Those citizens of Moscow who paid heed to such matters would still see his limousine, its curtains drawn, circulating at the usual times between Leontiev's residence and the Kremlin.

With the roster of full Politburo members in Moscow now complete, Lunin summoned them Wednesday evening to a meeting in his office. He would not allow any questions.

"With your permission, the subject is going to be discussed at length at our regular meeting tomorrow. Until then, there would be no point in our speculating what measures would be in order, should Konstantin Leonidovich indeed prove unable to resume his duties for a time."

He emphasized the last part of the sentence, as if that were indeed the worst that could happen to his old friend. He looked around. There were no dissenting voices.

"Until tomorrow, then."

They filed out, each clasping the host's hand. Kondratiev was the last to leave—Lunin wanted to be reassured that there had been no leaks abroad.

"Absolutely, Pyotr Nikolayevich. As instructed by you, we have refrained from as much as hinting to our foreign missions that something untoward has taken place." And, though knowing this would sound fatuous, Kondratiev added, "Let us hope there is encouraging news by the time we meet."

After returning to his own office, he leafed mechanically through the dispatches from the Middle East: nothing urgent. He might as well go home and try to relax. Tomorrow was bound to be a strenuous day, perhaps decisive. He thought of calling Kuliabko, but the latter anticipated him.

"May I come over? I need both a drink and company very badly."

A few moments later, Mykola was seated on a sofa facing him.

"If company and drink is all that is on your mind, we could go and have supper at my or your house."

"Perhaps later. Here we can talk more freely. But first the drink."

Mikhail Alexandrovich spoke through the intercom: he was not to be interrupted, except if the message was of the utmost urgency. He then walked up to the row of bookshelves lined up against an entire side of the room, and pressed what looked like a light switch in the paneling. Two middle shelves filled mostly with classics of Marxism in the original German sprang aside, revealing a refrigerator in the wall and a tray with bottles and glasses.

"You will have, I take it, your native drink?"

"Yes, I do not share your cosmopolitan taste in spirits—whiskey and gin. Do you think they would approve?" said Kuliabko, pointing to the opposite wall where the pictures of Marx, Engels, and Lenin dispassionately surveyed the scene.

"Marx thought of himself as a connoisseur of wine, and Ilyich would occasionally take a glass of beer." He poured scotch and soda for himself and a sizable shot of *horilka* for his friend, and sat down next to him.

"Better put the bottle on the table," said Kuliabko, tossing down the glassful of vodka. "This atmosphere of gloom has got on my nerves. Of course this is sad, but it was hardly unexpected. Lunin is acting like an old woman rather than a veteran Bolshevik . . . We must not speculate! Why doesn't he lock us up in individual cells, the way they do it with the cardinals before they elect a new pope?"

Kondratiev complied with his wish and resumed sipping his own drink. Finally, he said, "Out with it, Mykola. Before you've had too many."

"This is the last. You're quite right. I have not come here just to drink and chat. We may have trouble on our hands, or conversely an opportunity, if we act fast—it's Kubiak."

Kuliabko then launched into his story: An old friend of his ("We have not seen or talked with each other for years, but we come from the same village"), now a Party official in Rostov-on-Don, had called him the night before and in a roundabout way inquired if anything unusual was going on in Moscow. That morning he had attended a closed meeting of Party officials that had been addressed by Kubiak. "I asked him not to say anything more over the phone, but to get here as soon as possible. We had a lengthy talk just before we all met at Lunin's, and it came out: Kubiak has started on his little—or perhaps not so little—game."

"The speech in question . . . its text had been read and approved by us last week before the incident in Baku. It could not contain any clue, unless—"

"Precisely, unless," and Kuliabko went on to quote what his visitor had told him about some passages in the speech. "And that is not all. Later on, when our friend Valentin found himself taking refreshments with the local people he thought he could trust, he gave vent to rather strong feelings concerning you and Smirnov as potential successors."

"I can well imagine what he said about me: 'Son of a former tsarist officer.'"

"And as a young man, charged with a political crime. Later acquitted, but you can never tell about these things."

Kondratiev remained silent a while before asking, "And about Smirnov?"

"Physically not up to the job; 'Kulak' origins that he has tried to conceal."

"But Kubiak must be out of his mind! How could he think all that would not reach us, sooner or later? He is cutting his own throat."

"He has little to lose; he knows what will happen if either of you takes over. And if this impasse continues, he may build up enough support—even within our little group: Vishnevsky and Georgadze are friendly with him. Lunin seems to have lost his head. We may have a completely new situation."

"Then it has to be done right away—tomorrow. Is your man still here?"

Kuliabko hesitated: "I advised him to go right back. I'd rather not have him brought into this unless *absolutely* necessary." He poured himself another drink. "Misha, you know Kuliabko is not my real name. You also know that I changed it when my elder brother was sent to a camp in '37. I told you he died there. Well, he did insofar as I was concerned. He never forgave me for not trying to contact him until after Stalin's death, and wouldn't accept any help from me then. It was Kubiak who got him readmitted to the Party, and started on a new career . . . Yesterday and today we saw and talked with each other for the first time in forty-five years, since he was twenty and I eighteen. I asked him why. He said he was worried, knowing how Kubiak felt about me. He'd rather betray his benefactor than his younger brother. After all these years . . ."

Kondratiev got up and paced around the room. When he came back to the sofa, he put his arm around Kuliabko's shoulders. "We won't need him. For the past three days Andronnikov's people have been monitoring all such meetings. It is inconceivable that Smirnov and Lunin won't hear the whole story before tomorrow's meeting. I shall drive you home and deliver you personally to your wife, with instructions to make sure that you are in condition to attend tomorrow's meeting, which you won't be if you keep drinking. Then, to my own place to await the call from Lunin."

"What if it does not come?"

"Then I shall get after Andronnikov, but I am sure it will."

The call came after midnight, and Kondratiev, who had not undressed, arrived at Lunin's within minutes, but not much ahead of Viktorov and Smirnov, both of whom had evidently not gone to sleep either. Their host had—he wore a dressing gown over his pajamas—but the emergency restored his self-assurance. He was a different man from the one who, only a few hours before, had seemed to be on the brink of a breakdown.

"We might have anticipated some difficulties with Valentin Valentinovich, but this really goes beyond bounds," he said, as he distributed copies of the report on Kubiak's recent activities.

"Still, this is what one might have expected," said Viktorov, having finished reading.

Smirnov gave Kondratiev a sharp look, as if to remind him that he had proposed to chastise Kubiak some months before. The latter shook his head.

"As for me, I am amazed. I knew that he was ambitious, but not that he was naive enough to think this kind of mischief could work. And—"

"Naïveté is hardly the word for it," interjected Lunin. "I think we are all agreed what has to be done concerning Comrade Kubiak. Here is how I propose we go about it . . ."

■

In contrast to the customary racket that preceded most general sessions, the Politburo room did not reverberate with loud talk on this occasion. Even the outsiders, the few nonmembers who had been invited to attend in connection with the original agenda, quickly sensed a changed atmosphere and confined themselves to whispers. Lunin entered exactly on the hour, taking his usual seat; the one traditionally occupied by Leontiev remained empty. The whispers immediately ceased. Lunin's face was pale, but he spoke decisively, and without the occasional tremor detected in his voice at the meeting the preceding evening.

"Most of you already know that the general secretary suffered a cerebral stroke following his speech in Baku last Sunday. He is now in the Kremlin clinic, his condition stable, but is still suffering from a partial paralysis of his left side and a loss of speech. Comrade Smirnov has been in constant communication with the doctors. Their prognosis is uncertain. There may be a full recovery, or on the contrary, in view of Konstantin Leonidovich's age and previous medical history . . ."

Here he paused, but no one said anything. "In any case, our rules provide that in the case of incapacity of a leader, it is the next senior secretary of the Central Committee who should exercise the leader's functions, until and unless the majority of the full membership of the Politburo decides otherwise. I shall then pose this question later on today, when—"

"I don't think that would be necessary," interrupted Smirnov. "We don't need a closed meeting to express our full confidence in you, Pyotr Nikolayevich."

The other full members chorused, "Agreed."

Lunin bowed his head and said almost inaudibly, "If it pleases you." Then, in his usual tone of voice, "As the rules also provide, the person thus entrusted may choose two other persons to share the burden of leadership with him. I so designate Comrades Kondratiev and Smirnov."

There was an approving murmur, but this time several heads turned toward Kubiak.

Lunin continued, "And so, with your approval, the three of us will continue jointly to discharge the functions of the general secretary until such time that our dear chief can resume his post."

"Pyotr Nikolayevich," said Viktorov softly, "I am the oldest here and will speak without any inhibitions. We all fervently hope for a full recovery, but it would take a miracle. We respect your personal feelings, but should we not prepare our people for what appears to be inevitable?"

"No," said Lunin, firmly. "There is always a chance. The official communiqué to be issued today will announce that our chief is suffering from a severe influenza that will necessitate a prolonged period of recuperation and rest. If you insist on another statement, I could not go on presiding over this body . . . I do not believe that Comrade Viktorov, who has known me for almost fifty years, could find a single instance where I have put my personal feelings above what I consider my duty to the country and the Party."

Kondratiev, who was watching Kubiak out of a corner of his eye and noticed his smoothing of his graying mane, a habit he had before launching into speech, spoke up hastily, "I must reluctantly agree with Pyotr Nikolayevich. Why create premature anxiety among our people? Why give Beijing and Washington any incentive to try to spring something on us in the belief we are too preoccupied with our own affairs to react to their tricks quickly and decisively?"

"And the Poles," chimed in Smirnov. "God only knows what they might do if they get an idea that we are in trouble. Things are touch and go in Poland, as it is."

"There will be rumors," said Viktorov.

"There are always rumors," retorted Kondratiev. "But if our friends in Washington and Beijing cannot be sure, they are more likely to behave. And our people trust us."

"In this connection, should we not put some of our forces on the alert?" asked Marshal Vorontsov.

But the senior secretary, sensing that he had now made his case, spoke in tones of command: "Absolutely not, Ivan Yakovlevich. Everything should appear completely normal. Does anyone else here have any questions or comments? If not, I propose that we defer the subjects we were to discuss at the enlarged meeting until next week. Our closed session will convene in half an hour. Agreed? Thank you, Comrades."

"Well done, Pyotr Nikolayevich," said Kondratiev, once he and Smirnov had joined Lunin in his office. "Kubiak was going to say something, but evidently thought better of it and held his peace."

"He will now have his chance," nodded the older man, grimly. "We shall proceed as planned, with you, Misha, leading. And now, if you and Dmitri will excuse me, I shall lie down for a few minutes, and then make those telephone calls."

"Should we perhaps have a longer recess?" asked Smirnov.

"No, let's get it over with."

"Let's hope he doesn't have another stroke right here and now," whispered Smirnov, as they left the office.

Mikhail Alexandrovich shrugged his shoulders. "For all of his attachment to the Chief, he is too much of a Bolshevik to permit himself to collapse at a time like this."

And indeed, Lunin was composed and businesslike as he opened the second and crucial part of the proceedings. "Our next topic was to be personnel changes in the Council of Ministers. But in view of some recent developments, this too must be postponed. Perhaps we shall have to hold an extra meeting next week. Comrade Kondratiev, will you proceed with your special report?"

Several of those present appeared startled. Viktorov, who of course knew what was coming, put a hand over his eyes and leaned back in his chair. Kondratiev, who took a quick look around the table while pretending to fumble for his reading glasses, thought that the old man must be reliving similar incidents from his past. Was it, perhaps, when Beria had been cornered in this very same room and had to be carried out screaming and cursing? Or when Leontiev had turned on Karsavin, accusing him of plotting, with the KGB's help, to seize the leadership?

He pulled out the dossier from his briefcase and began to read, "Concerning charges of a breach of Party discipline by a member of the Politburo of the Central Committee . . ."

There was now an audible stir, and someone exclaimed, "What? What?" but Kondratiev did not pause. "The news of Comrade Leontiev's stroke was communicated to all the members of this body, except the two away on foreign missions, by last Monday night. Comrade Kubiak was reported as having received it at 11:05 P.M. The very next day, Comrade Kubiak addressed a closed session of Party officials of the southern regions, in Stavropol. The text of the speech, as is customary, had been circulated to the full members of this body the week before. But in his oral presentation, Comrade Kubiak departed from the written and approved text in several places.

One such interpolated passage read: 'Above all, there will not be a marked improvement in the management of our economy as long as the crucial decisions there, as in other areas, are made by a small and exclusive circle. To effect a significant advance, we must draw on the creative energies and expertise of a much larger and more representative group—our several hundred-member-strong Central Committee—the brain of our Party, as Great Lenin called it. They should have the ultimate say in how our Socialist Fatherland is governed . . .' Am I quoting you correctly, Valentin Valentinovich?"

"Yes, but surely—"

Kondratiev did not let him continue, but went on, raising his voice. "Then let me remind you—others in this room undoubtedly remember this—of the rule adopted by the Central Committee on October 15, 1964, following the resignation of Nikita Sergeievich Khrushchev. This rule remains binding on us to this very day, and it reads, 'No member of the leadership will advance proposals concerning powers, competence, or the manner of operation of the highest Party organs without first submitting them to the Politburo of the Central Committee and obtaining an explicit approval of them by the absolute majority of its members.'" He took off his glasses and looked straight at the man. "How then do you explain your statement, Comrade Kubiak?"

"But surely, Mikhail Alexandrovich," Kubiak attempted to impart a tone of incredulity and sincerity to what he was saying, "you cannot describe my statement as a formal proposal. It was just impromptu remarks designed to stimulate intra-Party discussion."

"You chose a very peculiar moment to initiate such a discussion." Smirnov was closing in on the kill, and Kubiak now threw caution to the wind, turning on the man who he obviously thought was the instigator of the affair.

"I am not a schoolboy or a suspect under interrogation, Dmitri Pavlovich. Are we responsible Party leaders or some lowly instructors who are supposed to recite, word for word, set pieces from *Pravda*?"

"That is precisely the point, Valentin Valentinovich," Lunin said softly. "We are supposed to be *responsible* leaders."

The cornered oligarch looked imploringly around the table, meeting, for the most part, impassive expressions on the faces of his colleagues. Only Georgadze and Vishnevsky averted their eyes.

Smirnov spoke again. "I beg to offer a motion before the Politburo of the Central Committee of the Communist Party of the Soviet Union: That Comrade Kubiak's speech represented a flagrant breach of trust, and as such disqualifies him from continuing as a member of this body and secretary of the Central Committee."

After a moment of silence, Lunin turned to the culprit: "Valentin Valentinovich, I would prefer not to have this motion put to a vote. Wait!" he checked Kubiak as he was about to speak. "You would have the right to appeal our decision to the Plenum of the Central Committee. But in that case, I must warn you that your entire public and private behavior during the last few years would have to be discussed, and the consequences of such a scrutiny might indeed prove very serious to you and your family . . . Won't you draw the appropriate conclusions from what has already been said here?"

Kubiak stood up; his face, pale at the beginning, was now flushed. He reached for the carafe of mineral water, but his hand shook so much that he spilled most of it, and did not even try to bring the half-filled glass up to his lips.

"Take hold of yourself, man," whispered Viktorov. "It's not like in the old days."

Kubiak gave him a wild look and practically spat out, "Thanks for reminding me, Alexander Ivanovich. I would not have known . . . I never betrayed the Party's trust. I stand by my words. You will have my resignation."

After Kubiak had left the room, Lunin looked at Smirnov and Kondratiev, who both nodded. Lunin said, "We had to ask the KGB to take some precautionary measures. But since he is technically still a member of this body, the order to place Kubiak under house arrest must be countersigned by all of us here." He walked over to the recording secretary's table and picked up one of the phones. "Lunin. Yes, send him in."

"We all know Comrade Grigorian, Assistant Chairman for Special Tasks of the Committee of State Security," said Lunin as a thickset, swarthy man in a lieutenant general's uniform entered the room and saluted the senior secretary. Lunin pulled out a single sheet of paper from the portfolio handed him by the recording secretary.

"You will witness, Comrade Lieutenant General, as all of us sign the authorization."

After the document went around the table, Lunin handed it to the security official, together with a sealed envelope.

"You will open this in the presence of Comrade Andronnikov. It contains the list of people on Comrade Kubiak's staff and some others who are to be detained until further notice. The whole operation is to be carried out in the utmost secrecy and without the slightest recourse to violent measures. The detained are to be treated courteously. You will be personally responsible for the scrupulous execution of this order."

"I fully understand, Comrade Secretary of the Central Committee."

There was a moment of silence after the door closed on the KGB officer, and then Georgadze asked what further measures should be taken in regard to their ex-colleague. "And what would he suggest?" asked Kondratiev, reflecting on how awkwardly the man was trying to cover up his tracks.

"Well, I should think he ought to be detained . . . until . . . until . . . the question of the Party's leadership is fully cleared up."

Lunin did not try to conceal his irritation at the Georgian's words. "That might lead precisely to the kind of troubles we wish to avoid. *Comrade* Kubiak will be released once his resignation is received and publicly announced. A matter of a few more days, at the most."

"And afterwards?" inquired Vishnevsky. "Should he not be brought before the Control Commission?"

For the first time since the news of Leontiev's stroke, they saw Lunin smile: "You *are* a martinet, Dmitri Vasilievich. Comrade Kondratiev, what is your suggestion concerning our erring colleague's future?"

"Well, by a fortunate coincidence, the post of ambassador to Czechoslovakia has become available. Don't you think, Comrades, that Valentin Valentinovich would make a very effective envoy to Prague? He has a good nose for intrigue, and would quickly sniff out any trouble brewing among our Slavic brethren."

The others nodded, and only Smirnov saw fit to add, "Hardly a suitable punishment for what he tried to pull: to undermine the basic structure of our leadership. Oh, well, as long as he goes away."

The chairman, though visibly weary, reminded the members that there was still some business remaining to be transacted. Though their numbers were now effectively reduced to ten, this was hardly the moment to select new members to their body and present them to the Central Committee. Or did anyone feel differently? There was no dissent. With the leadership of the Party in a precarious state, any attempt to enlarge the Politburo would have been a laborious and contentious task, pitting the pro-Smirnov forces against those favoring Kondratiev.

Lunin continued: Kubiak's expulsion meant that an important department of the Secretariat, that tending to agriculture, was now without a head. It was imperative that the position be filled without delay, and under the circumstances, preferably by a full member of the Politburo. The floor was open to nominations.

"I move that Comrade Kuliabko be made Secretary of the Central Committee, once Comrade Kubiak's resignation is received and accepted," said Smirnov brusquely, without, as was customary, expatiating on the candidate's merits. Everyone present knew what he thought of Kuliabko: a follower of Kondratiev's and a buffoon, to boot. But it was he who at that conference at Lunin's had proposed the genial Ukrainian for the post. No one could think of Kuliabko, even apart from the fact of his not being Russian, as a contender for the general secretaryship. His new job would very likely absorb his energies to the point of making him less able to exert himself on Kondratiev's behalf. Lunin cast a peremptory look around the table.

"Any other suggestions . . . Approved unanimously, with Comrade Kuliabko abstaining."

The new secretary stood up, his round face displaying just a hint of a smile. "I thank you, Comrades. You may be sure I shall do my utmost to justify your trust. I started shoveling manure on my father's plot when I was five years old, and I believe I can cope with some of the consequences of Kubiak's stewardship of our agriculture."

Lunin frowned—this was hardly the time for witticisms, but the others could not refrain from laughing. The tension that had hung over the meeting from the first moment was broken.

The chairman cut short the merriment. "We must all stay in Moscow. Let there be no cancellation of previously announced public engagements. But when it comes to out-of-town events, let the alternate members or other leading Party figures substitute for us."

He was about to adjourn the meeting when the recording secretary, who had been called out of the room, came back and placed a note before him. The old man's face broke into a smile. Konstantin Leonidovich's condition had improved.

"His speech is coming back. Thank God."

CHAPTER 11

MOSCOW, NOVEMBER 1982

The official communiqué about the general secretary's condition aroused varied reactions. Governments and Kremlinological circles in the West tended to be skeptical: the seventy-six-year-old man who had reportedly suffered a cardiac arrest some years before and been supposedly fitted with a pacemaker was probably experiencing a much more serious ailment than an aggravated case of the flu. But then some eminent American medical specialists interviewed by the press were willing to grant that, especially in a man of Leontiev's age, the kind of influenza currently widespread in Eastern Europe could indeed have produced a prolonged debility requiring the patient to move to a location with a more benign climate than that of Moscow in November.

In the capitals of "the friendly socialist countries," their Communist bosses had more tangible reasons to be dubious about the official version. Their contacts in the USSR more than hinted that there was a real possibility of a change of the guard in the Kremlin. The leaders of Hungary, Bulgaria, and so on, were fearful of the prospect; they had felt comfortable with Leontiev, who did not like changes and new personalities in the top positions and who closed his eyes to his old pals' peccadilloes. The same sentiments animated the upper and middle ranks of Soviet bureaucracy; Leontiev was easy to get along with, disliked variations in the official routine. As to his potential successors, each of them aroused a different kind of anxiety within the Soviet and satellite elites: Kondratiev was rumored to be a potential reformer; Smirnov was a disciplinarian who would undoubtedly crack down on the corruption and nepotism so rampant among the Communist officialdom. Kubiak? Well, he might try to turn everything upside down, somewhat in the style of the late N. S. Khrushchev.

Kubiak's demotion was not revealed until the Plenary Session of the Central Committee held on the eve of the anniversary of the November Revolution. There were some voices from the floor inquiring about the reasons for Comrade Kubiak's ejection from the Politburo and the Secretariat. Smirnov, presiding over the session in the absence of Lunin, who was suffering from arthritis, replied brusquely that the Politburo had decided on the step unanimously and for good and sufficient reasons. Would one of the questioners identify himself, and offer a motion for a fuller discussion of the reasons that prompted the leadership to accept Comrade Kubiak's resignation? No one did, and the Central Committee voted unanimously to accept the Politburo's recommendations to accept the resignation.

SOVIET LEADER VICTIM IN SUCCESSION STRUGGLE was the headline in the *New York Times*, and various other Western journals also expatiated on the theme. But a high-ranking State Department official who refused to be identified confided to the press that it might not have been a demotion, after all. From his post in Prague the erstwhile Politburo member could be expected to stand watch over Eastern Europe as a whole. A prestigious person was needed for the job, in view of the still precarious situation in Poland and its possible repercussions on the other "people's democracies."

Messages to the general secretary wishing him a speedy recovery poured in from local Party organizations, factories, and collective farms all over Russia. But the true measure of the average Soviet citizen's feelings on the matter was probably represented by a little dialogue between two slightly inebriated men who were overheard by a French journalist in a Moscow restaurant. Seeing that the customer at the next table was obviously a foreigner and assuming incorrectly that he did not understand Russian, one of them pushed a copy of *Pravda* with the official announcement under the other's nose, saying, "Leontiev might croak."

"So what?" replied his companion. "There'll be another one just like him. They are all the same."

"So your father has a shot at the top job," said Lisitsin to Pavel Kondratiev. They were sitting and taking tea in the latter's apartment, having just prepared another pamphlet to be Xeroxed and clandestinely distributed, quoting Western sources on the practice of confining dissidents in psychiatric wards.

"I doubt it," said Pavel, his emotions divided between filial attachment and his loathing for the regime. "He is too cultivated for that gang."

"Well, it's between him and Smirnov, and the latter is an impossible boor even by the standards of our current rulers." Igor paused, and then said uncertainly, "Pavel, could there be changes if your father—"

Pavel Mikhailovich shook his head vigorously, as if trying to chase away the thought. "And what changes could there be? Would he abolish the KGB, free the prisoners? Even if he wanted to, the others would not let him. But he wouldn't try. My father evidently had some independent ideas when he was young, but since then he's been entirely swallowed up by the system . . . Igor, if you don't mind, I'd rather not talk about my father."

The November 7 anniversary parade had in the past been eagerly watched as possibly providing some clues as to the relative ranking of the individual Politburo members. Foreign observers placed great importance on the manner in which the leaders who reviewed the parade arranged themselves on the stand above Lenin's tomb: who was on the right and who on the left of *the* leader; which full and alternate members of the Politburo rated the first row; and so on. This year, special care was taken to discourage such speculations. Lunin climbed the steps with some assistance to take the central position, with Viktorov on his right and Vorontsov on his left, none of the three presumably in the running, the first two disqualified by their age, Vorontsov by his military background. Kondratiev and Smirnov stood next to each other on the extreme left. Following the parade, the dignitaries, weary from the ordeal of standing for hours in frigid weather, refreshed themselves with tea and vodka, and dispersed to their homes.

As usual, several of them hosted little parties in the evening, the big banquet for several hundred top officials and foreign guests from the fraternal countries having taken place the night before in the Kremlin.

At Smirnov's, all other guests, mindful of the presence of three Politburo members and their preoccupied air, made their excuses shortly after the supper. The host then invited Remizov and Kuliabko to join him in some Armenian brandy. "You've had enough of your native drink, Mykola," he said, noticing him grimacing, "and this stuff, I am told, is as good as the best of French cognacs. I wouldn't know, not having our friend Kondratiev's cosmopolitan tastes and expertise."

"I'll join you, though when it comes to drinking I usually follow the preferences of my Ukrainian peasant ancestors."

Remizov readily agreed, but chided the host, "You, Dmitri, have had more than enough. Your doctor has been watching in dismay as you downed one after another. The Party needs you. Several times today I thought Lunin was going to faint right there on the stand."

"This is a special occasion," insisted Smirnov. "The Revolution is sixty-five years old. One more toast and then I'll switch to mineral water." He downed the brandy in one gulp. "This is an inheritance from *my* peasant ancestors. Kondratiev sips his brandy as a gentleman should." His voice was growing hoarse.

"Dmitri Pavlovich," said Remizov imploringly, "let's not get into that business. This is a celebration, a holiday from politics."

"We Communists never take holidays from politics. That is why we have been winning over the capitalists."

"There I agree with Dmitri," said Kuliabko.

There was a pause, during which Smirnov, disregarding his pledge, poured himself another brandy, but this time sipped it. "There can be no doubt now. The doctors say it is at the most a matter of weeks, possibly days. And then we shall have to decide . . . You, Arkadi, and you, Mykola, are like myself, peasants' sons." All of a sudden there was a note of bitterness in his voice so strong that Remizov, who had been reclining, sat up, while Kuliabko frowned, emptied his glass, and poured himself another drink.

"How can you two wish for the Party to be headed by a man who is a *barin*'s son, whose ancestors whipped and exploited our forefathers? Tell me."

"You are the host," began Kuliabko, but Remizov broke in.

"Dmitri, I have not said or decided how I shall vote, when and if. But for Heaven's sake, this is not 1920. And even then—Lenin was a hereditary nobleman, and a lawyer."

"But his grandfather was an illiterate tailor, born a serf . . . Yes, class origins do matter. More now, probably, than in 1920. Our young people are beginning to ape foreign capitalist ways. Where is that sense of mission and dedication that our people had even when all those terrible things were taking place in the thirties?"

"*I* have decided how I would vote," intervened the other guest. "You've done a lot for the Party, Dmitri. But are you suggesting that Mikhail Alexandrovich is not a true patriot and communist? Look at his record in war and peace. What does the accident of one's birth matter against that?"

"I would be the last to deny his great services. But his mind—"

"Yes?"

"—is that of a Russian nobleman nurtured on foreign ideas, not rooted in our native soil. Have you seen him address a Party or workers' meeting? One can sense his distaste at having to talk to such uncouth people."

"Permit me to say, this is nonsense," Kuliabko's face was becoming red. "I still run into people who remember him when he was a minister—most solicitous of the workers' welfare, humane and considerate in dealing with the rank and file. Not like some people I could name among our present ministers. If the choice falls on you, I shall do everything in my power to assist you in that heavy task. But if the choice of the majority falls on Kondratiev, as I believe it will, there is nothing that could be done about it, and I am sure you, as a loyal Party man, will employ your great talents in helping him. And now, Dmitri, let us end this conversation."

Smirnov nodded and shifted talk to Lunin and what an irreparable loss it would be if he also became disabled.

"We need younger blood," said Remizov sententiously. "For all his great achievements and merits, Konstantin Leonidovich had one weakness—he did not like new faces around him."

Later, Smirnov ushered them out, and then gazed out of the window as his colleagues' limousines pulled out of the driveway. He returned to the room where they had had their conversation and rang for the servant to remove the glasses and plates. As the maid lifted the tray, he snatched the bottle and poured himself another brandy. He sat for a minute with the glass in his hand, then put it down and whispered, as if confiding a secret to the empty room, "Yes, there *is* something that can be done."

Superficially, the general secretary's condition improved during the first days of November. He could sit up, and once in a while would, with assistance, get out of bed and walk for a few minutes. His speech returned, though he slurred words and grew weary after half an hour's chat. Lunin, Smirnov, and Kondratiev, who waited on him the morning after the Anniversary (it had been tacitly agreed that only those three of the notables, and collectively, should call on him), found Leontiev in better spirits than heretofore.

He was even trying to joke. "I should be brought before the Party Control Commission and given a severe reprimand for being sick at a time like this."

"I think in view of your past services, Konstantin Leonidovich, the Control Commission would just give you a warning to mend your ways in the future," retorted Kondratiev in the same spirit.

The sick man looked at him fixedly, obviously trying to compose an answer. "You always have . . . had . . . a way with words, Misha," came out.

Lunin, with some effort, bent over and kissed Leontiev on the cheek. "You're so much better, Kostya, but we must go: the doctors' orders."

The sick man smiled, but whether in relief or resignation it would have been hard to say.

In the attending physicians' room they found Anna Leontieva talking with the doctors. She exchanged greetings and a few banalities with her husband's colleagues, and after embracing Lunin, left the room. Professor Samuilovich asked them to sit down.

"You undoubtedly found him more animated, but please don't draw any false conclusions. I wish I could be more optimistic, but . . ." He slowly shook his head.

"Yet he does seem so much better. Then why?" insisted Lunin. And when the doctor remained silent, he continued as if begging for crumbs of comfort: "Even with the primitive medicine of those days, Vladimir Ilyich stayed alive for a year and a half after his stroke. And now we have all these drugs and treatments."

He is close to cracking up, thought Kondratiev. Why does he drag Lenin's case in? Does he think being the Party leader confers some special powers of survival on the man?

Professor Samuilovich looked at him and Smirnov, as if expecting them to explain to their colleague why his old friend's days were numbered. But as both of them remained silent, he surveyed again the charts in front of him and, without raising his head, addressed the questioner: "Comrade Lunin. These here," he tapped the papers on his desk, "show the patient's fairly satisfactory recovery from paralysis, but also, and unfortunately, continual weakening of his heart action. There is no drug, no treatment that can long delay the inevitable. You have authorized us to seek help from foreign specialists. We have flown in two leading cardiologists." He mentioned two German-sounding names. "Unhappily, they fully confirm the prognosis."

Back in his office, Kondratiev returned to the scrutiny of dispatches from abroad and digests of the Western press. Having quickly skimmed through each document, he would then hand it to his assistant, a red X marking items that were not to be filed away but kept for his further scrutiny.

News from America was unpromising. Nothing indicated that the popularity of the current administration was on the wane. Soon they would have to decide whether to renew the negotiations with the United States now, or whether to wait until 1985, when the American people would have gone through their quadrennial folly. But then if the present administration continued, the Yankees' position on both strategic and tactical nuclear weapons and other matters would very likely become stiffer. Normally, he would think that now would be the appropriate time—the mere fact of the negotiations' being renewed would embolden the Western Europeans to stand up to Washington and to refuse, or at least try to delay, the deploying of NATO's nuclear missiles on their soil. But with Leontiev about to die, and all that was likely to follow his demise, the Americans would attribute the Kremlin's willingness to resume talks to the "succession crisis," and might be hard to deal with.

When, then, would be a good time to return to the negotiating table? Obviously 1984, the presidential election year—the menstrual period of American politics. A voice within him kept urging that it brought bad luck to anticipate such events—to project what he would do when and if. But another part of his mind sheltered a vision of Mikhail Kondratiev, General Secretary of the Central Committee of the Communist Party of the Soviet Union (and by that time firmly in control on the home front), meeting with the president of the United States sometime in July or August 1984. No, he would not need any experts to advise him how to handle the Americans at a summit meeting.

"And then there are these," said his assistant, placing another stack of reports on his desk—summaries or occasionally entire versions of articles and columns culled from the Western press. The bulk of them dealt with the Soviet domestic situation, principally "the succession crisis." The general tone had become quite derisive about Leontiev's prolonged "minor respiratory ailment." Speculation as to his successor was now rampant. And in the imagination of the foreign experts and journalists, yet another candidate had entered the list: Marshal Vorontsov. Quite a few of those seers saw him backed by both the army and the KGB, who by the same token were allegedly firmly opposed to the previously most highly touted contestants, Kondratiev and Smirnov. The former was allegedly opposed by the military and secret police notables because of his liberalism; the latter was thought unsuitable because of his inexperience in foreign affairs.

Kondratiev chuckled and turned to his assistant. "You must have read through a lot of this nonsense, Ilin."

The young man was embarrassed. "Well, not really, Comrade Kondratiev. I simply select the materials that, judging by their headlines, should be of interest to you."

"Quite right—no reason to fill your head with all that trash."

Vorontsov as *the* leader! In the nine years Ivan Yakovlevich had sat on the Politburo, Kondratiev had never seen him as much as open his mouth on anything not concerning military and international affairs, and on the latter, he invariably echoed Leontiev. Imagine him dealing with agriculture or the Party apparatus in Leningrad!

But if the idea of the old soldier's being elevated bordered on the preposterous, another name mentioned in that context made Mikhail Alexandrovich laugh so heartily that Ilin looked at him in bewilderment: with all those weighty problems of the moment and his own future at stake, what could have made his boss so lighthearted?

"It's all right, Boris. Life would be too grim if our American friends did not provide us with occasional comic relief."

What had provoked his mirth was an article in a leading American magazine, written by a man described as an authority on Soviet Central Asia. The author maintained that despite all the indications to the contrary, the next general secretary was very likely to be a non-Russian. For one, other ethnic groups were gaining on the Russians within the population of the USSR. For another, the selection of an Asian to head the regime would thrill the Third World, and add very greatly, perhaps decisively, to Soviet prestige and influence in that crucial battleground between the Kremlin and the U.S. And so the man of the hour was none other than Gabayev: "The wily Uzbek has been on the Politburo for seventeen years and is known to have been, quite unobtrusively, a strong influence on Soviet foreign and domestic policies."

Kondratiev returned to reading the other materials. But his mind was still on the piece about Gabayev: on second thought, maybe it wasn't so funny. Of course, that idiot had as much chance of being elected as, say, Ilin. But it *was* a fact that the foreigners were waking up to what, in another generation or two, might become the Achilles' heel of the regime: the Russians' share in the overall population was going down; all those Uzbeks, Kazakhs, and the like, were breeding much faster. *Something* had to be done to arrest the trend.

He was a Party man, but also to his core, a Russian. Generations of Kondratievs had helped to build and defend this state. The Americans used to call their own society "a melting pot." Well, the Soviet state and society had to continue to bear the Russian imprint upon it. It was not a question of chauvinism: what else could hold the Soviet state together? What other nation could have withstood all the trials and devastation that for centuries had been its lot and yet gone from strength to strength, now constituting both the nucleus and the leading force of the mightiest state on earth?

No reason to slight the contributions of Ukrainians, Armenians, Jews, and others of the country's innumerable nationalities. But ultimately, it was the patriotism of the Russians, and not merely because they were most numerous, that had proved decisive in saving the Fatherland in the war and raising it to new heights of power. Since they were most numerous, they also had suffered proportionately more than the others from the cruelty of their own government—on the eve of the Hitlerite invasion, practically every family mourned a victim of Stalin's Terror. And yet when the hour of trial came, they did not turn against their ruler, who apart from his viciousness, had failed to prepare the country for war. They rallied around their government to repel and then smash the enemy.

Foolish and envious foreigners would babble about the slavish streak in the Russian national character. But in fact, what made them act the way they did was the nation's healthy instinct that the Fatherland could not survive without being great, and that no sacrifice was too exorbitant if it assured greatness and hence survival.

Did the young Russians still understand this imperative need for national greatness? Kondratiev could not help thinking of his two sons, both, in different ways, contaminated by noxious ideas seeping in from the West: Pavel, seized by intellectual arrogance, assuming that being thirty years old gave one the right to feel superior to one's community and its values; Nikolai, sunk in mindless hedonism. Add up his sons' flaws, and you got what in the West is known and extolled as freedom. How could any sensible man fail to see how that precious democratic freedom has already ruined the English and the French, their countries reduced to the status of third-rate powers, and how in time it must do the same to America, outwardly still powerful, but its society increasingly rent by license, crime, and racial and ethnic conflict?

Well, *he* would not allow this phony idea of freedom to get a grip on the minds of Russia's youth! But of course, it could not be done, as Smirnov and his ilk would have it, through mere repression. The Party had to be revivified; right now it stood in danger of coming to resemble the mortal remains of Vladimir Ilyich Lenin, a mummy rather than a vital and electrifying force. The term *Communist* had to become once more exciting and challenging for the young, just as it had been to Misha Kondratiev when he was in his teens.

He leaned back in his chair. "I'm afraid I've had enough for today, Boris. Reading too much of bourgeois papers tends to create a cacophony in one's head."

Ilin nodded. "That is what amazes me, Comrade Kondratiev. When I go through their journals to select items of importance, serious news gets all but lost amid all the disturbing stories about crime, sex scandals, and the like, that go on for pages and pages. How can people in the capitalist countries go about their daily tasks after having their minds filled with such depressing and enervating stuff? And how confused they must get; all those different opinions and interpretations."

"Quite unlike our own press, eh Boris?"

But the young man was quite serious. "Oh, yes, ours concentrates on really important issues, and still, at the same time it is . . . well . . . soothing, on one's nerves."

Kondratiev grimaced as his assistant left the room. There you have it: a graduate of Moscow University, who had studied abroad, who had mastered English, French, and German, and yet . . . Wasn't there some middle road between the Boris Ilins and the Pavel Kondratievs?

▬

The sequence of events that was to transform the lives of the Kondratiev family, and affect the destiny of a vast country, began in the afternoon of November eighth and ran through the fifteenth. In the time that was left to him, Mikhail Alexandrovich could only marvel at how many unusual episodes, each leading inexorably to the next, were crowded into those eight days, and how the entire story appeared as a replay of his adult life and, in a sense, of the last fifty years of his nation's history.

The afternoon promised to be a routine one. It began with the regular conference with Filimonov and his main deputies from the Foreign Ministry. It took some effort on Kondratiev's part to persuade the minister to tone down his harsh rhetoric about the U.S., and conversely to not sound too optimistic and almost supplicatory concerning relations between Moscow and Beijing.

"By excessively belaboring the White House and the Pentagon, we only succeed in rallying American public opinion behind them."

At the same time, they must not create the impression of begging the Chinese to become friendlier. This could only make Deng and his gang puff out even more, to the point of pressing harder with insolent demands on the USSR to pull out Soviet troops from Afghanistan, cut off Moscow's close links with Vietnam, and God knows what else.

"If we are more reserved toward our Chinese comrades, it is they who will come running to us to propose a rapprochement. They need time, as well as our help, to restore their economy, ruined by all those follies of Mao's."

Filimonov, more sour looking than usual—he did not like being read a lesson in the presence of his subordinates—finally agreed to be more circumspect in his statements. To save face, however, he felt constrained to add that both issues deserved a fuller review by the Politburo.

Kondratiev would not let him squirm out: "As you will remember, Andrei Andreyevich, we *have* discussed it at length, and I am simply stating what was the sense of the meeting."

He felt no reason to spare the feelings of Filimonov. The man was a brute, and as an alternate member, he would not vote when the all-important moment came.

The next session on Kondratiev's schedule was with Gorbunov, and Uzmanov, another official of his branch of the Secretariat. Here the discussion touched on the peace and antinuclear campaign currently gaining momentum in the West, and how its activities could best be steered in a desirable direction. They ought to make sure, argued Gorbunov, that all those prominent clergymen, politicians, academicians, and the like, who were setting up those committees for nuclear disarmament and for keeping Western Europe free from weapons of mass destruction, do not attack the Soviet Union as well as the United States, for being guilty of piling up nuclear arms.

"In other words, our friends should be in firm control of all those activities and movements."

Uzmanov disagreed, saying it was a mistake for the Soviets to try too blatantly to control the peace movement. "Let there be quite a few genuine pacifists and moderates on those committees. And it would be helpful if *occasionally* they criticize us, too."

"You must have acquired such Machiavellian notions while studying at the Sorbonne and Stanford," said Kondratiev severely. "You certainly could not have learned those sinful stratagems in our Party schools." He kept a serious face while both young men were hugely amused.

What a pity, thought Mikhail Alexandrovich, that his Central Asian aide was much too young and junior in status to replace the moronic Gabayev. Well, they would see about it in a few years

. . . Then he caught himself: of late, he was tending more and more to think in terms of *when*, rather than *if*. He mustn't jinx himself.

As if in answer to his silent self-reproach, a security aide rang to announce that a courier from the general secretary's office was waiting to deliver a special message. There were strict regulations concerning the delivery of such messages to members of the Politburo. Gorbunov and Uzmanov had to leave the room before the courier, a lieutenant colonel of the KGB, personally handed Kondratiev a red-bordered envelope. Mikhail Alexandrovich signed a receipt specifying the location and the exact time of delivery of the message. The officer placed it in his attaché case, saluted, and left.

There were three items in the envelope. Two bore the signature of Lunin: one, a printed card announcing that a meeting of the "narrow" Politburo had been scheduled for 11:00 A.M. on the tenth; the other, a note in longhand, reading—"Mikhail Alexandrovich, it is imperative I see you tomorrow afternoon or evening. Please call and specify the time." The third was a photostat of a letter that Kondratiev scanned impatiently before replacing it along with the other two messages in the envelope, which he resealed and locked in the safe.

He sat down at his desk, trying to control the excitement surging within him. By the time he summoned the aides back and they reentered, he appeared completely composed, ready to continue with the business at hand. During the next two and a half hours, the young men watched in vain for any indication as to whether and how the undoubtedly very important message he had received might have affected Kondratiev's mood.

The only possible hint came toward the end of the conference. Gorbunov wondered aloud whether the antinuclear campaign in the West was really going to result in solid advantages to the Soviet Union.

"Everything we hear and read indicates that the Christian Democrats will come to power in Germany, and that the present American administration is bound to be reelected in 1984. If so, no amount of noise and demonstration on the part of the peace groups would stop NATO from installing missiles that could reach the heart of our country in five or six minutes."

"You are young, Mitya, and therefore impatient," said Kondratiev indulgently. "Some benefits always come to us from these campaigns. More and more people begin to perceive that it is those anti-Soviet fanatics in Washington who threaten the security of Western Europe and would expose it to the threat of nuclear devastation, rather than ourselves. They will *start* deploying Pershing IIs and cruise missiles—no doubt. But then they will have second thoughts about it. And the American people themselves will eventually get tired of spending billions upon billions on new weapons. Yes, patience and perseverance are the keys to our besting the capitalists. It is when we get hot under the collar and in a hurry, as the late N. S. Khrushchev occasionally did, that we stumble."

He got up, indicating that the conference was over. "And another reason we prevail is that we can keep secrets," he added with a smile that reassured his assistants—the boss was evidently not displeased by what was in the message. And their future was so much tied up with his.

Kondratiev had considered inviting Gorbunov for a drink, but then decided he'd rather be alone: he would have to give serious thought to what lay ahead in the next two days.

Yet perversely, he became exasperated to learn on arriving home that his wife was at another of those cultural evenings of hers with a reception to follow until quite late at night. How could Irina not realize what was going on and that she should be at her husband's side, rather than attending some damned exhibition of Romanian folk arts and crafts? Or—a thought that had not occurred to him in years—perhaps she had a lover? One of that crowd of painters, writers, and composers with whom she hobnobbed. A young man who could provide more in the way of sexual and intellectual excitement than a seventy-year-old husband, forever engrossed in politics. There had been, after all, that episode with the French movie producer at the Cannes Film Festival—that was about the time they had the Czechoslovak crisis.

"What made you do it, and with a man you just met?" he had stormed at her when Irina confessed a few weeks later.

"For months you have not paid any attention to me," she replied quite evenly, though there were tears in her eyes.

It was true. There had been one crisis after another: the Israeli-Arab war, Karsavin's attempted coup, complications with Vietnam and China; he had been preoccupied, constantly on missions to Cairo, Hanoi, Prague . . . They ended by asking each other's forgiveness, but their renewed closeness did not last very long.

Well, that was but an episode, and Irina, for all her naïveté about politics, knew that a woman in her position must not launch into a real affair: it would not remain secret, and its repercussions might reach far beyond what it would do to their marriage. It was enraging to think that even that brief indiscretion of more than fourteen years ago may well have been recorded in the KGB files.

Had there been another "episode," then? Suddenly, he was seized by a feverish suspicion, verging on certainty, that a tryst was taking place at that very moment, and felt an irrepressible craving to visualize it in all its seamy details.

As if from a distance, he heard his servant's voice: He had not touched his supper; should she prepare him something else? Kondratiev assured Marfa that he had had a snack at the office. By the time he was in the library having coffee and brandy the degrading trance had broken. What nonsense: the loyal, dignified Irina transmogrified into a nymphomaniac, all because he had been furious at not finding her home to share his excitement and appease his anxieties.

His thoughts turned to real problems: the letter, a copy of which was delivered to him that afternoon. It was signed by forty-one members of the Central Committee and requested the Politburo to put an end to the present situation within the leadership.

"It is embarrassing to the Party and the government to keep our people in the dark concerning the real state of health of our beloved leader."

The letter also urged the appointment of an acting secretary general if, as the rumors seemed to indicate, Leontiev would be unable to resume his office in the near future. The signatories were for the most part elderly people, retired from their Party and government positions, who thus had presumably little to lose by their unprecedented challenge, at least in the last twenty years or so, to the prerogatives of the Politburo. Still, what they implied must have reflected a widespread feeling among the Party officials: the leadership ran the risk of appearing ridiculous to the people, not to mention the world at large, by keeping up the sham of Leontiev's being "temporarily indisposed." And as throughout the entire Soviet history, the Party bigwigs, for all their lip service to "collective leadership," did not feel comfortable with a committee, rather than one man, heading the regime. He thought he knew what Lunin would tell him. But then he could be wrong—or, to put it differently, one's judgment was fallible when ambition and the thirst for power were involved.

Irina entered the room and, as if divining what was on his mind, sat down on the sofa and put her arm around his shoulders. He felt a tremor of self-revulsion: how could he have ever imagined . . .

Later on, Mikhail Alexandrovich was to realize that his shameful fantasy of that evening had not been just a fit of folly triggered by an old memory. For a moment he had allowed himself to become an entirely private person; something in his mind was still at odds with the public role he had played for forty years. The conflict would have to be resolved, and other memories—much more painful—decisively suppressed, before Mikhail Kondratiev would be able to grasp and hold the supreme power that had been his goal all those years. It had been a warning.

■

"I must then ask you, Mikhail Alexandrovich: Is there anything that might make you unable or unwilling to serve as the general secretary?"

"As to the first, you know my record, and I shall abide by your judgment," said Kondratiev slowly. "As to my willingness, I recall what you said once: No Communist has the right to refuse to shoulder the responsibilities entrusted to him by the Party."

His intuition had proved right. Pyotr Nikolayevich had canvassed their colleagues: in a contest between him and Smirnov, the majority would vote for Kondratiev. "As for myself," Lunin stated, "the doctors have confirmed what I had suspected—I will not be able to continue in public life, let alone in my present post, much longer." He had presented his conclusions to Smirnov, who, after initial reluctance, agreed to move that the election be made unanimous. Dmitri Pavlovich insisted that the election be confirmed, but not presented to the Central Committee and made public until the current incumbent died.

"I pointed out to Smirnov that that would be a sheer formality. Konstantin Leonidovich's condition has worsened, and it is now only a matter of days. I don't think holding up the announcement would make any difference." The knowledge of his own fatal disease had evidently enabled Lunin to face with equanimity the approaching end of his friend.

And so, at 11:53 A.M. on November 10, 1982, the Politburo elected Mikhail Kondratiev Acting Secretary General of the Central Committee of the Communist Party of the Soviet Union.

On taking the chair, Mikhail Alexandrovich expressed his thanks, adding that they all realized this was not the time for policy statements. "We shall continue along the path prescribed by our dear Konstantin Leonidovich. And concerning him, I believe, if you comrades think it advisable, that an official communiqué should indicate the seriousness of his condition and prepare our people for the inevitable."

There was no disagreement, but Smirnov asked whether the Politburo would be summoned immediately to present its recommendation to the Central Committee, once the unhappy event took place.

"You know the standing orders as well as I do, Dmitri Pavlovich," said Kondratiev curtly. "They provide for a twenty-four-hour interval before the convening of the leading organs."

He just wanted to make sure that the rule was still in force, explained Smirnov. There was a tremor in his voice, but at the time, Kondratiev did not ascribe any special significance to the apparently pointless question. After all, the man's hopes had been shattered. How could he avoid becoming disoriented and bitter?

The Politburo's decision was confided just to the top Party and government leaders throughout the country. But even in the Soviet Union, something known to several hundred people could not remain a secret. A high official of the International Department of the Central Committee unwittingly dropped a hint to a visiting Italian Communist notable. That was enough for the news of Kondratiev's forthcoming succession of Leontiev to spread like wildfire through Moscow's foreign diplomatic and journalistic community.

LEONTIEV'S DEATH EXPECTED MOMENTARILY, and KONDRATIEV TO SUCCEED AS GENERAL SECRETARY were the typical headlines filed by American correspondents.

The evening of the eleventh, Kondratiev, along with other Politburo members, attended a reception at the Chinese embassy. That in itself would have created a sensation at any other time: no Soviet official of comparable status had set foot in the building for almost twenty years. But as far as everyone present was concerned, this friendly gesture toward the People's Republic was far overshadowed by the appearance of the man of the hour. Kondratiev listened sympathetically as his host expressed his government's anguish over the recent news concerning Leontiev's health. ("His influenza has led to serious pulmonary complications, and it now must be assumed that the general secretary will not be able to resume his duties for an indefinite period of time.") The ambassador sounded most convincing as he extolled Comrade Leontiev's great contributions and expressed the hope of the Chinese people that their revered friend would fully recover.

"Konstantin Leonidovich will be very moved by your message," said Kondratiev gravely, pressing the envoy's hand. What hypocrisy, he thought. Everyone knew of Leontiev's almost visceral hatred of the Beijing leaders, and how they heartily reciprocated his sentiments!

Other Soviet notables were almost ignored as the guests pressed around Mikhail Alexandrovich. He shook off a crowd of admirers from the fraternal countries to find himself face-to-face with Arthur Hill, who had just arrived as the new American ambassador.

"Am I witnessing a thaw in Sino-Soviet relations?" asked the latter, after shaking hands.

"Oh, yes, our difficulties from the past are receding, something I am sure must be causing great satisfaction in Washington. As we and the Chinese get to know each other better, our relations are bound to grow more and more friendly," replied Kondratiev, with just a hint of a malicious smile.

The American could not refrain from responding in kind: "But I thought the source of the trouble was precisely that you and the Chinese understood each other too well."

"Ah, Mr. Ambassador, even the most sophisticated people in the capitalist world find it difficult to realize that the two Communist countries cannot really have a basic conflict of interest. We've just been having a family quarrel."

Hill felt sorely tempted to rejoin, "Those are the worst," but thought such sarcasm ill-fitting for a newly appointed ambassador. Instead, he became very much a diplomat: "One cannot help hearing rumors. Would it be indiscreet for me to offer—"

"Sshh," Kondratiev put his finger across his mouth. "You would not want me to congratulate your president on his reelection, which will not take place for another two years? I hope you have a pleasant and fruitful stay in Moscow, Mr. Hill. Many of us still remember you fondly from your stay here some years ago."

He moved on, leaving Hill abashed: had Kondratiev heard about that old business about his first wife and the British newspaperman, and the KGB? Of course, they knew everything about the people they had to deal with, damn them!

Mikhail Alexandrovich was now pounced on by a group of Western journalists who, in a variety of ways, tried to elicit information as to what was transpiring on the Soviet Olympus. He parried their questions easily and without visible irritation: Yes, Comrade Leontiev's condition was causing serious apprehension, but he had a sturdy constitution inherited from his southern Russian peasant ancestors. No, the direction of Soviet foreign policy did not depend on personalities—its main lines had been laid down a long time ago by V. I. Lenin.

"Our enduring goal is peace and the security of all nations, small and great."

Afghanistan? A limited Soviet troop contingent was there at the *invitation* of the Kabul government. They did not intervene uninvited in the affairs of sovereign nations, as another power did, even in the case of countries thousands of miles away from its borders. Finally, a veteran American correspondent, evidently emboldened by several glasses of a fiery Chinese liqueur, took the bit between his teeth.

"Do you plan any basic changes once you become secretary general?"

"That, Mr. Clark, is a very complicated question to ask in a conversation that is rapidly coming to an end." He turned to Kuliabko, who happened to be standing by, viewing diffidently a variety of Oriental drinks and hors d'oeuvres being dispensed by the waiters. "Save me from the Americans, Mykola, or I'll start giving away state secrets."

Kuliabko took him by the arm to lead him aside. "You should not waste your time in idle chatter. I did not like Smirnov's tone yesterday morning. He still may have some tricks up his sleeve."

"What could it be? It's a question of days. He is sinking quite rapidly."

Their conversation was interrupted as the Chinese ambassador approached to introduce new members of his staff. It was being enlarged, he explained, in the hope that now (he obviously meant once Leontiev croaked) their two countries would greatly expand their commercial, cultural, and scientific intercourse. The two Politburo members made noncommittal noises.

Finally Kondratiev, prompted by Kuliabko's frown, made his excuses.

"No, you are not going home yet," said Mykola firmly. "We've got to go over all the possible contingencies and numbers, especially numbers. Let's do it in my dacha. My wife is visiting her mother in Kiev. There is no one there but the housekeeper, and he is deaf."

Once there, they went through the list of Politburo members, with an eye to any possible change in the Kondratiev versus Smirnov lineup.

"I simply don't see how it could change in the next three days," concluded Kondratiev after scrutinizing each of their colleagues' positions and attitudes. "Only Vishnevsky, Gabayev, and Georgadze were prepared to vote for Smirnov, and would, given a chance, do so again. So it would still be five to three in my favor."

"Can you be sure of Lunin on the second round? You've never been a particular favorite of his."

"Oh, if he followed his inclinations, he would probably be in Smirnov's camp. But that would create a four-four deadlock and would necessitate bringing the candidate members into the process. He told me quite frankly that that was why he voted for me and persuaded Smirnov to move it be made unanimous."

Kuliabko looked steadily at him and laughed. "I appreciate your delicacy, but there was obviously another reason."

"Yes, Mykola, he does not want the choice to be decided by the votes of three non-Russians."

"Well, for your sake I am pleased that the old crock is a Russian chauvinist." He paused, scratched his head: "Still—one vote. What if something gets into Vorontsov, Smirnov persuading him you would cut down the defense budget drastically, or something? The old marshal is not very bright, and Dmitri is capable of anything. Look, Misha, you now call the tunes. Why not have a meeting—tomorrow, they are all here—and co-opt two more people into our admittedly small group. I think we could swing the election of Andronnikov and of Korolyov or Berg. Then there would be no question."

Kondratiev appeared to mull over the idea, and then shook his head. "The Party statute requires confirmation of the election by the full Central Committee—"

"The statute be damned!" cried Kuliabko. "Who would stand on such ceremonies at a time like this? Even Smirnov would not want three hundred people horning in on something that is none of their business. If he did, the others would shout him down."

"Maybe not. Vorontsov does not like Andronnikov—the old business of the army and the secret service being like cats and dogs. He made it difficult to promote our friend to full general, which has always been a perquisite of the head of the KGB. Lunin has a bee in his bonnet about Korolyov; he is supposedly too soft on the intellectuals. We might have to go to the Central Committee with a split Politburo. How would you like that?"

Kuliabko sighed. "No, I would not. A meeting before Leontiev dies—what an opportunity for Dmitri and his pals to make trouble." He continued a bit sheepishly, "Forgive me, Misha. I had to get a rise out of you. You seemed to be enjoying yourself much too much tonight. You are not there yet. This is no time to relax and joke with foreigners."

"As if once there, I would really be able to take it easy, eh, Mykola?"

"Well, it is like this saying of Tolstoy's about marriage that you like to quote. When the job is finally yours, the burden will be on your back, but your hands will be free . . . Enough. Let us have one more, and then to bed."

"What shall we drink to?"

"Vigilance," said Kuliabko.

At his desk at seven the next morning, Kondratiev kept thinking of last night's conversation while scanning mechanically the confidential report about foreign reactions to the impending succession. He could not have told Kuliabko his real reason. To elevate Andronnikov to full membership on the Politburo would make it all the more difficult to get rid of him as chief of the KGB later on. It was not like the old days: a nod from Stalin and the man would topple, no matter how high his position or recent his elevation. No votes, no fuss. And it would be awkward to promote others and bypass Andronnikov.

He impatiently pushed aside the report: nothing but the usual mishmash of nonsense and platitudes. Could Andronnikov have caught on? Sasha's behavior was that of a friend and a dutiful protégé. And yet friendship was a perishable commodity in their business, and a timely betrayal often a profitable venture. Kondratiev recalled Khrushchev's indignation when he had tried to hint that the premier's chief of police was not exactly a paragon of virtue.

"Just because you had that unpleasant incident when you were young, you tend to suspect that any man in that job might turn out to be a swine like Beria. Karsavin is devoted to me. Not like some of our dear colleagues who would just as soon knife me in the back, the way those bastards tried in '57. Denis keeps tabs on them. Besides, what would he have to gain? I made him. Without me, he would still be a Komsomol instructor in the boondocks."

And so, while poor Nikita was basking in the sun on the Black Sea, Karsavin, back in Moscow, was masterminding the plot to overthrow him. The turncoat was handsomely rewarded: full membership on the Politburo and Party secretaryship.

To be sure, Karsavin did not enjoy the fruits of his betrayal very long. A few years later, he tried to pull a similar trick on Leontiev. This time he tripped and was relegated to a minor Party post in the provinces. He never got there. The car in which he was traveling smashed into the rear of a truck. The bodyguard-chauffeur who survived testified that the victim, who had been drinking, had insisted on taking the wheel. Even so, the man got five years at penal labor. Andronnikov, who shortly thereafter was appointed to his present job, once tried to intimate that there was more to the accident than the official report stated, but Kondratiev had not chosen to pursue the subject.

No, he must not get into the habit of suspecting foul play in every accident, seeing treachery lurking in everybody. That way lay madness, that "occupational insanity of despots," as Perventsev once characterized Stalin's behavior during his last years. Mikhail Kondratiev would never allow it to get hold of him, any more than he would let things stagnate the way they had during the last ten years. The Russian—Soviet—people deserved better than that. His colleagues were in for some surprises. And he was about to see the one colleague who was due for perhaps the largest shock of all.

Suddenly, Alexander Andronnikov was before him and speaking good-naturedly. "It was almost exactly forty years ago that Lieutenant Andronnikov reported to his new commander. Even then, the commanding officer had sensed that here was a young man who would go very far. And now the chairman of the State Security Committee awaits the instructions of the general secretary." Forty years ago—yes, it was at the height of the battle of Stalingrad that they had first met, not a pleasant reminder, given his current feelings about the man.

"I remember it, Sasha. You were fresh from the hospital, but insisted on going right away to the front. I was not thinking of years ahead, but only whether either of us would get out in one piece from that hellhole. But I am afraid we have no time for reminiscences. For one thing, this unhappy business of the funeral arrangements."

Andronnikov pulled out a number of papers and charts from his briefcase. Kondratiev studied them, at times peering over his glasses at the visitor, who maintained an impassive expression.

"Does this meet with your approval?"

"But, Sasha, this is almost an exact copy of the arrangements after Stalin's death."

"That is the only real precedent we have for this kind of occasion."

"At that time, Beria was supposedly afraid that the people might go berserk, storm the Kremlin, God knows what else. But now! Sure, there will be crowds expected to pay their last respects to Konstantin Leonidovich, but there is no reason to anticipate the slightest trouble. We don't have to seal off the center of Moscow with security troops, and take all these special precautions to guard public buildings. The militia and regular army detachment can keep order within the immediate vicinity of the funeral rites. Your people should look out for any potential troublemakers, though again, I don't see why there should be any."

The KGB head hastened to assure him that they would try to change the arrangements. "If there is time, Mikhail Alexandrovich. I understand the doctors fear it may come any day now."

"Do try. If we turn Moscow into an armed camp, it might lead to all sorts of rumors among the people, and would make us look silly in the eyes of foreigners. What is the general mood?"

The surreptitious poll of public opinion carried out by the KGB had predicted largely what might have been expected: people would be moderately sad at the passing of Konstantin Leonidovich, who with age and his visible debilities had assumed something of a grandfatherly image. There was little indication of the kind of apprehension that preceded previous shifts in the leadership.

"But . . . Andronnikov paused. "Mikhail Alexandrovich, people don't understand this *acting* general secretary business. It does make for some anxiety. Which leads me to another point . . . May I speak as your friend, and not as the chairman of the KGB?"

"Need you ask, Sasha?"

"I cannot help being a bit anxious myself. When it comes to the confirmation of your appointment, it could still turn on one vote: Lunin's."

Here it comes, thought Kondratiev, and he decided to anticipate his next move. "I am not unduly worried. What is uppermost in Pyotr Nikolayevich's mind is the Party's good name. And it would make us seem a bit ridiculous and intrigue-ridden—Kondratiev now, Smirnov one week later—not the kind of orderly, staid procedures we've maintained over the last eighteen years. But yes, I've been thinking of possible reinsurance: like trying to enlarge our august body by bringing you in, and maybe Korolyov. But how would Lunin react? In the first place, it would clearly suggest that I do not trust him. In the second place, being such a purist, he would object to the Party rules being passed over. No, it is too risky."

If Andronnikov's hopes were dashed, his face did not betray it. "I was not thinking of myself. Whether Alexander Sergeievich Andronnikov becomes a full member of the Politburo now or later, or not at all, is of little consequence in comparison with what is at stake: a rejuvenation of the Party that can be done only under your leadership. I am very fond of Konstantin Leonidovich, but clearly some changes are overdue."

Kondratiev got up from the sofa they were sharing—he never received important visitors sitting behind his desk—and walked to the window looking out on the courtyard. Directly across it was Leontiev's suite of offices, which should soon be his.

The man was still breathing, still struggling to eke out a few more days or hours, but all over Russia people already talked, as the two of them did, not only as if he were dead, but also as if he had never mattered at all. What mattered was the office, the once prosaic sounding "General Secretary" now evoking a vision of power far surpassing that of the mightiest monarchs and dictators of yore. Even the funerary rites, to be honest about it, would be held not to commemorate the man but to extol the power that emanated from the office he had held.

As a human being, Konstantin Leonidovich Leontiev, whose name for eighteen years had resounded from one end of the country to another, was now virtually forgotten. Once the doctors had rendered their definitive verdict, neither Kondratiev nor any of his colleagues, with the exception of the ever faithful Lunin, had found time to visit the dying man. Mikhail Alexandrovich had kept in touch by phone with Anna Leontieva, and was neither surprised nor shocked by the fact that her main concern appeared to be whether and for how long she would be able to retain their present apartment and country residences.

Conferences with other Party secretaries and ministers succeeded each other for the remainder of the day. But throughout, Kondratiev could not shake off an uneasy feeling left by the interview with Andronnikov: something about it did not quite fit.

In the evening there was a brief meeting of the Politburo, with all full members in attendance. They heard the latest communiqué from the hospital: the patient's condition remained unchanged. In view of this fact, urged Viktorov, they could not go on postponing some decisions, lest important branches of administration become stalled. The Ministry of Finance was without a head, Comrade Zavodny having suffered a stroke about the same time as Leontiev, and they were at a crucial phase of preparing the next year's budget. The comrades would remember that before Konstantin Leonidovich was stricken, they had discussed the advisability of replacing Comrade Sitnitsky as minister of nuclear power stations. With various irregularities in the management of several plants having come to light, the decision ought not to be delayed.

There were other matters somewhat less urgent; but still, if the present impasse should continue . . . After a brief discussion, it was decided to empower the acting general secretary to have full discretion to suspend ministers and chairmen of government agencies, and to designate, in concurrence with the prime minister, persons to act as their heads until the Politburo approved permanent replacements.

Before they adjourned, Smirnov raised another issue: Was this the time for the KGB to stir up additional anxiety among the people by announcing the arrest on charges of corruption of several persons whom idle gossip might connect to members of this body?

Everybody knew to whom he was referring; those announced as detained this very day included Vishnevsky's brother-in-law and a member of Gabayev's personal secretariat in Uzbekistan. Lunin hastily intervened: the investigation that led to the arrests had been authorized by him several months ago; no imputations could be drawn as to their colleagues. Still, the timing was most unfortunate, insisted Smirnov. Would Comrade Kondratiev see to it that no further measures were taken that might unduly agitate the public mind? He would certainly look into the entire matter, promised Kondratiev.

A strange thing, thought Mikhail Alexandrovich after his colleagues dispersed: he had known about the investigation and that the arrests were overdue, but Andronnikov had not even mentioned them this morning. Well, Sasha was undoubtedly awaiting a call from him, and would be ready with some explanation. But by the time he had moved to his little side table and lifted the receiver, he changed his mind and instead called for his bodyguard and car.

On the thirteenth, an early morning call from Professor Samuilovich informed Kondratiev that the end could be expected within twenty-four hours. Members of the Politburo and other notables were notified to be prepared for a summons at a moment's notice. Coded telegrams and telephone messages were being sent throughout the vast expanse of the land, to the leaders of the fraternal countries, and to Soviet embassies and missions abroad.

Kondratiev stayed at his desk. There was no reason to advertise the imminence of the event by canceling his reception with the visiting Japanese businessmen's delegation, nor the other audiences and conferences scheduled for the day. His aides moved around gingerly and spoke in hushed tones. He himself felt no tension, but at seven in the evening, fatigue took over. The committee to discuss the funeral arrangements was to meet in two hours, though in fact there was little to discuss, the amended plans having been delivered that afternoon to Remizov, who was vice-chairman of the commission, himself to be its titular head.

He stretched out on the sofa, leaving instructions not to be disturbed except for any communication from the hospital. And so when the bell rang, it had to be it. The officer on duty sounded embarrassed.

"I hope I am not going against your instructions, Comrade

Secretary of the Central Committee, but Citizen Pavel Kondratiev is here, and he claims it is most urgent that he see you."

Pavel had never visited any of his father's offices. What could have brought him here now? It would have to wait. But then Kondratiev was struck by a premonition. "Let him come up."

His son's expression was strained, but for a moment curiosity prevailed over his agitation as he surveyed the unfamiliar surroundings.

"I don't have much time. You must know what is going on," said the elder Kondratiev. "So what is this all about?"

Pavel looked momentarily bewildered, as if he'd forgotten what had brought him there. Then, without raising his voice: "You signed it, Father. It was a lie, what you said about your arrest."

Mikhail Alexandrovich felt a strange kind of relief. "Sit down and tell me what this is all about." He brought out a bottle of brandy and two glasses, and set them on the table next to the settee. Pavel hesitated, then filled his glass and emptied it in one gulp. (His father recalled Kuliabko's conversation with Smirnov, "Kondratiev sips his brandy, as befits a gentleman.") "I am waiting."

He had been summoned early this morning to a security official's office. When he protested that he had a lecture to deliver, Pavel was told that the matter was urgent. In the office, he was received by a man who identified himself as Major Ryabov. After the usual preliminaries, the major informed him that they had a sworn deposition by a man he would not name that identified him, Pavel, as one of the organizers of a clandestine organization that called itself the Union for Democratic Society. What could he tell him about that conspiratorial circle?

"I was so astounded that instead of being angry, I laughed in his face, and told him some of their agents must be hallucinating." The man said it was not a laughing matter. They had, he repeated, sworn statements. Perhaps their informants had exaggerated. In any case, it would be best if Pavel told him who the people were with whom he had been conversing, criticizing the Soviet system, and discussing ways of undermining it. "I pointed out that the Soviet constitution provided for the freedom of speech, and as for undermining anything, it was people like him who, by using lying informers, were undermining the law. I had nothing more to say."

It was at this point, continued Pavel, that Andronnikov had entered the room and dismissed the interrogator. "Uncle Sasha, who had obviously been listening to the questioning as it was recorded, was at first full of apologies. The whole thing, insofar as it concerned me, was started without his knowledge. And now it was out of his hands. Unless . . ." Pavel would have to make a frank avowal of his contact and, as Andronnikov phrased it, of those "slightly illegal" activities in which he had engaged with those other young men.

"I kept shaking my head, and finally said that I would rather have my day in court. He then grew very theatrical and, practically in a whisper—how stupid, since obviously it was still being recorded—confided to me that it was you who were the real target of the affair. If I persisted in my refusal to cooperate, I would be charged with conspiring against the Soviet power, and there was enough evidence to damn me. It had already been leaked to some foreign correspondents that a son of M. A. Kondratiev might be charged with supposedly trying to organize something on the order of Polish Solidarity. If I made a clean breast of my associations with dissidents and of those illegal activities in which I had participated, I would get at the most a suspended sentence; more likely, the case would be quashed with a warning. Those serious slanders would be disproved. And my . . . carelessness . . . would not reflect on you. But it was inconceivable for the Party and country to be led by a man whose son had been trying to overthrow the Soviet power." He stopped.

Mikhail Alexandrovich marveled at his own calm, but then nothing he was hearing was coming to him as a complete surprise. "Well, how did your friendly chat with solicitous 'Uncle Sasha' end?"

Pavel poured himself another glass, and after a sip, set it down. "I told him I was quite willing to tell my story whether in court or right there, but no names." Andronnikov then pretended to be quite perplexed and friendly and said, "Your father was not that fastidious when he was young. He cooperated with the security organs when he saw there was no way out."

Pavel had called him a liar to his face. His father, if he meant that affair in 1934, had refused to sign a false confession. Again the KGB head appeared deeply anguished. He excused himself, went out of the room, and returned with a thick volume. "He let me read two pages, a statement implicating seven men in the murder of Sergei Kirov, under it a facsimile of your signature and attestation of a witness. How could you sign it, Father, or was it a forgery?"

"No, I signed it. Do you want to know why?"

"Why? It was a lie! They were innocent!"

"So they were. They had already been condemned and shot. I wanted to live."

That was what Andronnikov had told Pavel, adding that, of course, these were different times. His friends would get off with, at the most, a year in a camp, much more likely just being sent out of Moscow to live in a provincial town. Was that so terrible?

Pavel had not said anything, and Andronnikov allowed that perhaps he was too shaken up to think clearly. So why didn't he come back first thing in the morning? In Pavel's place, he would not try to see his father—he was preoccupied with very important matters. But it was up to him.

Clever, but not clever enough, thought Kondratiev. Andronnikov obviously counted on the young man's pride keeping him from running to him. Or if he did, Kondratiev would order the investigation stopped. There would be a storm within the Politburo: Smirnov expostulating how the general secretary had allowed the good name of their two colleagues to be traduced because of something their relatives and subordinates were alleged to have done, while at the same time suppressing the really serious charges against his own son. There could be leaks to foreign correspondents and subsequent opprobrious stories in Western papers. All in all, enough for the old fool Lunin to throw up his hands and switch his vote.

He would have to move fast, before Andronnikov, clearly an accomplice of Smirnov's, came up with those and perhaps other tricks.

But what of Pavel, who was sitting silently, but not taking his eyes off his father's face?

"Nothing will happen to you. The whole affair from the beginning has been contrived against me, and I shall take care of it."

Pavel shook his head. "Something *has* happened to me. I want to leave this country."

"That is out of the question. You love Russia."

"Not this Russia. And if I am kept from leaving, I shall do my utmost to demonstrate how I detest this regime built on deception and disregard for human dignity."

"And what would you find abroad? We are at last discarding the accursed legacy left by that maniac, slowly but surely. The West is sinking ever deeper in corruption and rottenness. What would happen to you? Sooner or later, you would be got hold of by the Americans, expected to vilify your country in the press, exhibited before congressional committees, and turned into a source of amusement to those hyenas. And in a year or so, after you ceased being a sensation, you would be discarded, forced to live obscurely in a strange country, away from everything you've ever loved—an abomination in the eyes of your countrymen and in those of decent people in the West."

"I would not let myself be used. I shall do what I have not been able to do here: write and say what I think openly. Here I feel as if I were suffocating."

Here was an opening, thought Mikhail Alexandrovich: "I may have lied at a time when, as for many of my fellow countrymen, lying was the only way to survive. And you may choose not to believe me when I say that if it is within my power, there will be changes in this country, changes that will make it possible for you to feel free. And that is why I cannot allow you, or rather the people who want to strike at me through you, to ruin my dreams and plans for a better future. I see a future in which people like yourself will not want to *leave* this country. They will be going abroad and coming back as they please. The term 'defector' will become as anachronistic to our society as 'capitalist.' "

For an instant, the older man thought he saw comprehension in his son's eyes. And so the question came quite unexpectedly.

"Why, then, after Stalin's death, when you were already one of this country's rulers, did you not tell the truth about your role in the Kirov affair?"

Kondratiev got up. "I am afraid we shall have to discuss that and other personal problems of the Kondratievs some other time. Right now, there is extremely important business to which I must attend."

Immediately after the door had closed on Pavel, Mikhail Alexandrovich asked to be connected with the commandant of the Moscow military district. He then summoned Gorbunov. The latter was visibly startled when his boss began explaining what he wanted him to do. Kondratiev shook his head: "No questions, Mitya."

▬

"Lunin will not budge," said Viktorov, sinking wearily into a chair. "I told him what we found in these," he pointed at the stack on Kondratiev's desk—papers and tapes seized by Gorbunov from KGB headquarters. Pyotr Nikolayevich was in an uncompromising mood. Yes, he agreed that Andronnikov's attempt at suicide and the papers found in his files would tend to prove that he had tried to inveigle Pavel Kondratiev into a criminal conspiracy, thus to compromise his father. And if it is definitely proved that it was Smirnov who instigated the whole affair, he should not only be stripped of his position, but chased out of the Party.

But all that provided no excuse for Mikhail Alexandrovich's willful act, Lunin had averred. He should have obtained the Politburo's authorization. "We empowered him to dismiss ministers, but not to have them arrested or to use army officers to raid the KGB headquarters. Bringing the army into our intra-Party affairs! At a time like this . . . He has not as yet, thank God, been confirmed, but is already behaving like Stalin at his worst."

As he recounted Lunin's words, Viktorov himself became uncharacteristically agitated. "Mikhail Alexandrovich, what did drive you to that impulsive action?"

"You have seen and heard enough to know that I had good grounds to suspect that Andronnikov was Smirnov's accomplice in a plot to ruin my son and thus to bar my way . . ."

The old man shook his head. "It could not have been just that. You know as well as I do that parents are no longer punished for their sons' transgressions, as they used to be under Josif Vissarionovich . . . And once confirmed, you could have then unraveled that business about Pavel. I have never known you to act impetuously or to panic. So what was it?"

"You are right," said Kondratiev finally. "I probably would have waited, had I thought that all Andronnikov plotted was to strike at me through my son. But I feared that once he turned against me and conspired with Smirnov, he was capable of something worse, much worse, and I had to have those papers to parry the blow. I did panic . . . You remember, Alexander Ivanovich, when you told me about Stalin's last words before he lapsed into unconsciousness. 'Ask Kondratiev.' You wisely did not want me to explain what he might have meant, for then I could not have told you. But now, I must."

It was the night of November 30, 1934. Misha Kondratiev was staying up late: the accounts of the Leningrad Komsomol organization were in an incredible mess, and he, its second secretary, had been charged with straightening them out. His fellow youth officials undoubtedly partying or whoring that night, he, as an engineer, was supposed to make some sense of the disarrayed figures and atrocious bookkeeping. Shortly past midnight he was ready to quit, when a stocky fortyish man with a shock of graying hair had burst into the room. The newcomer looked confusedly around, mumbled something about this being the wrong room, and then his eyes rested on Misha, who on his entrance had jumped to his feet and stood at attention.

"Who are you, young man, and why are you staying up so late? You young people don't have to stay up until the morning hours on the chance *he* might choose to call you."

He lowered his voice to a confidential whisper. "You know that our great leader, Josif Vissarionovich, likes to work nights, so we his servants must do likewise." He took a few steps toward the table on which Misha's papers were spread, stumbled, and then finally sat down heavily in a chair. Sergei Mironovich Kirov, head of the Leningrad Party organization and a secretary of the Central Committee, a faithful "comrade-in-arms of Great Stalin," was very much drunk.

Misha's experience did not extend to dealing with inebriated potentates. Finally, he asked in a quavering voice, "Can I get you anything, Comrade Kirov?"

"I don't suppose you keep any vodka in the Komsomol office—in any case, I've had enough." He turned away from Misha and addressed his speech to the portraits on the wall. "Started drinking yesterday in Moscow after *he* told me I am to become the general secretary. He is going to concentrate on defense matters and foreign policy. 'You're the right man for the job, Mironovich; we must uproot all the treason and vileness, to begin with in our own ranks. There is going to be a war. In all probability, the Nazis and the Japanese will invade us. At the first shot, all those Zinovievs, Kamenevs, Bukharins, and their henchmen will turn traitors.' I am to be the Executioner General while he remains Father of the People." He began to laugh wildly.

Frightened, Misha concluded that Comrade Kirov must be suffering from some temporary insanity and hallucinations—how could Comrade Stalin have said all those things?

"I must leave, Comrade Kirov." He began with trembling hands to collect his papers.

"No, sit down and listen. 'We must rid Soviet soil of all that filth,' Josif Vissarionovich said. More killings. As if they haven't killed enough people already—millions of peasants." He looked at Misha as if he previously hadn't noticed him. "I thought this was my bodyguard's room."

"It is one floor up, just above. Shall I summon him, Comrade Kirov?"

"No, I won't need him." He patted his bulging right pocket. "Here is my protection, and one way out of the whole mess. Not tonight—my hand is not steady enough. Do you think I am drunk, young man?"

"I would not know, Comrade Kirov. I think you may need a rest."

"Yes, go and fetch Borisov."

Misha ran out and eventually found the bodyguard, who had been looking throughout the Smolny for his boss.

"Has Sergei Mironovich been saying anything?" Borisov asked anxiously.

"He spoke quite . . . incoherently, and I could not understand."

"Whatever it was," said the guard, "forget that you saw him. Forget every word he said—it is worth your life. Go home right away. You never met either of us tonight."

▬

"I was too young and naive to realize what was happening," Kondratiev told Viktorov. "Nine years later, when Stalin said to me that we shared a secret, it came to me in a flash: he had known all along that it had been suicide. And shortly before Stalin's death, I finally realized that he couldn't have been more responsible for Kirov's death had he himself pulled the trigger. There had been no doubt in his mind that Sergei Mironovich would take his own life rather than become general secretary and assume responsibility for unleashing mass terror. Stalin would never let go of real power. What other choice was left to Kirov? If you disobeyed Stalin's command, you would be branded an enemy of the people. Then not only was your life forfeited, but also your good name. Die by your own hand, and you could be reasonably sure you wouldn't be posthumously stigmatized as an agent of Trotsky, the Nazis, Japanese militarists, or some other fabrication. Kirov was proclaimed a martyr, the leader himself carrying the urn with his ashes to be buried in the Kremlin wall. Cities, factories, and warships were named after him.

"Dead, he was still made to serve Stalin by providing a pretext for mass purges. They began modestly enough, with the execution of Nikolayev and those thirteen other members of the nonexistent conspiracy. But that was but a rumble preceding an avalanche of terror that descended on our people in 1937 and 1938. I don't think even you would know how many people perished in those years."

Viktorov shook his head. "That's one set of statistics I never dared to probe. In any case, millions were killed, either by a bullet or from a slower death in the camps."

"And the vast majority of them were no more guilty than those fourteen 'assassins' of Mironovich.

"After that other conversation with Stalin, I became convinced that my turn was next; he sensed his own end coming and wouldn't want to leave behind anyone who knew the truth about the crime that started the holocaust."

"I still don't see—" began Viktorov.

"Wait! When he died, I remained the only man who knew the secret of Kirov's death. But how could I be sure? I should have come forth with my story when Khrushchev told part of the truth about Stalin and then tried to find out what had really happened in the Smolny on December 1, 1934.

"I rationalized my silence on the grounds that the Party and the country would only suffer by reopening the old wounds. Once I made it to the top, it would be in my power to make amends and help build a better Russia. Was I very wrong, Alexander Ivanovich?"

"Who can tell? We haven't dared to tell the truth about the

past to our people. But men like Lunin wouldn't forgive you for concealing it from us—the leaders. Strange, I could never bring myself to believe those rumors about Stalin and Kirov's death. Not that I thought him incapable of the most ferocious crimes. But it seemed out of character for him to honor and extol the memory of a man he had hated and destroyed."

"And now maybe you'll understand why I moved so quickly against Andronnikov. He knew all too well how vulnerable I was to anything touching on what happened in Leningrad on that day. He wove a web around my son. With Leontiev's end so near, why wouldn't he become more vicious? I could imagine him forging documents that linked M. A. Kondratiev directly to Kirov's death. Well, I was there at the time. I did sign a false confession, still in the KGB files. So I had to get hold of Andronnikov's papers and tapes right away before he put the finishing touches on the plot. There just wasn't time to ask for the Politburo's authorization.

"I didn't find what I was looking for, only those clumsy fabrications concerning Pavel, enough to damn Andronnikov and Smirnov, but not enough to justify my violating the rules. Damn the secret service, and not the least for what it does to the minds of those who work in it. Andronnikov had once been a brave soldier, a loyal comrade. I believed that it would soon be within my power to curb the KGB and remove that festering sore from our society."

▬

Konstantin Leonidovich Leontiev expired at daybreak. The official news of his demise came at noon. On the fifteenth, the newspapers carried under banner headlines a report of an extraordinary meeting of the Central Committee of the Communist Party of the Soviet Union held the preceding night. Comrade M. A. Kondratiev presided, and after extolling the life and services of the departed leader, he informed the Committee that the Politburo by a unanimous vote had charged him to move that Comrade Arkadi Remizov be elected general secretary. The motion was approved by acclamation.

An inside page showed two brief announcements: the Presidium of the Supreme Soviet had relieved A. S. Andronnikov of his post as chairman of the State Committee on Security (omission of "comrade" preceding the name suggested that the ex-chief of the

KGB had simultaneously been stripped of his Party card). And the Central Committee had acceded to the request of Comrade D. P. Smirnov that because of the state of his health, he be released from his duties as a member of the Politburo and secretary of the Committee.

▬

"Try to understand the politics of this confounded country!" exclaimed Arthur Hill to his wife over the breakfast table.

"Calm down. There's no reason for you to get so excited. You're spilling coffee over everything!"

"Yes, there is. I wired Washington that it was virtually certain that Kondratiev was in, with just an outside chance of Smirnov's getting the job. We're here because the Secretary of State persuaded the President that at a time like this, they should have someone in Moscow who really knows what's going on in the Kremlin. And now, you can be sure that there'll be leaks to the press that the State Department's leading expert on Soviet affairs, our man on the spot, goofed. I can see the editorials now: 'How can our foreign policy get out of the doldrums when our diplomats show themselves to be so inept and ill-informed?' Christ!"

His wife sought to stem the flow. "Come on, Art. You can't be expected to know more than the Politburo. And from the way they behaved at that reception, everything pointed to Kondratiev. Compared to those thugs, I rather liked the man. What do you suppose is going to happen to him now?"

"He's probably wondering, himself."

▬

But if Mikhail Alexandrovich felt any special concern about his future or anguish over what had just taken place, nothing in his expression or demeanor suggested it as he began his working day at the Secretariat at the customary early hour. His aides knew that they were going to be more than usually busy with arrangements for Leontiev's funeral, and with questions of policy and protocol that were going to arise in connection with the multitude of foreign potentates about to descend on Moscow for the occasion. Kondratiev warned his secretaries at the outset that he would be too busy to accept calls not directly related to the business at hand. He made an exception for Kuliabko. "I'm not going to talk about what happened," said the latter, "not now. But you ought to get some rest. Your voice sounds hoarse—you must not be getting much sleep."

"I'm all right," Kondratiev replied, adding that the two of them should get together soon, if possible even before the funeral. As he put down the receiver, he wondered how much Mykola did notice. During the tempestuous Politburo discussions, he knew he had slurred a few words, and faltered at one point in his nominating speech, fearing momentarily that he wouldn't be able to finish. But the brief spasms of pain in his side hadn't recurred since last night. He should see his doctor, but not right away—the next few days would be hellishly busy. To be away from Moscow at this time, or worse, hospitalized, would be the greatest, no, the second greatest political mistake of his life.

"I think this just about winds it up for tonight, Mitya," said Kondratiev, several hours later. They had just drafted a memorandum suggesting what should and should not be taken up by Remizov during his forthcoming interview with the vice president of the United States, who was coming to represent Washington at the funeral.

Gorbunov gave him a pleading look.

"What is it?"

"Forgive me, Mikhail Alexandrovich, the commentator on the BBC . . . He said you would still remain the power behind the throne."

For the first time that day, Kondratiev laughed. "There is no such office in the Party. But I'll be around for quite a while yet."

And why not? he thought as Gorbunov, still close to tears, took his leave. It was but a passing weakness that had made him hint to his wife that, in view of what had transpired, he might retire soon altogether.

"But you couldn't live without politics!" Irina had exclaimed.

She was right. And Remizov, when the two of them conferred after the election, begged him not even to think of resigning. Also true, they had to chart a new course. It would be fatal to let things drift. They were in danger of losing the younger generation. (Briefly, very briefly, his thoughts wandered to Pavel and whether he would ever see him again.) Remizov understood what had to be done, but he needed someone by his side who would prod him, someone who understood the West.

Still another voice within him warned that nobody who had reached for the highest prize and been rebuffed could expect to be retained in a position of power. But, come what may, he wouldn't quit.

▬

That same evening, Pavel Kondratiev boarded an Air France jet at Sheremetevo Airport. It had been a bewildering sequence of events. The day before, he had been summoned to the KGB office and informed that the case against him had been quashed. He immediately applied for permission to go abroad, and was ready to settle down for a long wait before the authorities acted on his application.

Pavel couldn't believe his eyes when, the very next morning, he received a packet containing his passport with a permit to go abroad for one year, French visa, and a plane reservation. Enclosed was a note, under the signature of a deputy chief of the KGB, wishing him *bon voyage*. There was obviously a connection between that near miracle and what he had just heard on the news. But whatever it was, he must not delay his departure. He'd unravel his thoughts later, far away from Moscow. He said good-bye in person only to his mother and Irina. They both begged him to see or at least call his father, but after their last conversation, he simply couldn't. Nor did he get in touch with any of his dissident friends. He didn't want to answer any questions or go through any effusive send-offs at the airport.

Once aboard, he tried to turn his mind to practical matters: whom to contact in Paris, where he could live, finances. It was only when the plane was in the air that he felt a sudden onrush of anxiety, with at once pity and anger at his father: how could he have lived for so many years with all those lies?

"Excuse me." Somebody was speaking to him. The passenger in the seat next to him, a Swiss businessman, had been thinking for quite a while about what kind of conversational gambit he ought to try on the young Russian sitting next to him, who, judging by his remarks to the steward, was fluent in French. "I know you people don't like to talk politics with foreigners. But your new leader, Remizov—not much is known about him abroad. Is he likely to introduce major changes in the economy and foreign policy?"

Pavel hesitated for some time before replying. "Policy might be different . . ." He paused. "But things change very slowly in my country."

CHAPTER 12

EPILOGUE, MOSCOW, DECEMBER 1982

From Pravda, *December* 3, *1982*

> It is with the most profound anguish that the Central Committee of the Communist Party of the Soviet Union, the Presidium of the Supreme Soviet, and the Council of Ministers announce the sudden death of Mikhail Alexandrovich Kondratiev, member of the Politburo and the Secretary of the Central Committee. M. A. Kondratiev spent his career in the service of his country in peace and in war. A talented engineer and industrial manager, brave soldier, accomplished diplomat, and outstanding Party leader, Mikhail Alexandrovich's entire life was devoted to the lofty ideals of Leninism, the welfare of the Soviet people, and the cause of peace. His services were highly esteemed by the people of the USSR: he was a Hero of the Soviet Union, recipient of five Orders of Lenin and three of the Red Banner and of numerous other decorations and honors. He had been Deputy of the Supreme Soviet since 1946, member of the Communist Party since 1931. He was elected a delegate to each Party Congress from the Nineteenth through the Twenty-sixth.
>
> The bright memory of Mikhail Alexandrovich Kondratiev will be treasured forever in the hearts and minds of the Soviet people.

December 6, *1982*

Irina was impatient to get home. At the reception following the funeral she declined Tamara Remizova's invitation to spend the evening with her and the general secretary. In contrast to her other, formal embraces, she hugged Kuliabko tightly and assured him that her sister (whom in fact she had not seen for years before this day and with whom she felt she had little in common) would be keeping her company. Yes, Irina would be coming very soon to visit with him and his family in their dacha. She wanted very badly to get away from the oppressive official scene and to be alone.

Yet, on arriving home she found to her surprise that she was pleased when Marfa, tears still streaming down her face, announced that Nikolai was waiting in the drawing room. She had been barely conscious of his presence at the funeral rites.

"Kolya, you should be with your mother," she said, kissing him this time with real feeling.

"Sonia is staying with her, and I thought you would not mind me coming and sitting around for a little while."

She stepped back and her heard pounded: his habitual frivolity dropped off like a mask; he looked amazingly like Mikhail Kondratiev of thirty years ago.

"I am delighted. My sister will not be here until later. You are most thoughtful." Irina found herself chatting animatedly about the ceremonies, even found herself able to laugh at some of the absurd features of the ritual. Then she fell silent, and Nikolai asked what had been on his mind all along.

"Any word from Pavel?"

"No, he has not yet forgiven your father for the times he and his country had to live through. Someday he'll come to understand."

"Do you think we will ever be able to understand . . ." asked Nikolai. "I mean, why it all had to happen?"